Marvels & Mysteries of Our Animal World

A Family Guide to the Fascinating Creatures of Earth, Sea and Sky

READER'S DIGEST

Marvels & Mysteries of Our Animal World

with introductions and a special supplement,
"Animals from A to Z," by Jean George

Coronet Books

THE READER'S DIGEST ASSOCIATION/PLEASANTVILLE, NEW YORK

CONTENTS

In these pages are the dramas and mysteries of more than 300 creatures of the Earth. The book includes animals of every important order in every major class. All are classified according to their place in the Animal Kingdom, either in the index or in the illustrated supplement, "Animals from A to Z." A chart of the Animal Kingdom appears on pages 314-315.

PART 1   EACH AFTER HIS KIND

PART 2   THEIR FATE AND DESTINY

PART 3 A COLLECTION OF WONDERS

PART 4 THE NATURE OF ANIMALS

PART 5   THE TIDAL FORCES

PART 6   THE SOCIABLE KINGDOM

SUPPLEMENT   ANIMALS FROM A TO Z 289

PART 1

EACH AFTER HIS KIND

The Earth's first creatures appeared in its warm waters more than a billion years ago, and developed into the mighty throng of invertebrates —the boneless animals. From them, in the next great period, came the amphibians, and from these the reptiles. In turn, the reptiles gave form to warm-blooded birds and mammals, which were to populate the Earth in all their splendid ways.

Chapter one

THE GREAT & THE SMALL

Mammals, the highest form of life, began their evolution some 200 million years ago during the great Age of Reptiles. There are fewer kinds of mammals than of other classes of beasts, perhaps only 3200 species out of more than a million on Earth. They range in size from the shrew, weighing two fifths of an ounce, to the mighty blue whale who plunges his 130 tons through the ocean.

Two striking characteristics distinguish mammals: they nurse their young, and they have at least a little hair at some time during their lives. Furthermore, all but the platypus and the echidna give birth to live young. These two lay eggs, being a link with the reptile world.

Scientists classify mammals in 18 large orders, according to whether they are flesh eaters (dog, bear), whether they gnaw (mouse, squirrel), whether they leap (rabbit, hare) and so on. (See pages 314-315.)

Of all the beasts on Earth, mammals are among the most secretive; many live out their lives hidden in woodland dells, buried under rocks, camouflaged in grass and leaves. Most of us have observed little of their habits and have noted even less about how they feel. Scientists who have lived closely with beasts and studied them have found that all mammals are emotional. They grow fearful, angry and aggressive, particularly when their young are threatened and when trespassers come on their land. Their emotions develop as they grow from infant helplessness to independence. No other beast is more dependent than the suckling baby mammal or more individualistic than the full-grown adult. And it is in the raising of their young that mammals reveal their greatest attribute—their tremendous capacity for warm affection.

THE KING'S LAST STAND

Jack Denton Scott

For over an hour we sat in our car in Kruger National Park in South Africa, watching a scene that seemed to have come alive from a wildlife artist's brush—morning mist was rising from damp grass in little gunsmoke puffs as a herd of graceful, foxy-red impala (a species of antelope) with milk-white bellies and black stripes on their rumps threw their heads up in quick, nervous motions. Drinking from a nearby pool were two giraffes, their legs propped at impossible angles. Four zebras stood behind them, as still as porcelain.

Suddenly my wife gasped and pointed. Coming out of the high grass to the left of the impala was a big male lion wearing his yellow mane like a golden crown, shuffling along head down as if he couldn't care less about the prey a few hundred yards away.

"We're about to see something spectacular," whispered the South African in the rear seat. "*There* is a lion with a plan!" The plan seemed to be for him to sit like a big dog and stare. He sat for 15 minutes. At last from beyond the nervous herd came the sound of coughing. The lion's ears twitched. He got to his feet and in an amazing burst of speed (most experts agree that a lion can run 100 yards in four seconds flat) started toward the herd, driving it between two grassy rises into a little valley. We followed the great cat, which now had slowed to a walk. There, in the middle of the valley, lay two dead impala. Beside them three creamy-tan lionesses awaited the lion.

Thus does a pride of lions use high strategy to outwit the fleet antelope. The lion we watched had actually herded the animals into the death trap when the lionesses coughed to signal that they were in position. Planning and execution were perfect.

This was my dramatic introduction to Africa's larg-

est carnivore in action on his home ground. The world's most famous animal, the huge, tawny, amber-eyed cat needs little description. Most of us have seen lions in zoos, in circuses, in architectural and heraldic carvings. The lion is mentioned 60 times in Homeric tales, appears in almost every book in the Bible from Genesis to Revelation. Since the beginning of recorded time he has been the symbol of strength, nobility and courage.

But there are facts about this popular cat some of us don't know. For instance, not many realize that right now the lion is fighting for survival in Africa. Few of us know that a lion can swim skillfully and carry twice his weight; that, living as he does in a pride of from 6 to 20 lions, he is the most sociable member of the cat family; that the male is the sultan of a harem; and that the female probably originated the idea of baby-sitters.

The lion spends years learning the arts of survival. After the two-week courtship and gestation of 108 days, the lioness leaves her pride, seeking a secluded place near water, and brings into the world two to

six 12-inch, one-pound cubs, fluffy, striped and spotted. Normally no more than three, more often two, cubs survive—nature's method of selection, perpetuating the lion race from the finest specimens. Enemies are rickets, hyenas and the greatest predator of all, man. Leaving the cubs only to seek food, the lioness nurses them for three months and also begins bringing pieces of meat or disgorging her own partially digested meal. When the young are three months old she usually rejoins her pride, where another female becomes the official baby-sitter.

Contrary to general opinion, the old-maid baby-sitter is usually fiercer than the mother. Stewart Edward White, who spent much time in Africa, was charged by a childless baby-sitter female so savagely that he had to shoot her, while the mother fled into the brush with her brood.

Lions use a number of sounds for communication, including coughs, grunts, roars and moans. The female often controls her offspring with a moan that sounds as if it were strummed from a bass viol. Early one morning my wife and I were sitting in a car watching

The most sociable members of the cat family, lions live in prides of from 6 to 20 animals.
During mating season, however, a male and a female retire from the pride to be alone

the animals in Nairobi Royal National Park when we saw two spotted lion cubs looking as if they had just stepped out of a toy shop. Curious, they came within 20 feet of us. Then there was a stirring in the brush by the roadside and their mother poked out her tan, gold-eyed head and moaned. The cubs fled to her side and the family vanished in the underbrush.

At five or six months the cubs are taken to a kill, where they attempt to imitate their mother as she eats. An English major once saw a lioness at an antelope carcass carefully instructing her cubs in the use of claws for stripping the skin off the meat, and dewclaws for holding the meat down when eating. The youngsters sat like schoolchildren watching a teacher's pointer trace cities on a map.

At about three months they are weaned, but as their canine teeth don't develop for another six months they remain completely dependent upon their mother. After weaning, serious training begins. Safari organizer Donald Ker once watched a lioness stroll along the leeward side of some Thomson's gazelles, ignoring the drinking herd until it was between her and a reedy swamp. Then she streaked into the herd, scattering the panic-stricken animals into the gum of the swamp. At this, lions, lionesses and half-grown cubs (an entire pride) poked their heads above the high grass where they had been hiding and rushed after the trapped animals. Ker saw eight gazelles killed in less than a minute, with cubs inexpertly assisting. This was an involved lesson, illustrating several techniques: hunting at the right place (near waterholes); pride coöperation; using the wind properly; killing method—and, above all, patience.

The lioness is a better hunter than the male, fiercer and more lithe. She usually is the scout and the executioner, with the lordly-maned sultan lending his superior weight and power only if needed. Even when the lioness is hunting to feed herself and her cubs, the male is apt to take his share first. I saw a lion eat his fill before he permitted his family to eat.

Unlike most cats, lions are unafraid of water and become skillful swimmers. Even in this action they show superior intelligence, avoiding crocodiles, which they cannot cope with in the water, by crossing a stream only where it is swift and shallow. Despite some opinions to the contrary, they can climb trees and are amazingly agile. Lieutenant Ludwig von Höhnel saw a lion hurdle a gorge 12 yards wide, and lion expert F. Vaughn Kirby watched a lioness jump without effort to the top of a 12-foot embankment.

But all of this marvelous physical ability comes only with time. The young stay with the mother (who may mate again meanwhile) until they are two, when

their stalking and killing techniques are well developed. Two-year-old males often form a bachelors' pride, working together to secure food. Their manes grow at three and they mature at five; in the wild they live for 15 years and up to twice that long in captivity, where they seem to thrive.

Largest member of the cat tribe, *Felis leo* is (together with the tiger) the most highly developed and specialized of all carnivores. His domain was once all of Africa, India, Greece, Persia, Syria, Palestine, Armenia, the Balkans and even, in ancient times, the British Isles. Man, always his greatest enemy, has driven him out wherever he could. Egyptian, Assyrian and Persian monarchs considered it their symbolic duty to war on lions. A Mogul emperor of 17th-century India hunted them with an army of 100,000 men. In a period of 40 years the Romans brought over 50,000 lions to Rome. By the end of the last century lions were extinct everywhere except in parts of India and in Africa, and even here they were hunted unmercifully. In South Africa, with the spread of farms and civilization, they were shot, trapped and poisoned until by the 1860's the most handsome subspecies, the black-maned Cape lion, was exterminated.

Given a fair chance, however, the lion can take care of himself. His charge is one of nature's most awe-inspiring sights. When the big cat decides to rush, he drops his head; his tail twitches, then stands stiffly erect; he utters a series of rumbling growls, yellow eyes flame and he moves forward, gathering speed. The impact is shattering. Another factor that makes the great cat a dangerous animal is his talent for concealment. One hunter searched for an hour for a wounded lioness who virtually wrapped herself around an anthill on the open plain, blending with it so perfectly that she appeared to have vanished (black shading on the ears breaks up the head outline and the coat resembles dry grass). Lions take advantage of the smallest cover, flattening themselves so closely to the earth that they seem part of it.

But their main forte is strength. A lion can kill an ox more than twice its size, breaking its neck with a quick combination of fang and claw. He will attack a full-grown hippopotamus, that war-tank of flesh few animals have the courage or strength to molest. Lions have even been observed killing the fearful crocodile, and one was seen outmaneuvering and tearing in half a giant python.

It is the exceptional lion that weighs 500 pounds; most grow to about 400 and are 9½ feet or less in length, including the three-foot tail. The lion's ability to kill and carry animals much larger than himself is due to the skillful way he goes about it. Commenting on a lion jumping a fence with a cow in his mouth, J. A. Hunter, one of the best-known African white hunters, wrote: "A lion shows a special knack in getting partly under the carcass and shifting the weight onto his back while holding the cow's throat in his mouth. When jumping the barricade, the lion's tail becomes rigid, seems to act as a balance."

Unlike most cats, lions are not wanton killers: they slay only to survive. Lieutenant Colonel James Stevenson-Hamilton, who studied them for many years at Kruger National Park, claimed that a pride of six lions kills, on the average, two big antelopes a week. There have been a few notorious "man-eaters." The most publicized were two maneless lions at Tsavo which stopped the construction of the railroad through their domain in the Kenya bush for weeks, killing scores before they were destroyed. Another in Mikindani, Tanganyika, slew 380 people.

In *No Room in the Ark* the noted author Alan Moorehead wrote: "The hunting lion is one of the great natural spectacles left in the world, and they have a fascination which is beyond value. . . ." It will be a sad day when lions are seen only in cages.

Experts like Colonel Mervyn H. Cowie, director of the national parks of Kenya, don't think we will have this spectacle much longer. The lion can survive only where the wild grazing herds are kept intact. The national parks remain his last stronghold. How long this magnificent animal, our living symbol of courage and nobility, can last is a question only the African nations can answer.

THE RABBIT THAT WEARS SNOWSHOES
Alan Devoe

If a naturalist were to seek some single symbol of the northern winter—some one creature of outdoors whose name at once conjures the crackling blue-white silence of the north woods, the snow-bowed cedars and hemlocks, the curling of a man's breath like smoke in the frosty stillness, the squeak and crunch of walking boots on powdery snow—he might very well select the snowshoe rabbit.

This is the long-eared white haunter of the white silences that bounds away over the drifts almost as swiftly as the wind-whipped snowflakes themselves. This is the small white animal dot, cheery and companioning, that enlivens landscapes of darkly somber

evergreens, pale wintry sun and the gray scud of snow-wrack. This is the animal that wears upon its feet, as an outdoorsman himself must in the winter wilderness, a pair of snowshoes, and comes whisking efficiently over the drifts to wrinkle its nose at his campfire in weathers when no other beast stirs from the shelter of the firs and most birds are frost-numbed in huddled silence.

Wabasso is the north-woods Indian name for this larger cousin of the cottontails and second cousin of jack rabbits. The textbooks call him the "varying hare," because of his dramatic alterings of seasonal coat, from warm grays and tawnies in summer to snow-whiteness when the winter comes. He is an arresting reminder both of the strength and the triumph of life, and of the strength and the triumph of death. The proliferation of varying hares is something so stupendous that in the great "wave" years, which recur periodically, a man might easily kill 500 in a day without making a visible reduction in the populace. But when the "wave" is to subside there comes an epidemic plague of such fearful effectiveness that

The snowshoe rabbit is also known as the "varying hare" since its coat varies with the seasons: white in winter to blend with the snow, brown in summer to match the earth.

a "trough" year may find whole territories in which not one single snowshoe rabbit remains alive.

A snowshoe rabbit commonly lives out the whole of its small, quick life on a very small patch of earth. From the time it comes into being, as a small brown infant in a litter of three or four in a casually fashioned nest in a stump or a leaf-lined hollow, until that day when its dim little rabbit-consciousness winks out, it may undertake no wider wayfarings than can occur in one big tamarack swamp. Nor does this restricted adventuring involve any bright cunning: the snowshoe rabbit is not a wily strategist; it escapes its enemies mostly by simple speed. It thrives by protective coloration, by omnivorousness and by fecundity. Though gentle-eyed and fond of play, the male rabbits in mating season become locked in savage fights in which they seek to disembowel each other.

Wabasso has no fear of starvation when the snow lies deep. He can subsist not only on clover and grass and leaves but on very nearly anything else. Snowshoe rabbits eat poplar bark, willow bark, birch bark. In a pinch, they can eat the violently pungent cedar and spruce—eat it in such quantities that their flesh becomes so tinctured with rosin as to be humanly inedible. There are records of snowshoe rabbits stealing the frozen meat from traps and eating *that*.

The change of coat, of course, is Wabasso's most arresting endowment. He is brown in summer so he may hug the earth and "disappear"—white in winter so he may hug the snow and similarly vanish. It was long supposed that the actual color of the hairs changed with the passing of autumn into winter, as a human being's hair gradually silvers with the passing of his years. Wabasso's change, however, is in fact a molt of one coat and the growing of another. The chemistry of the change is very strange. If, for instance, a snowshoe rabbit is bereft in autumn of a tuft of his fur, the new fur which grows in will be snow white, in anticipation of the overall winter change, which may still be many weeks away. Conversely, in the early spring a lost tuft of white fur will be replaced with a growth of tawny brown, in anticipation of the coming summer coloring.

Wabasso's feet are just about twice as big as a jack rabbit's or a cottontail's. The toes, instead of being compactly together, are splayed widespread. With the approach of winter, new white fur begins to grow abundantly on the rabbit's feet, until finally, by snowtime, it has "feathered" them into broad, soft, light pads that can carry him over the most powdery drifts without sinking. Where the deer may get stalled, and even a great stilt-legged moose bog down, the small snowshoe rabbit can go his fleet way, making his great ten-foot bounds, and only dimple the drifts. He can also, should the odd need arise, swim as powerfully as though he carried a pair of paddles.

Nevertheless, Wabasso is at nature's disposal. He is preyed on by hawk and owl and lynx and fox, by dogs and men and weasels and any other predatory thing that may occur in the rabbit's territory. Parasites internal and external, in incredible abundance, thin down the rabbits' numbers. Every fang and talon in the woods is against Wabasso. Should he evade them all and begin to multiply until his numbers approach a "wave," he is then subject to epidemic death.

There is a certain fitness in the fact that the snowshoe rabbit, symbol of the northern winter, should be intimately linked with the bird that is the equivalent symbol in feathers: the little black-capped chickadee, his fellow darer of sub-zero weathers and the drifting whiteness. When a chickadee builds its northern nest in a birch stub, it likes to line it with soft warmth. The fur of Wabasso, so bewilderingly changeful, is in the end a symbol of the interweave of nature's shifting life when it becomes, as it regularly does, the insulation for a nest of new young birds.

GIANT OF THE DEEP
Roy Chapman Andrews

So far as is known, the largest animal that has ever lived is the blue whale—and this is not excepting those giant extinct reptiles, the dinosaurs. The largest whale which has been measured was 100 feet long, while the largest specimen ever weighed—in sections, of course—totaled 136.4 tons. The wonderful strength of the blue whale is almost beyond belief. My friend Captain H. G. Melsom reported to me that while hunting off the coast of Siberia he struck a blue whale which ran out 3000 feet of line and, with the ship's engines at full speed astern, towed the vessel forward for seven hours, never at less speed than eight knots. Some years before this in Norway he shot a blue whale at five p.m. which dragged the ship with engines at full speed astern until 11 p.m., when the captain slowed down to half-speed; at one a.m. he changed to dead slow and finally killed the whale at two o'clock in the morning.

Many touching stories are told of the affection which whales show for one another. When a school of devilfish whales is attacked by whalers, if a cow is wounded the bulls refuse to leave until she is dead.

The orca or killer whale is unmatched in ferocity and will break through ice floes to chase its quarry. Able to tear apart other, far larger whales, it is the greatest carnivore of the globe.

A captain once told me that while hunting a pair of devilfish whales he shot the female, and the male would not leave his dead consort, but kept close alongside, pushing his head over her body.

A herd of bottlenose whales will never leave a wounded comrade while it is still alive. The hunters take advantage of this loyalty by harpooning a second bottlenose before the first is dead. The whales crowd about the wounded ones, and sometimes 10 or 15 can be taken before the school is lost.

Data upon the breeding habits of whales is difficult to secure. However, in mating season they administer blows with their long fins, and these love pats may be heard for miles. The period of gestation is about one year; the calves of some species are about 15 feet long when born (the newborn blue whale, however, is about 25 feet in length) and probably live exclusively on milk for about six months.

The gray whales, as well as other large cetaceans, have only two major enemies—man and one of their own kind, the orca or killer whale. Although twice the size of the killers and correspondingly strong, the gray whale becomes terrified when a pack of orcas appears; either it dashes wildly for shore or, paralyzed by fright, it turns belly up at the surface with fins outspread. One killer puts his snout against the closed lips of the gray whale, forces the mouth open and tears out the tongue. Of 35 gray whales which I examined after they had been killed, seven had tongues eaten to a greater or less extent and one had several large, semicircular bites in the lower lip. Fins and flukes are also shredded by the killers.

Whales were probably once land mammals; they have bodily activities essentially the same as those of any land mammal. When below water, they must hold their breath. However, some whales can hold their breath for as long as 45 minutes. Breath thus contained under pressure is highly heated, and as it is forcibly expelled into colder air it condenses into a column of vapor, which in some cases may be from 12 to 15 feet high. Whales have no vocal organs. During spouting, however, the rush of air through the pipelike nostrils produces a metallic, whistling sound which can sometimes be heard a mile away—a sound mistaken for the whale's voice in the statements that whales have "bellowed like a bull."

Whale meat, which is eaten in many countries and is one of the staple foods in Japan, is coarse-grained and tastes something like venison, but has a flavor peculiarly its own. I have eaten it many days in succession and found it not only palatable but healthful. In fact, a chemical analysis shows that whale meat contains about 98 percent of digestible material, while ordinary beef seldom has more than 93 percent.

Humpback whales are playful, and there is never a dull moment for those hunting them. Once in Alaska we raised a humpback's spout and ran up close before the animal submerged. Ten minutes later, without warning, the floor of the ocean seemed to rise and a mountainous black body, dripping with foam, heaved upward, almost over our heads. It paused an instant, then fell sidewise to be swallowed up by a vortex of green water. With the camera ready in my hands I stared at the thing. Even the nerves of the harpooner were shaken, and he clung weakly to the gun without a move to use it. The whale had dropped back scarcely 20 feet away; if it had fallen the other way, the vessel would have been crushed beneath its 40 tons.

Sometimes a whole school of humpbacks will throw their 45-foot bodies into the air, each apparently trying to outdo the others. In what the sailors call "lobtailing," the whale literally stands on its head, with the entire posterior part of its body out of the water, and begins to wave the gigantic flukes slowly back and forth. Faster and faster they move until the water is lashed into clouds of spray.

Frequently a single humpback will play tag with a vessel. He will come up first on one side and then on the other, "double" under the water and rise almost at the stern. Sometimes this will last two or three hours until, tiring of the game, with a farewell flirt of his tail he will dive and swim away. If he is allowed to continue his elephantine gambols unmolested, he is as harmless as a puppy. But once embed an iron in his sensitive flesh and it is wise to keep well beyond the range of his powerful flukes, which strike with deadly, crushing blows. Just before a whale dies it goes into a death flurry, and any ship nearby stands an excellent chance of being rammed, for the animal is utterly blind in its rushes. A 60-ton whale once drove into a ship, crushing her side like an eggshell, and the crew just managed to get a small boat over before she went down.

Whaling began more than 1000 years ago and it continues to this day; the present annual catch is about 40,000. While this may not mean total extinction, whales could become so reduced in numbers that they would never again be abundant. Enormous animals are usually slow breeders. To protect the whale, the International Whaling Commission was founded in 1946. Participating nations have agreed to observe a closed season on whales, to accept a limited overall annual catch and to spare the lives of whales under a certain size and any cow accompanied by a calf. Surely this greatest of all members of the animal kingdom deserves no less.

Chapter two

THE WINGED BEASTS

In an ancient age a lowly, reptile-like bird called *Archaeopteryx* somehow turned his scales into feathers and achieved the first true flight. Since that momentous deed, forest, field and waters have become adorned with the color and music of the most beautiful creatures of all—some 8600 species of birds that we know today.

The feather distinguishes birds from all other living things. It is the lightest and strongest structure for its weight ever developed by nature or man, and it forms a part of the world's best insulating system. Not only the feather but the whole body of a bird is built for flying: hollow bones, strong breast muscles, no weighty teeth.

Because most birds are active by day and do not hide from danger, we know more about them than about any other animals. As they flit among the leaves, splash over the water or dart through the woods, we can easily observe their highly instinctive habits. An oriole can find an orange milkweed in a meadow, strip it into fibers and weave them into a basket nest. And all orioles will do this with no variation and no lessons in either botany or sewing. Thrushes characteristically make nests of mud, doves use sticks, the goldfinch works in thistledown.

Scientists have grouped the birds in 27 orders: the wedge-winged (penguin), the night hunters (owl), the ocean-dwelling (albatross and petrel), to name a few. (See pages 314-315.) The sweetest of these is the order of perching birds—the only one with birds that sing. Their voices (and it is usually the males') purl out the boundaries of a territory or proclaim war between two rivals. To most men's ears their songs are beautiful, and the voice of the whistling cardinal or the meadowlark is a sound of enchantment and happiness.

MAJESTY ON HIGH
Donald Culross Peattie

The United States of America has a king. He shows himself in every state of the Union except Hawaii and is seldom seen elsewhere except in Canada. He is king of the air, undisputed ruler of the sky, the American, or white-headed, eagle.

As a proud monarch should, he has regal features— a snowy head, an aquiline nose, a piercing eye. Congress chose well when, in 1782, it picked this species for the Great Seal of the United States, rejecting the golden eagle originally proposed by the designer. The darker bird, though also found in the United States, has been for centuries a heraldic symbol in such undemocratic states as Czarist Russia, the Austrian Empire, Napoleonic France, the Prussian Empire, the Roman Empire—indeed, a symbol of tyrannies and dictatorships running back to Assyria.

Handsome the golden eagle may be; as a harrier of young stock it has a thousand marks against it for every one that can be charged to the American eagle, whose favorite diet is fish. Honest old Ben Franklin, who wanted to make the strutting and stupid turkey gobbler the national bird, charged the American eagle with being a coward, a bully and a verminous thief. He did not know, apparently, that this bird is attached to its home, is faithful to its mate and spends more care in the education of its young than any other in our skies.

Eagles mate for life—a claim made for many birds, but often falsely. The eagle pair do stick to each other, in breeding season and out, until death does them part. Only then will the bereaved one disappear from its accustomed haunts to roam the skies—now so often empty of eagles—till somewhere it finds a new mate and leads it home. Courtship begins in November and lasts until June. In their eyrie, usually at the top of a tall tree not far from water, the couple live in fierce and ardent devotion. There seems reason to think that the mating act is repeated at dawn and sunset every day until the eggs are laid and even after—as if the union were not for reproduction only. One ornithologist tells of the wild cry that rings out from the mating birds, over the tops of the trees steeped in shadow and awed silence.

No other bird is so deeply attached to his home. The eagle never leaves his bailiwick except to seek a mate or when failure of his food supply forces him to migrate. Most birds desert the nest at the end of one season; it is to them not a home but a cradle. But the eagle each year builds a new nest on top of the old one. And an eagle may live as long as 30 years. So the nest grows and grows, and serves as a permanent home, summer and winter. One nest in a tree that blew down near Lake Erie was found to weigh nearly two tons and represented perhaps a half-century of occupancy. Another, found on a rock off the California coast, contained several wagonloads of sticks and leaves. Coarse branches sometimes six feet long formed the breastworks of this bird castle. Within, it was lined with soft grasses, lichens, moss and feathers. And the view from such a wilderness mansion is usually the grandest in the countryside.

The female eagle lays two or three white eggs. These are relatively tiny—not three inches long. An eagle's egg is smaller than the Canada honker's and only half the size of a whistling swan's. From such small beginnings grows the king of the air. The parents take turns at incubating, which lasts for about 35 days. Without stirring, one bird will sit as long as 72 patient hours. When weary it will signal the mate with a chittering sound. Then the change of guard will be made swiftly. If it becomes necessary for an eagle to leave the nest unguarded, the sagacious creature roughs over the top of the nest with dead leaves to make it look deserted.

The eaglets, being born so small, have a long infancy. And the life they are to lead is so much more complex than that of most birds that their education is long. At first the chicks get food popped into their

This living symbol, the bald eagle, was first used on a coin in Massachusetts in 1776 and later it became the official emblem of the United States. Originally "bald" meant "white."

mouths, but when they should begin to feed themselves the parents tear up a fish before the youngsters' eyes to show them how to do it. Presently they bring a whole fish and stand back while the little fellows learn to quarter it themselves.

Eaglets in their nursery play with sticks, just as children play with toys, and learn to grasp objects with their talons. Before they can fly they must first pluck out their gray down and develop and preen their new, strong white plumage. They are taught to exercise every day. Their parents show them how to jump up and down on the ample platform of the eyrie, flapping their wings. They do this by the hour, squealing and stamping like children in a game. All this is preparatory to flying, and to fly as an eagle flies is something that is learned, it seems, only by weeks of practice.

At last the young eagles make a first terrified flutter from the edge of the nest. Usually they tumble back again as fast as they can. If they are too slow about trying again, the parents discipline them by withholding food. Tantalizing morsels are dangled just beyond their grasp. When at last an eaglet completes his first solo flight, he gets a reward of food.

Like girls and boys approaching maturity, young eagles, once they can fly, spend less and less time around home, until toward the end of their first year they go off to seek their fortunes in the world. They do not mate until the fourth or fifth year, when they begin to wear the snowy crest and white tail that distinguish the adult bird, but long before that they are on their own as masters of all they survey. Their tremendous wingspread of seven or eight feet is matched by the internal strength of their great pinions—the flight feathers. The longest primary feathers are up to 20 inches long. The wing tips are slotted— that is, the eagle can spread the primary feathers apart like fingers.

This slotted wing tip is a feature of all birds which can soar without flapping the wings. It seems to act as an antistalling device. With such equipment the eagle is the absolute master of flight. Airmen have found him flying at almost 10,000 feet above the earth. His marvelous eyes have been known to detect a fish three miles from the spot where he was soaring; he then captured it in one long, slanting dive. It is this power that makes him the dread of the fish hawk or osprey; the king of the air frequently forces one of these birds to drop a fish, which the eagle catches with superb dexterity as it falls.

The eagle has many dangerous enemies—all of them human. For a century eagle eggs were at a premium with the class of collectors who rightly call themselves "fanciers." And unnumbered thousands of dusty, molting, stuffed eagles still adorn the top shelves of drugstores, barbershops and country offices. Many a farmer who misses a hen thinks, if there is an eagle nest about, that he may pay it a punitive visit. Added to such injury is human libel—a charge so criminal that if it were true it would justify retribution. But there is no truth in the hoary newspaper story of the eagle snatching the baby from its cradle. No American eagle has ever been known to make an unprovoked attack upon a child. For a number of years the National Audubon Society has painstakingly followed up each of these accusations, and every one melts away to fable.

Only in 1940 did Congress get around to passing legislation to protect the symbol of America's proud freedom. Today, after two amendments to the original law, it is unlawful to kill, shoot at or capture Uncle Sam's birds, or to take eagle eggs or molest the nest. But the enforcement of this law is no stronger than the vigilance of game wardens and the attitude of judges. In addition, a new threat has appeared on the scene: a marked decline in the bird's ability to reproduce. Scientists at the Federal Wildlife Research Center at Patuxent, Maryland, working under a mandate from Congress, suspect that DDT may be the villain in the case. DDT has been used extensively for mosquito control along the coast, which eagles inhabit, and it has been found in many fish, which form the principal item in the eagle's diet. Experiments conducted at the Research Center since 1945 have proved that non-deadly doses of DDT lessen the reproductive ability of both bobwhite quail and pheasants.

In spite of all that Americans have done to exterminate their grandest bird, it is still not uncommon wherever the fishing is good. It is most abundant in Alaska and Florida, around the Great Lakes, along the Mississippi river system and off the Atlantic and Pacific coasts.

If you are fortunate enough to see the American eagle, you will never forget the experience. He may be sitting in motionless, unblinking majesty upon the highest limb of the tallest tree in all the countryside, keeping guard over mate and nest, over wood and water. Or you may first see him in a power dive from the skies as he pounces upon the shapes beneath the waters. Or perhaps you will watch a flock of eagles soaring, circling, up and up until they become specks against the blue. Then it is not the dark spread of wings that is the last to vanish from sight, but the flash of the proud white head, like the twinkle of snow on distant mountains.

The mockingbird has earned a unique reputation by its amazing ability to mimic the songs of 40 different birds.

LISTEN TO THE MOCKINGBIRD
Lewis Nordyke

Great poets immortalized the nightingale and the skylark, but a barber captured the melody of that saucy little mimic, the mockingbird. Richard Milburn, a natural-born whistler who accompanied himself on the guitar, first whistled a tune based on the bird's trill in his father's barbershop in Philadelphia a little more than a century ago. One day composer Septimus Winner heard Milburn's melody and wrote the words—the poignant story of a man who has lost his love and hears the mockingbird singing over her grave. Published in 1855 under the title "Sentimental Ethiopian Ballad—Listen to the Mockingbird," it has been a worldwide favorite ever since.

The mockingbird is an opera singer without a fancy costume, a slim gray bird the size of a robin, with yellowish-orange eyes and a long, sharp beak. Patches of white in the wings and tail show when the bird is in flight, giving dash and sleekness to his lines.

This sober-suited songster is famous for mimicking the songs of other birds. But the mockers are nonconformists; some of them mimic and some of them stick strictly to their own songs. This has given rise to argument among naturalists: is the bird actually a mimic or is he a singer born with a marvelous repertoire? People who love the mockingbird say he "can mock anything," including the squeak of a wheel or the whistle of a youth who has just beheld loveliness across the way. Some years back, several English nightingales were sent to Florida in cages. One night there was great consternation. Nightingale music rang from treetops up and down the countryside. But the nightingales hadn't escaped. Mockingbirds had picked up the imported music and were improving on it.

The mockingbird is mainly a resident of Dixie, but in recent years he has infiltrated new territory and now is heard in the Great Lakes region, in New England and occasionally in Canada. A slightly different singer known as the western mockingbird ranges from Texas westward to California and southward into Mexico. Mockingbirds do not migrate with the seasons, but the singers that live in village and city sometimes move in winter to the nearby open country, to a more stable supply of food.

In Mexico there is a legend that the gay, extravagant songster, impressed with his own brilliance, decided he was lord of the sky and of song. He was flung to the ground in rebuke. Since that time of chastisement his song has commenced with "*Con el favor de Dios*"—"If God wills it." On a bright spring morning, when you hear the first mockingbird's song you can, if you use your imagination, discern that Spanish phrase of pious submission.

Except for the hermit thrush, the mockingbird has the sweetest, most musical voice of any feathered songster in the United States, and certainly the greatest variety of song. Cocksure that his stuff is worth repeating again and again, he trills each phrase at least six times; this gives his song a musical fullness that no other bird can equal. What is more, he sings more frequently than any other of our familiar birds.

The male does the singing, and his song is part of courtship, mating and raising a family. Early in the spring he selects his individual territory, which includes a perch from which he can oversee his empire. From here he opens the season with tentative notes, like a violinist tuning up. Within a few days he is in top trilling form and there is a female flitting about the lower branches; then, as Longfellow said in *Evangeline*, there comes "from his little throat such floods of delirious music that the whole air and the woods and the waves seem silent to listen."

Soon the loosely constructed nest is built—never in the top of a tree or vine, but about midway up it. While the dutiful female lays four to six turquoise-colored, brown-flecked eggs, the male spends the greater part of his time nearby on the perch, pouring out music. Occasionally he pitches high into the air, turns half a dozen flip-flops and pirouettes back to the perch without missing a note. He works overtime, braving the scorching sun of midday and trilling on through moonlit nights.

While the young are in the nest, the perch is a watchtower. A Texas woman once telephoned her local newspaper that a large brindle cat had strolled under a nest in which hungry young mockingbirds were squawking. Screaming like half a dozen mad jays, the singer plummeted off his perch and hit the cat behind the ears, making the fur fly and bringing blood. Then he soared to a tree limb, screamed and dive-bombed again. He rose to the eave of a nearby garage. Using this as one vantage point and the limb as another, he shuttle-bombed until the frightened cat, apparently attacked from all sides, scatted.

Audubon marveled at the mockingbird's courage. While painting birds in their natural haunts in Louisiana, he produced a canvas showing three mockingbirds attacking a rattlesnake that had taken refuge in the fork of a tree. In reality the mockingbird is an individualist; he goes into battle alone. He does fight snakes, dive-bombing their eyes; he attacks hawks and crows that threaten his home, and doesn't hesitate to dash into a tree filled with shrieking blue jays. Protection of the young sometimes requires still greater courage. If the little birds are captured and caged and left within reach, the parents continue to feed them.

If a mockingbird were to encroach on another's domain, he would probably find himself in battle. Workmen on the University of Texas campus happened to lean a window against a building so that it reflected like a mirror. This was in a mockingbird's territory, and when he glimpsed his own image, he attacked again and again with screaming fury until the window was removed.

There is an argument as old as the Jamestown Colony over the correct operatic billing of the mockingbird and the nightingale. Thomas Jefferson took a persuasive stand on this question when he wrote: "I have heard the nightingale in all its perfection and I do not hesitate to pronounce that in America it would be deemed a bird of third rank only, our mockingbird and fox-colored thrush [hermit thrush] being unquestionably superior to it."

As he flies our skies, singing with the joy of the emancipated, the mockingbird embodies the liberty-loving, fire-breathing, self-reliant spirit of the men who started North America on its way. In all his cascade of song there is never a note of fear.

LEGEND WITH WINGS
Donald and Louise Peattie

There is a legend that before it dies a swan finds its voice in true song, for just that once. Scientists, of course, made a joke of such a sentimental myth. But these old stories often have a disconcerting way of turning out to be true.

Dr. Daniel G. Elliot, a great ornithologist and one of the builders of New York's American Museum of Natural History, shot a swan for the museum and was astounded to hear the wounded bird, as it came sailing down from the sky, begin its death song, which continued, plaintive and musical, till the bird reached the water half a mile away. And when Dr. Elliot questioned local gunners, he found they had heard this last melodious singing, so unlike the bird's call in life.

In appearance, too, the swan is almost too beautiful to believe. Its snowy plumage and the proud and graceful arch of its neck give it a regal look. And it actually is a royal bird in England, where all swans on open and common waters belong to the Crown. The swan that is familiar to most of us—the one seen on park ponds in Europe and North America—is the mute swan, a bird domesticated for centuries. There are two other species in Europe, and in North America two wild varieties—the trumpeter and the whistling swan. All swans except the black, native of Australia, and the black-necked bird of South America wear the radiant pure-white plumage.

All are as loyal as they are majestic. Swans mate for life. When one of a pair is bereaved, it may build a hopeful nest for several seasons, as though believing that the beloved may return. Legend? No, fact again. In January 1959 a flock of swans paused in migration to rest on the lower Detroit River; one pair lingered too long, and the female became frozen into the ice. Conservation officers rescued her, sick and weak, and for a month nursed her back to health. But out on the bitter waters her mate swam anxiously about, evading all capture. When at last the female, restored in health and strength, was released on the river, the pair met, looked long at each other, then moved with that exquisite serenity downstream and out into Lake Erie till the watchers could see them no more.

For hundreds of years, both in the Old World and the New, the skies and waters were snowy with these shimmering great birds. In 1496 the secretary of the Venetian ambassador to London, writing to his master, said, "It is a very beautiful thing to behold one or

A mute swan, the variety we see on our park lakes and ponds, is actually a noisy bird. Although usually thought of only as a graceful swimmer, the swan can fly up to 50 miles an hour.

two thousand swans upon the river Thames," and a 17th-century poet called Ireland "the swan-abounding land." As for the North American trumpeters, Audubon described their abundance on the Mississippi: "As I gazed over the icebound river, flock after flock would be seen coming from afar and in various directions, alighting toward the middle of the stream. Through the dim light I could discern the graceful curve of their necks as they gently turned them backwards to allow their heads to repose upon the softest and warmest of pillows."

In Denmark, an ideal swan land with its many waters and marshes, hunting had depleted the numbers of wild swans in the 1920's to three or four breeding pairs. In 1931 Denmark established a closed season on swans all the year around. By 1950 at least 385 pairs could be counted and the number is constantly growing, so that today the traveler in Hans Christian Andersen's country may see flocks of the serene white birds rafting upon blue waters in fearless peace.

Swans may congregate independently, often in remote wilderness spots, or they may be found in man-made sanctuaries. One such is at Abbotsbury on the south coast of England, owned by Lord Ilchester. Years ago the great Russian ballerina Pavlova came to this sanctuary to study the birds in preparation for that most famous of her dances, "The Dying Swan."

It is in such surroundings that swans are most easily observed, and since the semidomesticated swan is the "mute" swan, its habits are the best known. Far from being mute, it is rather noisy at times, having a vocabulary of eight different sounds. It can blare like a bugle, snort, or hiss with ill-temper. A mother bird will summon her brood by a sound like a puppy's bark, while the general-alarm call has been written as "Herbert! Herbert!" You will know this swan when you meet it, perhaps on a public lagoon, by its black forehead knob, very arched neck and pinkish-orange bill. No other all-white swan has that notable knob above the beak, which produces a look of stern gravity, and no other except the black swan arches its neck with such a proud grace. A full-grown mute swan may weigh 27 pounds, have an eight- to nine-foot wingspread and fly as fast as 50 miles an hour. When angered or frightened while swimming it will sink low like a heavily laden ship, but when confident and happy it rides high.

Valiant is the male mute swan in defense of his own. He makes as devoted a father as he does husband. He guards the eggs or chicks—more exactly called cygnets—against thieving rats, foxes, otters and birds of prey. A blow from the knucklebone of his wing can break a man's arm.

For five months the cygnets, which break from the eggs 4 to 12 in a clutch, are under parental protection, both the dam and the sire swimming watchfully around them. On signal a cygnet will climb into the downy hollow of its mother's wings, there to be carried cosily as she paddles the waters. They are not pretty children, for their feathers are dingy gray—as all the world knows from Andersen's wise tale about the ugly duckling that turned out to be a swan. When the rapidly growing cygnets weigh about 20 pounds, the gray feathers give place to gleaming white.

Far different from the semidomesticated world of the mute swan is the world of the wild North American swans, the whistling and the trumpeter, and lucky the bird-lover who glimpses one. For their multitudes have been decimated, and their range is limited. The whistling swan, which breeds on Canada's arctic coastal islands and in Alaska, goes south in winter, chiefly to the Atlantic coast, Chesapeake Bay and especially to Currituck Sound. These are great places for duck-shooting, which spells death to many a swan. For although they have legal protection against hunters, the great white birds, while feeding, swallow the shot that lies in the marshes and die of lead poisoning.

The trumpeter swan has one more convolution in its windpipe than the whistler, and can call more loudly and deeply than any other swan. It is the greatest of all North American waterfowl, with a wingspread of as much as ten feet. In flight the trumpeter has been known to go a mile a minute, and its great wings, regularly beating, glisten so that they can be seen three miles away. When alighting, it uses a long runway, hitting the water near the shore and braking with opened wings and then with its feet, always calculating the direction and force of the wind. But the trumpeter, which as late as 1883 nested as far south as Iowa, has receded with the wilderness. It could fight coyotes and eagles and win; its enemies have been hunters' greed and encroaching civilization. A single breeding pair requires a full square mile of solitude. Only in far and lonely places, then, can the trumpeter's loud, deep bugle call be heard.

Once this call was nearly silenced forever—a survey conducted in the early '30's located only 73 of the birds in the United States. Today, thanks to the establishment of sanctuaries in Montana and other western states, there are some 1800, about 1000 of them in Alaska. Canada, where the Royal Mounties are ever watchful of their safety, has some 500. So, though still rare, the trumpeter has come back to stay, it may be hoped. For every swan alive lends a little touch of fairy tale to this everyday world.

Chapter three

IN THE WORLD OF WATERS

Five hundred million years ago, when mountain ranges were rising above
the shallow seas, and sponges, starfish, clams and snails inhabited the waters,
the first fish evolved. It was an extraordinary experiment, for the new
creature's skeleton was not on the outside—like the skeletons of the
well-established mussels and crabs and insects—but inside its body. To our
knowledge, no "link" connected this new beast to any previous form of life.
The fish just appeared, with that structure which divides all animals
into higher and lower life: the backbone.

The fish was supple and free to move swiftly through the dense medium of
water. It had gills for breathing and scales for protection. It was
propelled by fins. And these ancient devices still characterize the fishes,
for the experiment was an enormous success. Today there are some
20,000 species—more than the reptiles, birds and mammals put together.

Present-day fishes have many shapes because they have adjusted to
every possible water environment. In the open sea they are streamlined for
speed; on ocean bottoms they are flattened and colored to match mud,
sand or coral. Some, shaped like weeds, ripple in the current.
Eels are designed for cracks and burrows, while the dark ocean canyons
force others to carry lights.

The fins of fishes are as varied as their body shapes. The sea robin's
lower fin developed into legs on which it creeps along the ocean floor. The
triggerfish has fins that release a spine, like the trigger of a gun, and the
remora's top fin is a suction disk that holds it to the bellies of sharks.

As many as three million fish travel in one school. Though declining
in numbers, they are still so prolific that fishermen's nets twinkle and
sparkle every year with 40 billion pounds of them—man's most
abundant protein food.

LIFETIME JOURNEYS OF THE SALMON

Edwin Muller

At an early age a young salmon is seized with an uncontrollable impulse to go on a journey. The pilgrimage he makes is one of the most fascinating phenomena in nature. Where he goes and what he does baffled scientists for years, and his actions have only recently been detected.

The life of the salmon begins in the egg—a red globe the size of a buckshot, which lies buried in the gravel bed of some swift-flowing northern stream. After the little fish emerges from the egg, he stays there in the dark for many days, living off the yolk sac which is still attached to him. He may, if he is lucky, live eight or nine years, but this is the only time in his life when he is perfectly safe.

When the sac is finished he pushes his way up out of the gravel, and his troubles begin. Still only a fraction of an inch long, he is prey to a lot of hungry predators: trout, bass, eels, ducks, swans and herons. Within a few days many of his hundreds of brothers and sisters have been gobbled up. He in turn gobbles creatures smaller than himself. He grows much more slowly than the trout and his other neighbors. After spending perhaps as long as two years near the gravel bed in which he was born, he still is only a few inches long and weighs no more than a few ounces.

Then one morning the impulse seizes him and all the other salmon of his age, and together they start downstream toward the sea. As the current carries them along, their heads are pointed upstream, as is true of all fish moving in fast water. Dangers multiply. The salmon is swept down swift rapids where the white water boils over the rocks. He is carried over steep waterfalls. He may go for hundreds of miles. (Down the Yukon River salmon have traveled as far as 2000 miles to the sea.) At last the current slackens and the river broadens into quiet reaches where the water is brackish, then salt. As he takes his first taste of salt water the little fish turns, heads out to sea.

For years no one knew the whereabouts of salmon at sea. Recently tagging programs of Pacific salmon, notably one conducted by the University of Washington's College of Fisheries, revealed their migration patterns, which range from a few miles offshore to hundreds of miles away.

An irresistible instinct drives the salmon upstream from the sea to the same pool in which his forebears spawned.

George Rees, a British naturalist, sets forth the hypothesis that Atlantic salmon go as far as the Arctic Ocean, coming from the rivers of North America and of Europe and joining in two great silver columns which converge under the arctic ice. Here they would find a salmon heaven. Shrimp and prawns, for example, exist in incredible numbers. When an arctic floe turns over, its under surface is inches deep in a wriggling mass of shrimp. Feeding on shrimp under the ice, the salmon could lie there and eat and eat, fairly safe from attack.

Wherever he goes, near or far, if he survives he comes back. After an interval which may be one year or as many as five, he returns—and usually to the mouth of the very same river in which he was hatched. An extraordinary change has taken place. When he went to sea he was the size of a sardine. Now, after only a year in salt water—a year in which he has stuffed himself prodigiously on small creatures of the sea—he is 18 inches long and weighs as much as seven pounds. If he has been at sea longer, he may weigh 60 or more pounds—a great, silvery fish, beautifully proportioned and strong. He needs this strength, for as he starts the return journey toward the gravel bed where he was hatched he must contend with a new set of enemies. Off the river mouth are porpoises, harbor seals, lampreys. As he swims upstream, otter and mink lie in wait. If he stops to rest in a shallow pool, a hungry grizzly may stalk him from behind. Man is his worst enemy. Off the mouth of the river, fishing vessels sweep the water with their nets. In every pool on the way upstream, fishermen are casting their lures.

The salmon swims steadily, making three to ten miles a day depending on the force of the current. He does not stop to feed. But his strength endures. He can drive up through the swiftest rapids. He can surmount a ten-foot sheer waterfall, making it in one mighty leap. Sometimes when a fall is 40 or 50 feet high there are shelves here and there and the salmon gets up by leaping from one to another.

As the salmon move up the river, most groups find with sure instinct the small stream in which they were hatched. The fish begin to pair off. When a pair reaches the right gravel bed, the female swims close to the bottom, turns on her side and fans violently with her tail. This digs a trench 12 to 18 inches deep. Now she expels her eggs, dozens at a time. The male covers them with a cloud of sperm as they sink to the bottom of the trench. The female now pushes the gravel back, covering the eggs. Then they repeat the process, extending the trench, expelling and fertilizing more eggs. This may go on for five days, for the female

lays up to 20,000 eggs. By now the pair are completely exhausted. Pacific salmon always die after the act of reproduction. Those of the Atlantic sometimes manage to get back to the sea. There they recuperate, returning to the river to spawn again.

In due time there is a stir of life in the eggs. The cycle starts once more. This is what is known of the extraordinary life of the salmon. Even more fascinating is what is *not* known.

How does the salmon find his way back through hundreds, perhaps thousands of miles of the trackless ocean to the same river and same gravel bed where he was hatched? No satisfying explanation has ever been made. We do know, however, that his homing instinct is shared by other fish. An experiment was made in a Canadian lake into which flow many brooks. In each brook hundreds of trout were trapped far upstream, marked, carried by truck and boat to a central point on the lake and released. Within 48 hours nearly all of them were back in the traps, each in his own particular brook.

Today there are only two or three salmon rivers of any importance in the eastern United States, most streams having been spoiled by pollution, obstruction or overfishing. On the west coast, however, from California to the Yukon, salmon come up almost all the big rivers.

The supply of salmon is maintained by artificial hatching. Eggs are stripped from the female, fertilized by sperm pressed out of the male, and hatched in gravel pens where they are safe from their natural enemies. Like normally bred salmon, these go to sea and in due time return as near as possible to their birthplace.

To the sport fisherman a salmon is something to set the blood racing. The fly fisherman does his fishing upstream, in a Pacific river or one of the famous rivers of New Brunswick such as the Restigouche or the Miramichi. He wades out into a broad pool where the current moves in slow swirls and eddies. He flicks the fly to a point where the current carries it slowly past a rock. A shadowy shape rises toward the surface. The fly disappears in a tiny whirlpool. Waiting a few seconds, the fisherman lifts his rod and sets the hook. At once there is a violent tug. The rod bends and the reel sings as the line runs out. The fish takes out 50 yards on his first run. Then he comes out of the water in a beautiful, curving leap, shaking his head to try to get rid of the hook. Again and again he jumps.

Sometimes the man wins the fight. More often the salmon wins, tearing out the hook or breaking the leader. Then doggedly he resumes his long journey upstream, toward the gravel bed where his life began.

DOBBINS
OF THE DEEP

Deena Clark

I fell in love with sea horses in Hawaii. As they sported in the undersea playground of the Waikiki Aquarium, some circled slender sea grass with their graceful tails and slid like little firemen down their poles. Others locked tails and played an underwater game of tug-of-war. One particularly acrobatic little steed coiled his prehensile tail around a sea branch and slowly revolved in an incredible number of complex somersaults.

Mother Nature outdid herself when she assembled the sea horse. This bizarre creature has the arching neck and head of a stallion, the swelling bosom of a pouter pigeon, the grasping tail of a monkey and the color-changing power of a chameleon. It has eyes that pivot independently, so that while one orb scans the surface the other can be directed underwater. To top this fantastic make-up, the male sea horse is equipped with a kangaroo-style pouch from which the little ones are born.

The Greeks dubbed this freakish fish *Hippocampus* —"the sea-monster horse." There are more than 40 species, ranging in length from one inch to two feet, and they inhabit the waters of almost every warm sea throughout the world.

The sea horse is a master at camouflage. While most are dark gray or bronze-black, those in the Indian Ocean and Mediterranean often wear waistcoats splattered with pink, yellow, blue or white. At the approach of danger, a resplendent tropical sea horse, fins rimmed with topaz lights, can turn to dusky brown and impersonate the surrounding rocks.

An Australian relative trails seaweed-like filaments, looking like a refugee from a ribbon counter. Orange-brown "antlers" sprout from the crown of his head, and kelp-textured strands float from snout, body and tail. Even a sharp observer might mistake him for a fragment of seaweed.

The sea horse is a fish without scales. From top to squarish tail, his body is sheathed in a tough, parchment-like cuirass of bony plates. Because of his rigid armor, he swims standing up, propelling himself in stately manner by fluttering a tiny, yellow-fringed, fanlike fin on his back. Ramrod straight, he moves forward or backward, up or down, by manipulating that fin so speedily that it is almost invisible. Two transparent fins flare like tiny manes at the sides of his head, waving incessantly in synchronized figure 8's. The worst thing that can happen to a sea horse is to get a puncture, for his buoyancy is stabilized by a bladder. If a single bubble of gas escapes the chamber, his specific gravity is disturbed and he sinks helplessly to the bottom. There he must remain until he is able to manufacture enough gas to fill up his tank. The sea horse feeds on plankton and *Daphnia*—infinitesimal plant and animal life in the ocean. Brittle, prickly and leathery, the sea horse himself makes fit food for neither man nor fish.

The courtship of sea horses is a fantastic performance. In an elaborate 24- to 48-hour wooing dance to the accompaniment of tiny, drumlike mating signals, the bride and groom swim in delicate circles around each other, the female pursuing the male. At the height of their *pas de deux* the two little creatures meet in a trembling nuptial embrace. At that moment the bride transfers one or several of the eggs she has created to her husband's brood pouch. She meets him in mid-water again and again until she has given him 250 to 300 brick-red eggs, each one fertilized at the instant of transfer. Her marital duties over, she swims away free from care.

For approximately 45 days Papa nourishes the nestlings in his steadily swelling incubator chamber. At the end of this period a single little sea horse prances out, then another and another. In some species they are no bigger than a comma. Finally with a convulsive movement Papa ejects a herd of young clinging together with air bubbles in the shape of a ball. As this ball rolls toward the surface 50 or 60 infants dart out from it in all directions. The process continues until hundreds of nimble little sea colts have emerged. Each baby is an almost exact replica of its parents, except that the body is so transparent that you can see its tiny heart beating. Pigmentation appears later.

Sea horses have fascinated men from time immemorial. Long ago in Athens the sea horse was credited with dark powers. Steeped in wine, it was regarded as a violent poison. But the ashes of the sea horse, taken in honeyed vinegar or mixed with pitch, were believed to be a powerful antidote to other poisons. Pliny recommended it for the cure of hot flashes, skin eruptions, baldness and the bite of a mad dog. A 16th-century Frenchman suggested dipping sea-horse ashes into oil of roses to produce a mixture that would cure chills and fever.

Even today in Chinese apothecary shops in New York and San Francisco the attendant behind the counter may smilingly assure you that powdered sea horse is his fastest-selling aphrodisiac.

The female sea horse transfers her eggs to her mate's brood pouch, so it is he who gives birth to the young. Shown here, an albino and a red sea horse and between them a brown, carrying eggs.

THE BEAUTIFUL WORLD OF THE UGLY CATFISH

Jean George

One of the ugliest creatures alive is the catfish. Frog-mouthed, bearded like a lynx, with pointed, sometimes poisonous spines on his back and sides, he is, as poet Oliver Herford said, "unmixable as vitriol and vichy—a thing of furs and fins." Yet science has now discovered that the ugly catfish is remarkable for an entirely different reason. Endowed with more senses than humans have, this trash-picker of the fish society is attuned to worlds beautiful and unreal. With his super-acute senses, he hears the sound of young crayfish stirring in their mother's apron, he "feels" the dying minnow far away in the pickerel weed, he "senses" whether he is swimming right side up, and sees above him a distorted kaleidoscope of trees and boats and boys fishing on the bank. For the common catfish is exceptionally sensitive.

The most refined of his senses is his ability to taste. Fleshy barbels, usually eight of them, hang down like a beard from his jaw. Covered with taste buds, they constantly "sip" the mud for flavors. It is as if you were to run your tongue over the floors and furniture as you go about the house, for the whiskers bring to the catfish the taste of sticks, flies, snails, weeds and rusty cans. He savors these things not only with his barbels, but with his scaleless body and tonguelike tail. This is the reason the catfish has skin instead of scales—to taste with. A Potomac catfisherman put it this way: "The catfish is such a sophisticated eater he can taste crayfish with his chin, salty mussels with his side, while all the time his tail is drooling over a sip of turtle. There's no part of a catfish's body that doesn't lick its chops."

Because the catfish eats just about anything, he is the ideal catch for small boys. They need no fancy equipment or special knowledge—just a pole, a piece of string, a hook, and a button or a piece of leather, a watermelon rind or an old bone. Moreover, catfish make wonderful eating. I remember how one morning several years ago, when we were vacationing in Ohio, my eight-year-old son brought in a three-pound catfish he had caught. Although proud of his catch, he handed it to us gingerly, and I soon saw why. He had learned the lesson all boys must learn: catfish, with their barbed spines, can cut the hands of

Barbels or feelers are the distinguishing feature which all catfishes have in common. Shown here: the channel cat.

the unwary and leave nasty sores that won't heal for weeks. But the reward seemed to be worth the pain, for when it was cleaned, rolled in cornmeal and fried, my son, who generally does not care much for fish, agreed that this one was delicious beyond compare.

There are a thousand different kinds of this unusual fish, from the five-foot, 120-pound blue cat of the Mississippi to the delicate little willow cat of the mountain pools. Along the Gulf Coast, the barbed, right-angle prominences of the sea catfish so resemble the figure of Christ on the Cross that fishermen have dubbed this variety the "crucifix fish."

Catfishing is a big industry along the Mississippi River and its tributaries. Some 12½ million pounds annually are pulled out of the rivers to make catfish the second most popular freshwater fish in America, outranked only by carp. To catch them, commercial fishermen use "trots," long lines with smaller lines branching out, or haul seines, nets anchored at one end to the shore and hauled by boats that travel in a wide arc.

At Peoria, Illinois, the catfish center, the fish are put alive into tank cars and shipped all over the South and Midwest (with the exception of the Great Lakes area, which has its own catfish industry). Restaurants keep them alive in cement tanks until the moment they are skinned, fried and served with hush puppies. Prepared in this way, they are called a "catfish fry."

Several years ago I learned about the second sense of the catfish—smell. I was watching a fisherman in Morgan City, Louisiana, haul in a trot line of seven monsters. The water was roiling red with mud and sticks, and I asked him how the fish found the bait in such mire. "They sniff around down there," he explained, "running the water in and out of their 'nose' holes until they get a scent. Then they track it right to the source like an old hound dog."

Sniffing underwater seems incredible to me, possibly because all my instincts tell me not to take water into my nose. But the catfish's "nose" does not open into his throat and lungs as ours do. There are two sacs, each with a pair of nostrils, lined with scent glands. The water circulates through these, bringing the scent of turtle or worms almost instantly, for smell, like sound, travels fast in water.

The catfish's world is further enriched by his keen sense of "hearing." Because he is tremendously sensitive to vibrations transmitted through air, ground or water, he can "hear" the carol of the song sparrow while swimming close to shore. He can "hear" beetles biting the stems of pond lilies, or caddis flies stacking tiny stones and gluing them tight. He can "hear" the cautious step of a fisherman walking on the bank, thereby making the old adage, "Be quiet, the fish will hear you," an accurate statement.

The organ that picks up the low swish of snakes or the breast stroke of frogs is the "lateral line," a tube of mucus running down the side of the catfish. It is the stripe or design you see when you turn a fish on its side. Nerves and pores are attached to it, bringing to its owner strange and wonderful sensations. This lateral line brings to the fish one sense we will never understand—the "touch" of things far away. The catfish can "feel" the mussel closing his shell door a few feet away. A snapping turtle swimming upstream can be felt as if the catfish had reached out a hand. Of special importance is the news of the coming of spring which the lateral line brings to the catfish. A kind of thermostat, it tells the fish how many degrees the water has warmed and how long to sit before his body has adjusted and he can move to a higher and warmer spot. In this way the catfish moves upstream with the spring season.

The feel of warming water, the sound of birds singing on the shores, the sense of passing time eventually bring the common catfish out of the mud and silt to the edge of the water to breed. Now the sense of sight assails him, for light penetrates the shallows, and he looks up and sees the land. His view is strange, however. Due to the refraction of light on water he sees the land as if he were peering through a tube.

When pulled up on shore the catfish sees a blurred and watery world, such as you and I see underwater, for his lenses are more rounded than ours. Underwater this roundness puts everything in sharper focus, which is important to a catfish, for he is a devoted parent and must keep his small fry in sight.

In May and June, along the edges of the streams, ponds and rivers, catfish gather to select their mates. Each female lays a mass of eggs, and a male fertilizes them. In most species the father almost immediately takes the eggs into his mouth and, not eating during the entire two- to three-week incubation period, holds them there until they hatch. Once they have hatched, the parent still keeps the fry in his mouth until all the food sacs are used up. Then he spits them into the weeds.

As soon as the fry come spewing into the world the parents escort them around the shallows. The father will take them into his mouth again if he "feels" the enemy turtle approaching, or when he smells the legs of the stalking egret. At night the fry return to his mouth until they are too big to get in.

I used to love to watch the tiny baby catfish, with their big heads and black whiskers, swim around a pond in Pennsylvania, vacuuming the weeds as they went. One day my dog ran up beside me and apparently loomed so demonic in their little eyes that they scattered in 27 directions. Patiently the parents found them behind leaves and sticks, picked them up and put them together again in a tight group that looked like a black ball. It took them a worried hour to reassemble their funny fry.

A dramatic time in a catfish's life is the day the young go off to seek their fortunes. Suddenly the fry are terribly appetizing to their parents. Fighting temptation, the parents speed off into the deep water, while the fry, sensing that all is not well, scatter into the weeds, independent creatures who must now develop their own special abilities.

When the parental instinct dies in a catfish, it dies with a thud. One day I watched a male cat in a laboratory tank take his own and a black-bass fry into his mouth. He spat out his own; but a few days later when he took in small cats and bass—he spat out nothing. His tour of duty was ended. He felt no more loving instincts. That night the aquarium keeper removed the old cat from the tank.

All these remarkable attributes—plus one more— have made the catfish a part of American folklore. To many of us the catfish is a symbol of summer—of lazy drowsing on riverbanks, small boys with fishpoles and straw hats, fish fries in the long summer evenings. For catfish and people seem to go together.

Chapter four

"UPON THY BELLY THOU SHALT GO"

Three hundred and fifty million years ago, when the waters were teeming with life and plants were beginning to flourish on the land, a fishlike creature left the sea and crawled ashore, where it prospered. But there was one way of life this pioneer could not change: each spring it had to return to the water to lay eggs so that its young might be cradled by the gentle sea. For this cold-blooded animal was amphibian—living half in water and half on land.

A wide variety of these amphibians dominated the swamps for almost 100 million years, then died away until today but three groups are still alive: frogs and toads; salamanders and newts; and legless, snake-like blindworms.

Over 50 million years after the amphibians appeared, a new creature evolved from them. It was an improvement, for it did not need the sea; it laid eggs on land, thereby freeing itself to discover the earth. This lung-breathing beast was the first true land animal—the reptile. Reptiles invented many new devices. Eggs were fertilized inside the female for the first time. Born on land, the young did not have to change from sea to land creatures; they arrived looking and acting like their parents. The reptiles grew armor—bony plates, horns and shield-like scutes—to protect themselves.

For 120 million years the reptiles were supreme. Some were magnificent. The best known—the dinosaurs—ruled the land in sizes and shapes never seen before or since. Today only five groups of reptiles remain: the lizards, the lizard-like tuatara, the snakes, the turtles and the crocodilians, which include the alligator. One long look at any of them can spin the imagination back to the primeval reptile.

CROAKER IN THE LITTLE POND

Alan Devoe

In a world in which newspaper headlines scream of international tensions, it is very easy for a man to forget that the elemental life of Earth goes on as usual. It is good for a man to remind himself of things like this—that there are venerable stabilities which the insanities of dictators are not able to overthrow. It is good, for instance, just to shut off the television for a while, throw away the newspaper and go out into the warm darkness of a country night and listen to the frogs. It is good for a man to shift his attention for a while to something permanent, such as a frog.

It is early in spring, when the first bloodroots are blossoming and shadblow has just come into flower, that the frog emerges from its winter torpor. Since early the previous fall it has been hibernating in a hidden place—the leopard frogs and green frogs buried deep in the soft bottom mud of creek or pond, the wood frogs concealed in interstices of rotting stumps and lichened fallen logs—and during all the time of cold the sluggish frog blood has scarcely circulated, the frog scarcely stirred in its deep sleep. In the spring, thawed by the returning sun, it issues forth, ready once more to hunt the creek banks, to doze in the shade and breed.

The universe into which the frog comes in the spring is made known to it chiefly in four ways: by sight and sound and smell, and by a subtle sensitivity to light and touch. On each side of the frog's head is a protruding eye, its rotation controlled by six muscles, its lens tremendous and nearly spherical. This eye does not permit keen perception of stationary objects, but it gives immediate awareness of any kind of movement. The stir of a cricket, the dart of a dragonfly, the slow, soundless progress of an earthworm through the grass—these things the frog's great protruding eyes immediately register. So bulbous are the eyes that they would soon suffer accident if the frog could not retract them at will into their sockets and if the two eyelids were not supplemented by a third, a nictitating membrane. As the frog hops along a creek bank in the spring sun, or floats half-submerged in the green-scummed water, the eyes are periodically protruded in search of prey and withdrawn at any passing danger.

The frog has no external ear for hearing the movement of prey or the coming of an enemy, but behind each of its bulging eyes there is a broad tympanic membrane. Inside the auditory capsule lies an inner ear, supplied by branches of the auditory nerve. As the tympanic membrane vibrates, waves of sound travel to this inner ear and transmit to the frog's small, convoluted brain an awareness of sound sensation. Underwater the frog hears much as a fish does: the sound waves traveling in the water are communicated directly to its inner ear.

By awareness of movement, of tympanic vibration and of scents received in its nasal cavities and communicated by olfactory nerves, the frog is equipped to apprehend its small, wet universe. Its fourth endowment—a delicate sensitivity to light—is not less important than these. The frog's body, like a garden slug's, is naked. Its cold green skin is filmed by a thin covering of mucus, which restricts evaporation. It is for this reason that frogs must live in damp places or near ponds and streams where they can readily immerse themselves, for without a constantly moist atmosphere or periodic ablution their skins would quickly dry and they would perish. Even the small, forest-dwelling, red-brown wood frogs, which visit streams only in the spring to lay their eggs, pass most of their time in the damp leaf mold and the humid interior of decaying stumps. A frog's sensitivity to light is as essential to its survival as sight and scent and hearing; it is what impels the frog to withdraw from summer sunlight into damp shade or water.

Equipped in this manner, then, the frog goes forth to pond and creek bank in the spring. The foods it seeks are such lesser fellow haunters of watersides and marshes as worms, midges, spiders and water striders; the frog waits immobile, in the shelter of a leaf or tussock, for these to come near. When one does, the frog darts out its tongue. A frog's tongue is

1. *Eggs, laid in the water by a female frog and fertilized by a male, adhere to water plants in a jelly-like mass.*
2. *Close-up of the eggs: the grooves indicate the beginnings of the tadpoles' backs.* 3. *After several days the tadpoles hatch from the eggs.* 4. *They feast on vegetation in the water, moving about like fish and breathing through gills.* 5. *In time the tadpole develops hind legs.* 6. *Then come the forelegs.* 7. *The tail grows shorter, eventually to be completely resorbed into the body, for frogs are tailless amphibians. The gills are resorbed because the frog develops lungs for breathing on land.* 8. *The tadpole, transformed into a frog, leaves the pond.*

rooted not to the back of its mouth, as are most vertebrates', but to the front; the frog can hurl it forth full-length, and the movement is quick as the flutter of a hummingbird's wing. The tongue is sticky; at a touch it adheres firmly to the body of whatever minute creeping or flying creature it has struck. An instant after contact has been made, the frog draws in its tongue again, and the squirming prey is gripped by the conical teeth of the frog's upper jaw. In a minute or two, convulsively, the frog swallows. If the prey is large or kicks, the frog raises its adroit little forelegs and pushes vigorously to stuff the victim in.

That is the way the frog feeds. The way of perpetuating its kind is this: In the spring the female lays a quantity of eggs—from 5000 to 20,000—when the water of pond or brook is at proper temperature. The eggs, in a mass, adhere to vegetation in the water. After fertilization, the jelly which surrounds the eggs swells and grows in bulk so that the developing embryos may be protected from injury.

Out of an egg, presently, a tadpole comes. It is a long-tailed creature, wholly water-dwelling. It has external gills, vestigial tiny cilia which as an embryo it used for effecting movement within the egg, and fine teeth wherewith it can scrape nourishment from the algae and waterweeds after it has used up the yolk in its alimentary canal. Fishlike, with wrigglings of its long tail, it moves along the mud of the pond or stream which was its birthplace. In time—the period varies among frog species—the tadpole forms four pairs of internal gills; the tuftlike outer gills vanish, and the inner ones take over their function. The tadpole now takes in water through its mouth and passes it out again through its gill slits and through an opening, the spiracle, on the left side of its body.

Other changes in habits and appearance quickly take place. On the hind part of its soft, slippery body there appear in miniature the hind legs of a frog. They grow quickly, developing powerful muscles, and the tadpole acquires the art of swimming with them. A little later forelegs burgeon, the small, delicate forelegs with feet like little hands. The tadpole's tail is growing very short now. It is being resorbed into its body. Resorbed, too, are the four pairs of internal gills, and forming in their place are the pear-shaped elastic lungs with which, as well as through its skin, a grown frog breathes. Only a little longer and the metamorphosis is complete; the tadpole is ready to take its place in the company of frogs, to sit on the brook bank in the shade of a skunk-cabbage leaf hour after hour, watchful for fly or spider, and—forcing air out of its lungs and into its mouth and back again—to emit the sonorous croaking which is its curious music.

A frog has many enemies. It does not often die of age. The yellow-eyed herons, wading the shallow water, are alert to spear its fat green body with their great beaks. The slow turtles, almost invisible in the bottom mud, are enemies; so are snakes, and sometimes larger frogs, and of course always man, who considers frogs' legs a choice delicacy. A frog does not die quietly. When it has been seized by a mottled water snake and is kicking and wriggling in the grip of the cold-fleshed jaws, a frog does something that it does at no other time in its life. Shrilly and piercingly, it screams.

Such is the life story of frogs. It bears no relation that I can see to the international situation. But frogs will be croaking and hunting and dozing in the summer shade as long as there are ponds to croak in.

THAT "TERRIBLE LIZARD"
George S. Fichter

While I was on combat training in Florida during World War II, our daily routine included a stint around an obstacle course. On the final stretch there was a broad, shallow pool. We were supposed to swing across it on a rope, but, hot and sweaty by then, most of us just swung to the middle and dropped in—until one day our enterprising lieutenant put an alligator in the pool.

From that day on, GI's left the ground 15 feet from the water's edge, soared high above the pool and sprawled flat in the dust well over on the other side, as far as they could get from the 'gator's jaws. Not that the alligator showed any interest in the humanity hurtling overhead. It usually lay motionless, sleeping or quietly soaking up the sun. But so fearsome is the alligator's appearance, and so frightening its reputation, that the mere presence of one below us was stimulation enough.

The early Spanish explorers in Florida sent back lurid descriptions of the "terrible lizards" they found there. In those days alligators (which are not giant lizards, but members of the crocodile family) existed in almost unbelievable numbers as far north as the Carolinas and west to the Rio Grande. An explorer in the 1700's reported that the huge reptiles, some of them 20 feet long, were so thick in Florida's St. Johns River he could have crossed the broad stream walking on their backs. He complained that their grunting

and bellowing kept him awake far into the night.

Today alligators are common only around Georgia's giant Okefenokee Swamp, in the Louisiana bayous and in the marshlands of Florida. For a time it seemed that the alligator, beaten back by civilization and hunted for his hide, might follow the passenger pigeon into oblivion. So great was the demand for its skin that nearly a quarter of a million beasts were killed every year. In the late 1940's, however, Florida lawmakers placed restrictions on this slaughter. They also made it unlawful to sell baby 'gators for pets; those you buy today are not really alligators but the closely related caimans, which are imported from Central and South America.

Conservationists gave two good reasons for protecting alligators. Not only are they important tourist attractions, but in the vast open ranges of subtropical Florida—where there are just two seasons, the wet and the dry—'gator holes may be the only permanent, year-round water supply. The alligator digs its cave in the bank of a pond or a stream or under the roots of a big tree, tearing away the tangle of roots with its teeth and loosening the dirt with its shovel-like snout. Then it kicks this material behind it with its feet and swirls it away with its tail. The result, a broad, deep pool in front of each cave, serves as a sort of reservoir. Here, during the dry months, cattle and wildlife come to quench their thirst. Here, too, vegetation grows lush and stays green even when the surrounding country is burned up under a blistering sun.

Since they have been protected by law, alligators in Florida have increased in numbers and moved closer to towns. You can stand at a bridge on some well-traveled highways and spot them sunning themselves along the bank, or see in the water below you the tiny raised-up tip of a 'gator's snout and the two bulbs of its eyes as the reptile glides along, leaving almost no wake. Here and there these in-town alligators have become nuisances. A four-footer somehow got through a fence and took up residence in a private swimming pool at Fort Lauderdale. In Bradenton an alligator came out of Ware's Creek, stalked a sleeping bird dog in broad daylight and snapped its victim almost in two. There have also been a few cases of people being attacked, but none fatally.

Small alligators are probably harmless, but one longer than six feet has an enormous appetite, tremendous power and a short temper. It deserves all the respect you can give it. The alligators particularly to beware of are the half-tamed ones, sometimes fed and sometimes left to their own devices. They may become brazen in their approach, and to tease them is to invite disaster. 'Gators are not the slow-moving, sluggish

The alligator stalks his prey beneath the water. When he strikes, fish, birds and amphibians take off in all directions.

creatures they appear to be, but can turn and attack with lightning speed.

The big alligators spend most of their time in their caves, leaving only to prowl for food or for a mate. During the spring mating period both sexes, but especially the bulls, wander from pond to pond. This is the time of year when they are noisiest. Standing in shallow water, the bull inhales deeply, then lifts his head high and lets out a deep booming noise, halfway between the roar of a lion and the bellow of a bull. Presumably this is the challenge to other males to battle. On a still night it can be heard as far as a mile away, and if you're close you can feel the ground tremble beneath your feet.

The female builds her nest on a spot of high ground by heaping up a pile of vegetation and debris as much as three feet deep. In it she lays several dozen eggs that look like long, leathery hen's eggs, covering them with more rubbish. The eggs are incubated by the heat of the sun and of the decaying debris. For nearly two months the mother lies nearby on guard. Then one day there's a stirring and grunting in the eggs, and she removes the top of the heap so that the little 'gators can make their way out.

Baby alligators, about ten inches in length, actually charge from their eggs ready for a fight. They will sink their needle-sharp teeth into anything that moves —even if it's a brother or a sister. Left to forage for themselves from the start, they live mostly on insects, frogs, mice, fish. Most of the young 'gators are eaten by other creatures of the swamp, but those that survive their first year will measure about a foot and a half in length and weigh half a pound. By the end of the third year they are nearing four feet in length and may weigh 15 pounds. Two years later they are ready to mate and are approaching the six-foot length. They now have a capacity for tackling bigger game—pigs, for example. Many Florida counties have an eight-month open season on 'gators over six feet. Not many measure more than ten feet, and probably the largest are 14-footers.

In an alligator's lipless, almost leering mouth there are from 70 to 80 conical teeth. Small prey are crushed and swallowed whole. But if an alligator gets something too big to swallow in one piece it jerks its head so swiftly and violently that the hapless victim is actually torn to pieces. When an alligator snaps its jaws shut it has a viselike grip on anything between. But the muscles for opening its mouth are unbelievably weak—once those powerful jaws are closed, you can hold them shut with one hand. Men who wrestle 'gators before audiences depend on this weakness.

A third of an alligator's weight is in its massive, muscular tail. With one swing of this appendage a large 'gator can upset a boat, knock a man down or break his leg. In swimming, the alligator propels itself with the tail—and few animals can match its speed traveling underwater.

The alligator has special adaptations which fit it for an aquatic existence. For swimming just below the surface, it has elevated nostrils and popped eyes. (At night, in the glow of a hunter's lamp, these eyes gleam ruby red at 300 feet, bright as the taillights on an automobile.) When the 'gator opens its mouth underwater, a valve closes off the windpipe, allowing it to grab prey without getting water in its lungs. Also, each eye has a third lid which, like a bird's, operates transversely rather than up and down. Transparent films, these lids slide over the 'gator's eyes when it swims underwater.

But to biologists the strangest fact about alligators is that they are found in just two places in the world: in the southern United States and along the Yangtze River Valley in China. Why did these creatures survive in only two such widely separated places? It remains an unsolved riddle.

THE CHARMING VOICE OF THE BOX TURTLE
Colin Fletcher

The day Archimedes came to share my apartment he was sick and depressed. A white patch of fungus was growing over one eye, and until I fixed a light in his room he sulked in the corner, looking very sorry for himself. The second morning he was still sulking and fasting and occasionally wiping at his eye, but that afternoon I got him out in the fall sunshine for a spell. By evening I had a 40-watt bulb warming his cardboard box, and he munched briefly at some bits of crisp, fresh lettuce.

By the fourth morning he was a changed personality. The fungus had gone. His wrinkled skin was beginning to glisten. He demolished a turtle-sized helping of raw hamburger, inspected the thermometer and plainly approved its 80° reading. Then he lumbered into the tin plate full of drinking water and sat there contemplating the deluge his bulk had displaced over the rim.

Archimedes was my first turtle. He was luckier than many firstcomers, because just before buying him I happened to meet a devoted turtle-lover. "You don't need to know much," he told me, "but if you want to keep him indoors this late in the year, you'll have to watch the temperature. Reptiles have no built-in warming mechanism, like us mammals, and they just can't function properly in cold or extreme heat. The best turtle temperature is around 80° during the day; for a box turtle, nights don't matter so much. Otherwise just give him varied food, enough water to drink and sit in, and a covered place out of the light where he can hole up when he wants to."

Box turtles, I found after knowing Archimedes, are docile and gentle. This may well be because—perfectly protected by the extraordinary defensive device that gives them their name—they naturally adopt a passive and peaceful attitude toward the world. The underside of the box turtle's shell (known as the plastron) hinges in the middle. Its inmate can pull both ends up tight against the upper shell (or carapace) and "box" itself in so efficiently that a thin knife blade won't slide through the crack at either end. Inquisitive dogs, finding no place the animal could have gone, turn the shell over and over.

Box turtles can be surprisingly responsive. Some have been taught to balance on their rear legs and "beg" for food—an act perhaps not too far removed from stretching up in the wild for succulent blackberries. In his *Handbook of Turtles* Dr. Archie Carr, one of the world's leading authorities, reports that a box turtle which was habitually fed on hamburger "soon learned to show its hunger by taking a station in front of the refrigerator."

Almost anywhere in America, pet box turtles will happily live outdoors all summer, eating what they can find. Winters, left to themselves, they will dig down into loose soil—sometimes as deep as two feet —and hibernate. Or they can be kept indoors, where they are much less demanding than aquatic turtles. For example, aquatic turtles need lots of water; the tiny green ones can't even swallow food unless they are submerged.

When it comes to food, a box turtle is like most humans—an opportunist. He will eat more or less whatever is going—not chewing, however, for he has no teeth and must shear off food with the sharp, bony sheaths covering his jaws. In the wild, insects are what he likes best. Fruits and succulent vegetation come next. But never forget that food is no good to your turtle unless he is warm enough to digest it. Turtles must have sunlight, too—preferably unfiltered by glass—to produce essential Vitamin D. However, a little cod-liver oil helps remedy any deficiency.

Perhaps the vilest torture inflicted on pet turtles

The box turtle looks upon the world with perfect confidence that nothing can penetrate his shell once he closes his trapdoor. The shell was perfected before the Age of Dinosaurs.

is painting their shells. An inelastic, airtight, waterproof layer of paint disorganizes bodily functions, deforms the growing shell and condemns the turtle to ever increasing pain and eventual death. The paint should be carefully flaked away with a razor blade or sharp knife, or rubbed off with nail-polish remover.

When is a turtle a tortoise? The question is unanswerable: the names are unscientific and inexact. But in America today the word "turtle" normally includes the whole tribe, while "tortoise" means "land turtle" (though "tortoise shell" comes from the sea-dwelling hawksbill turtle!). "Terrapin," from an Algonquin Indian name, usually refers to a freshwater or tidewater variety that people like to eat.

Box turtles straddle these definitions with a characteristic disregard for obstacles. They live almost entirely on land, almost never take a swim and have high-domed shells like tortoises—yet are more closely related to aquatic turtles. West of the Mississippi they are known as "box tortoises" or even "box terrapins." And herpetologists call the American box-turtle clan "Terrapene." All of which leaves us exactly where we were—in a state of rich, unscientific confusion.

Most people today, meeting a wrinkled, toothless, wizen-faced turtle, exclaim, "Now I wonder how old *he* is!" (There's something compellingly masculine as well as ancient about a turtle's appearance.) And turtles *do* grow old—very old. A box turtle's life expectancy is 40 to 50 years, and at least one is known to have lived 130 years. But even adolescent turtles look old—and in a sense they *are*. Turtles are an ancient tribe, far older than the dinosaurs. Some have changed a lot since their beginnings; yet when the last dinosaur died, about 100 million years ago, there already existed a turtle whose bones—and probably everything else, too—were exactly the same as those of a species that still lives in the jungles of the Amazon.

You don't really appreciate how bizarre a turtle is until you examine an empty shell (about five inches in length for an adult) and discover that the foundation of the upper part is formed by ribs—and that the rigid but still segmented backbone is built into this ribcage-in-the-roof. Such a vivid anatomy lesson finally demolishes the still popular folklore story that turtles crawl out of their shells to escape a fire.

Box turtles are no numskulls. They're surprisingly good at solving the maze puzzles used to gauge animal intelligence. And their eyesight is acute, especially at short range. They probably taste things, certainly smell them, and react instantly to the lightest touch. They are highly sensitive to land vibration and may well hear airborne sounds, too (they have highly developed inner ears, though no outer organs).

But that famous biblical passage, "And the voice of the turtle is heard in our land," has led many people astray. Turtles have no vocal cords; the quotation refers to what we now call turtledoves. The closest a turtle comes to utterance is when certain species grunt or roar at mating time. Otherwise they make only mechanical noises—a grinding of jaw surfaces, the creak of a misfit box turtle closing its shell. Surprised turtles often hiss as they draw their heads into their "turtleneck sweaters," but this is probably just air being expelled from suddenly compressed lungs.

Box turtles live solitary but tolerant lives. They move—almost entirely in daylight—within restricted areas that average barely 250 yards across; but they make no attempt to defend their territories against invaders, as many animals do. Indeed, several little "kingdoms" often overlap. At egg-laying time the females may rove as much as half a mile in search of a good nest site. Returning, they no doubt use their fairly efficient homing instinct, which is shared by the males. Experiments with flashing mirrors suggest that they orient themselves by the sun.

A female box turtle can retain live sperm for as long as four years. She lays from one to eight eggs in a shallow nest dug in soft soil—usually in June, almost always in late afternoon. She carefully covers and camouflages her eggs before leaving them to their fate (turtles began long before mother love appeared on Earth), but they often suffer heavy losses from marauding mammals and snakes.

The young hatch out after two or three months—and then seem to disappear. Naturalists have long been asking, "Where do baby box turtles go?" The answer seems to be that they go almost at once into hibernation. But in some areas, at least, it may simply be that they are extraordinarily difficult to see. They need their good camouflage protection. At first, unable to retire completely into their shells, they make succulent meals for coyotes, dogs, badgers, skunks, raccoons and even crows.

For 300 million years the turtle shell has done a superb defensive job. Inside it, the earliest turtles needed to fear few hazards beyond fire and freezing. As time moved along, unlucky individuals no doubt had their shells cracked by powerful-jawed animals —first by the huge carnivores of the reptilian age, later by alligators and possibly coyotes. In some parts of the world, too, eagles are reported to crack turtles by dropping them from a height. (A Greek legend holds that the poet and dramatist Aeschylus was killed by a turtle-carrying eagle that mistook his bald head for a rock.) But none of these dangers severely threatened the turtle. Calm and perfectly adjusted, he sturdily survived.

Then, barely a million years ago, there appeared a new animal that could create fire and wield weapons. That animal became by far the turtle's worst enemy. Its depredations have already wiped out several species. Others are threatened. Only 300 years ago huge fleets of green turtles roamed the oceans; today, soup-loving man has almost destroyed them. An English pirate once wrote of the giant Galápagos tortoises, "They are so extraordinarily large and fat, and so sweet, that no pullet eats so pleasantly." Between 1831 and 1865 American whaling ships alone slaughtered an estimated ten million of them for food.

Today we have at last become wise enough to start protecting the world's animals. We are trying to re-establish the green turtle's old breeding grounds; it is now illegal to kill a Galápagos tortoise; and here at home the box turtle is protected in many areas. What is more, the box turtle holds one vital advantage over many other species: we rarely eat him. And for good reason. Box turtles can apparently digest poisonous mushrooms with safety, but the poison remains in their bodies. It seems fairly well established that people have become seriously ill after eating them, and some have even died.

So, all things considered, we can rest reasonably assured that for a long time to come the charming and inoffensive box turtle will continue to be seen in our land.

Chapter five

THE MIGHTY THRONG

Lowest on the tree of life are many strange creatures so odd and different that some of them are hard to believe. They are the invertebrates— the teeming masses of animals without backbones. Most of them live in the ocean—amoebas, sponges, jellyfish, corals, worms, shellfish, starfish and lobsters, to mention a few. Some are soft-bodied; others, like the oyster and the clam, have veritable rocks for outside covering.

One group of invertebrates adapted to land are the insects, the largest mass of life on Earth. Some 800,000 species are known, and another three to four million may still be discovered. Insects are covered with jointed armor; their "blood" is green, yellow or clear, and is pumped by a simple heart—a "blood" vessel that contracts from one end to the other. An insect has no lungs; chinks in the armor bring oxygen to the blood. Its brains are knots, and it always has six legs. (Spiders are not insects; they have eight legs and belong to another class.)

Insects and spiders are the most imaginative of all beasts; they invade every possible corner of the Earth and have thought up every sort of mechanism to function there—glue, hooks, snorkels, wings, scubas, parachutes, swings. Think of something and an insect or a spider has invented it first—even internal clocks, triggered by heat, are set each year to awaken certain species. Insects and spiders have had sonar for millions of years. They have spun silk, made pottery, built cities, tunneled under mountains. Poisons, insecticides and preservatives were invented first by insects.

Some of these animals are the most peaceful examples of coöperative living. Ants, bees and wasps live in societies so beautifully regulated that man is blundering in comparison.

MASTER CATERPILLAR

Donald Culross Peattie

With book and with bell, with candle and Latin, certain caterpillars plaguing a town in southern France were once excommunicated. Or so goes the folk tale. But even this curse of the Church was not enough to drive out the heretical woolly pilgrims—pine processionary caterpillars, who move in single file, head to tail, wreaking destruction throughout the pine forests. So they were summoned to court, to be arraigned on charges of trespass, vandalism and theft. However, the counsel appointed for their defense showed that his clients could not remove themselves in time to comply with the court order, and he was granted a later date for their departure.

Well did all parties to this sly old nonsense know that at the approach of winter the processionaries would hole up in cocoons, to emerge the following spring as harmless moths.

For caterpillars, as every child knows, are the larval stage of moths and butterflies, the childhood of the insect. But what brats are these children! They eat and grow prodigiously, get into anything and everything and leave havoc behind them. The tobacco hornworm, the cutworm, the larva of the velvet-bean moth, of the codling moth and the clothes moth alone cause hundreds of millions of dollars' damage yearly. On the other hand, from ancient times a great commerce has been built upon the industry of the silkworm. All these children of nature are far more important than the adult forms of the same insects, most of which spend their time flitting about from one nectar-cocktail party to another, pollinating a flower here and there, or frivoling and flirting and promiscuously mating.

A butterfly, like all other true insects, has six legs. A caterpillar goes it two or five pair better. With these it ripples along on its mighty marathons, for it has a system of muscles that, in proportion to its size and weight, make it an Olympic champion. But some caterpillars, you will have noticed, move by humping or looping. That is because the middle pairs of legs are missing or undeveloped.

Caterpillars have a heart that keeps the yellow or green "blood" moving sluggishly, but no lungs; instead, pores on their bodies connect with a network of tubes and so aerate the blood. There are a crop and gut—trust these greedy creatures for that. And jaws, tireless jaws, that move sideways, not up and down like ours. Primitive sense organs, which will become the eyes of the adult insect, can distinguish light from dark. Apparently without ears, caterpillars move in a silent world, deaf even to their own constant munching. But they have a delicate sense of touch all over the body. Concentrations of nerves in a series of ganglia make up the brain centers of a caterpillar. Here nerve messages are received, and orders to the muscles dispatched. How stubbornly these orders may be carried out was shown by the great Provençal student of insect life, Henri Fabre. He set up a group of pine processionary caterpillars on the rim of a large flower pot, beside which he laid a branch of pine, their favorite food. It would have been perfectly easy for the caterpillars to reach this; instead they crawled round and round the rim of the pot for seven days.

The reason for this apparent idiocy was, from the caterpillar point of view, a sound one. These creatures, like spiders, are spinners, and each processionary, as he went, laid down a thread of silk for a guiding path. The threads formed a track the crawlers could not bring themselves to leave; they became prisoners of the game of follow-the-leader. Call it instinct or reflex, this persistence is a driving force with which a caterpillar is born.

To get born, the caterpillar eats its way out through the shell of its egg. Usually the egg has been laid on the caterpillar's favorite food plant so that the little glutton can immediately fall to. Or, with some species, if food is not at hand, the caterpillar quickly drops off its birthplace by paying out a silken rope and crawls off to seek what it may devour.

Young Master Caterpillar looks a tempting tidbit to many a bright bird eye. So some wary kinds of caterpillar feed underground or at night. Others are protected by a thick coating of hairs, many of which

Caterpillar of the spicebush swallowtail butterfly. The appetite of the caterpillar is prodigious, and it is usually born on a leaf so that it can begin its life of eating at once.

carry an irritant like that of nettles. Blown on the wind when the caterpillar sheds them, these hairs can cause a rash on people who have never even come into contact with the creature.

Even the hairless caterpillars have their ways of surviving. Many of them look like bare, dead twigs on the trees, having the same color, holding themselves at just the same angle of growth as real twigs. Others have a flavor disagreeable to the palates of their enemies. The puss-moth larva can put on a false face by pulling down an extra fold of skin. The result is a furious red "face," two big scary "eyes" and a false, fierce "mouth." Also there emerges from the hindquarters what looks like the forked tongue of a serpent. When disturbed, the caterpillar of the lobster moth can rear up, its front pair of legs looking like feelers, while the raised tail segments protrude false stingers. Whether or not enemies are frightened by such displays is a question.

While many of these underworld characters cost us millions, nature has its own way of eliminating them. I remember an influx of caterpillars into my neighborhood when I was a boy. The community was preparing an attack upon them with poisons and burning when a flock of warblers came through on their seasonal migration, and soon there was hardly a caterpillar to be seen.

As a boy, too, I captured the full-grown larva of a Polyphemus moth and put it with some oak leaves in a shoe box in my room. Soon my caterpillar began the restless weaving back and forth of the head that precedes the spinning of its cocoon. The material for this is produced by glands in the creature's head; it emerges as a viscous fluid which upon contact with the air hardens into silk of varying quality. Generally the cocoon is made in three layers: a coarse, loose outer casing, a lining of fine silken floss and a papery wrapping around the caterpillar itself. In the dark and silence of this retreat it passively undergoes its miraculous transformation.

But in some cases the hand of man interferes, and to great purpose. The silkworm has been domesticated for at least 4000 years, and not all the drip-dry synthetics yet discovered can rival the sheer or sumptuous beauty of silk. The silkworm, a creamy-gray caterpillar about three inches long when full grown, is an amazing little worker. In three days of constant weaving it spins a cocoon from which can be reeled off an unbroken filament up to 1200 yards long and only 1/1200 of an inch thick. Skilled workers unreel these filaments and twist them into thread. About 25,000 cocoons make a pound of raw silk.

The cocoons of many moths are lovely little pieces

 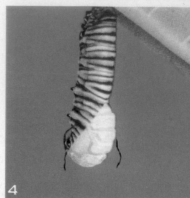

1. Egg of monarch butterfly, greatly enlarged. 2. The caterpillar just out of its egg.

3. The adult caterpillar. 4. It starts to spin a cocoon for the chrysalis stage of its life. 5. Inside the chrysalis the caterpillar is transformed into a butterfly. 6. Toward the end of the chrysalis stage, the wing pattern becomes visible through the wall. 7. At last the butterfly begins to emerge from the chrysalis. 8. The fully developed monarch, its wings thoroughly dry and ready for flight.

of deceit. The leaf-roller caterpillars snuggle between two leaves so fastened together with silk that the whole looks like one dead leaf twirling in the autumn winds. The maesa butterfly makes a hideaway that imitates a plant gall, with apparent "holes" through which you would say gallflies had escaped. The black hairstreak butterfly forms a retiring place so like a bird-dropping on a twig that even collectors are deceived. As for the hated clothes moth, its cocoon is a tiny case clinging to the fabric which the housewife may take for a speck of lint.

Within the privacy of its cocoon the caterpillar changes from the larva we knew in its crawling childhood to a pupa—the dormant stage. This has been likened to adolescence, for now occur in secrecy the alterations from child to adult. On the great day of emergence the latent creature finally cuts, or dissolves, or unplugs an opening in its monastic, dull retreat and crawls out, weak and damp. The wings, crumpled like leaves in bud, slowly expand; their possessor may wave them many times, drying and sunning them in the fresh air, until at last they are ready for the glory of flight.

Now the primitive sense organs of the caterpillar become the compound eyes of the adult, and for the first time color is perceived. Orange and red and yellow particularly delight the butterflies. The moths, night fliers for the most part, prefer white blossoms that show up in the dusk. And certain flowers which are especially adapted to pollination by moths open only at night, or exhale their perfume after the sun has set. For the sense of smell in this winged thing that was a caterpillar is now exquisitely developed. The odor of the female peacock moth will call the males from afar. Even a spot where she has alighted is enough to send these suitors fluttering around it in a frantic search for her. In the swallowtail butterfly, males carry this sensual allurement in their wings to attract the females.

Gone is the childish greed of the caterpillar. These airy adults live only on nectar, reached even in deep-throated flowers by their long, uncurling tongues. Some there are that never eat or drink at all, but live only to mate.

For such a life they pay a high price—brevity of life itself. Soon their lovely wings, now faded and torn, carry them in a last forlorn flutter to the forest floor. Or the beautiful little triflers drift to lake waters, or are borne away by some stream already chattering with cold. But somewhere, in some right place, the eggs have been laid. The light-winged mother does not stay to see more. The great circle of life, which has no beginning and no end, is complete.

STRANGE FORM OF THE SEA
Alan Devoe

Some of the thousands of kinds of animal whose home is the dim green ocean depths and the tide pools, and whose underwater landscape is furnished not with trees but with barnacled rocks and rotting wharf piles and the submerged skeletons of foundered vessels, are related to land creatures that are familiar to us. The horseshoe crabs that sidle up, dripping, out of the sea to lay their eggs along the tide marks of our eastern beaches are biologically linked with the scuttling and sidling spiders of our summer gardens. The lobsters have a kinship with the crayfish that frequent the banks and stony crevices of inland streams.

But there are other denizens of the sea world that are wholly alien to the land, having not even remote similarity to any living animal of our familiar environment. They are entirely marine. The only evidence that they are fellow animals of ours is their participation in the great central rhythms that are common to all our various lives—the rhythms of birth and growth and feeding and reproduction and death. Such a sea creature, for instance, is the common starfish, inhabitant of nearly all the coastal waters of the world.

The animals of our accustomed experience are bilaterally symmetrical—formed so that their chief organs are arranged in pairs on either side of an axis passing from end to end of the body. A man is thus built, as is a beaver, an ant, a fly and a spider. So habituated are we to this anatomy that the physical organization of a starfish constitutes the first difficulty in the way of fellowly recognition.

The body of the starfish is made up of a central area from which radiate five similar arms. The starfish is indeed a five-pointed star. Its calcareous-plated body, looking as inanimate as a pebbly stone of odd design, has not even the elements of usual internal organization to make it seem to us a living thing. Its world is without any directional quality—of forward and backward, right and left—and our habit of thinking in twos, in pairs, is not anywhere applicable to the processes of its dim and mindless underwater days. The processes, unmistakably, are our own; but the quality and pattern of them are as remote from our experience as might be those life sensations which some scientists believe to be experienced by plants.

Motionless, seeming inert as rock, the starfish lies with extended rigid arms upon the ocean floor. Small water spiders and caprellas drift upon its back and settle there. The currents of the water catch up its

spiny body and shift and tumble it. For hour after hour the starfish may float and drift thus, responding with no evidence that there is the drive of a life force in it. But, sooner or later, the stony pentagon makes a tiny stir that has not been caused by the water current. Slowly, more slowly than a snail, it begins gliding. It begins to demonstrate that, like mice and men and millipedes, it has the power to walk.

On the starfish's back, near its center, there is a circular structure which is a sieve. In through it, now, the starfish is sucking sea water. Via intricate canals, the water is coursing through its body, and by means of a series of interior valves and reservoirs is being carried out to the extremities of the radial arms. Along all the arms' undersides, which are deeply grooved from their tips to that central orifice in the starfish's axis which is its feeding mouth, there are quantities of little, transparent, tubular processes. They are about three quarters of an inch long, immensely delicate and elastic, and each of them terminates in a little sucking pad. They are the starfish's feet, the means by which the rigid, directionless body is performing its version of the walking of men and the prancing of deer. It is a locomotion achieved, quite literally, by the starfish's act of drinking.

In the water-vascular system of the starfish, resembling no physiological system known to us on land, the indrawn water flows out into the tube feet, filling them. As each water-filled foot is pressed against the ocean floor, the starfish rhythmically draws the water out from it again, and thus creates a tiny suction tube. Alternately fastening the tube feet and withdrawing them, making use of every pebble and seaweed stalk to which it can adhere, the starfish goes creeping through the water. It does not see where it is going. There is a tiny crimson eyespot at the tip of each of its arms, but these inform the starfish of no more than light and darkness. Now, as it makes its way, it keeps thrusting out a special tube foot, suckerless, at the tip of each of its arms—tapping and reaching and feeling with these instruments in a groping investigation which is its substitute for vision.

The starfish is hungry. Even as it walks, after a fashion, like an animal, so does it hunger like any other animal. When it comes presently to a clam or oyster, it has found its prey. The starfish is an omnivorous scavenger, engulfing in its slow transit of the ocean floor all kinds of fragments of marine life, but it has a special appetite for bivalves. Infinitely slowly, cumbersomely, the starfish creeps up on top of its discovered prey, gradually arches the central axis of its body and in a little while has contrived to straddle the victim. Or, more precisely, to surround it, for its five bent arms compose a kind of imprisoning cage. Now it begins to apply its sucker feet: foot after foot fastened with suction tightness to one side of the victim's two-part shell, foot after foot laboriously fastened to the other. When at last the tremendous grip has been fully arranged, with many slow gropings and settlings, the starfish begins to pull. It pulls with the enormous strength of steadiness, the steadiness with which a growing plant splits a rock. Constantly, unrelentingly, it pulls—a pull of as much as three pounds. No clam or oyster has muscles strong enough to hold its shell closed indefinitely against such prying. The starfish is unhurried and unwearying. It pulls, if need be, for hours, until at last the most tight-shut shell must fly open.

Out from the orifice in its underside, which is its mouth, the starfish slowly now everts its stomach. Farther and farther it extrudes the organ from its stony body, turning it inside out, and gradually, with delicate precision, inserts it into the shell it has forced open. It applies the stomach to the body of the clam or oyster and begins to pour forth its juices of digestion. The feeding is very slow, like all else in the life of this ambulant but sightless and mindless being, almost as slow as the feeding of a pitcher plant upon a fly. But in time the starfish has digested the last fragment of the cold, watery flesh and is ready to move on. Slowly it draws its stomach into its mouth again. With thrust-out groping feelers, and water-driven feet pulsing beneath it, it glides on.

Breathing and drinking and moving in a combined operation, feeding by an extrusion of its stomach—thus the starfish performs three of the chief animal rites. It performs the last great rite—reproduction—when, if female, it pours out a filmy exudate of eggs or, if male, floods the water with a cloudy jet of sperm cells. Commingling in the currents, the stuffs of life will presently blend to produce new millions of the little ciliated transparencies which are infant starfish. These, molting and metamorphosing, will grow to be a new generation of stony pentagons.

Land animals are subject to death by injury: by the lacerations of their enemies or the elements. But when the starfish is broken by the buffeting of the breakers, or perhaps torn in two and hurled back into the sea by some angry human fisherman who has found the starfish despoiling his oyster bed, the starfish does not necessarily die. Each half of its broken body, settling to the ocean bed, has in it a recuperative power of new growth which puts forth with infinite slowness new arms, new tube feet, new arm-tip eyes. What was a broken starfish becomes, in the course of time, two new ones.

A tenacious starfish pulling open a scallop. When the hungry starfish comes upon its prey, it surrounds the creature with its five arms and pulls with its suction pads until the shell parts.

A cowherd ant milking an aphid. This ant keeps herds of aphids for the sweet liquid they secrete.

WONDERLAND OF ANTS
Donald Culross Peattie

"Go to the ant," said Solomon, and so we may—to find a society as industrious as our own. For under our feet, unaware of human ways, ant tribes pursue occupations startlingly like mankind's. I found this out when I lived in the subtropics in a house with a large garden. Ants really owned the place; I merely paid the rent. Living among the magnolias and mimosas, there were four of us in the human family; of ants

there were several million, probably as many as there are people in Greater New York. With a magnifying glass I watched their ways of peace and their wars, when they fell upon each other's Ninevehs and Tyres and smote their foes with a great slaughter.

Some were the big, stiffly moving carpenter ants, which get into the woodwork of a house and, like termites, riddle it with their galleries. Some were harvester ants, which live on the seeds they gather and store for winter. Some species were cowherds and pastured their "cattle"—aphids that suck the sap of plants—upon trees and bushes; these ants bring their kine out each morning and "milk" them for the juice they secrete. There were thief ants and acrobat ants and kidnaper ants, which hide in the walls of other species' nests and steal their babies.

In the Mexican tropics I have seen the famous army ants, fierce nomads that move about in a compact herd, carrying their babies and their queen with them; they can divide columns and flank to the right and left to encircle their prey—yet they are wholly blind and have to smell and tap their way.

All over the world there are steamship ants, which invade ships as stowaways and so travel to distant ports, where some take permanent shore leave. There are big, ferocious slave-raiding ants which tear open the nests of other tribes and seize the hapless young to carry away and raise as slaves. In certain species, they send forth these slaves to do their raiding for them. Some slave-owning ants, indeed, have become so effete that, despite their warrior look, they cannot even feed themselves but have slaves put the food in their very mouths.

Sluggards indeed are these. But of all ants the most fascinatingly industrious are the parasol ants, so called because they may be seen in processions, each one bearing above his head a bit of green leaf. This is no Easter parade. The leaves will be made into compost, for these ants are farmers, perhaps the only farmers in the animal kingdom besides humans and certain termites. They deliberately sow, manure and prune; they weed, eat and again sow their crops. The crops are different kinds of fungus. Some seem to be related to the mushroom we raise; others are distant kin to bread molds. But so secret and subterranean are the labors of these little farmers, and so fiercely do they defend their nests, that it has taken scientists nearly 100 years to piece together what is known of them.

All the leaf-cutting ants are found in the Western Hemisphere, chiefly in the tropics. These efficient reapers are justifiably feared, for their swift depredations on crops and shade trees can spell ruin. But what they did with their harvest of leaves no one knew

A parasol ant carrying a bit of green leaf to be made into compost for its fungus-growing farm. Parasol ants were sowing, tending and harvesting their crops for aeons before man appeared.

until 1874, when the British naturalist Thomas Belt published the result of his first investigations in Nicaragua. He discovered that the ants do not eat the cut leaves but hash them up into a compost, on which they sow the spores of certain fungi. And the ant-farmers cultivate these fungi as carefully as a human gardener tends his cabbages. The little plants are not permitted to reach the fruiting or "toadstool" stage; instead the ants constantly prune them back, and with a purpose.

The repeatedly pruned fungus forms tiny knots, about the size of a pinhead, called "kohlrabies." These are eaten by the ants. The kohlrabi that we ourselves sometimes serve is really a greatly thickened stalk of cabbage; it is not seen in the wild plant but is the fruit of human horticulture. The kohlrabi of the ants is just as clear a case of horticultural know-how, dating back millions of years before human society began.

The hard-working ants eat up their kohlrabies about as fast as these come to a head. And it is by rationing the amount of kohlrabi eaten that the ants produce their different castes, four or five in number. Those fed on minimum amounts never grow up to be more than "minims," tiny workers who tend the fungus garden and feed the larvae or ant babies. A medium-rich diet develops the "mediae," workers who do most of the leaf-stripping. More food develops the big, fierce soldier ants who defend the nest; they can bite so savagely that they draw blood. And a still richer diet produces the idle males and the virgin "princesses," both of which are winged in preparation for the nuptial flight.

For this, on some enchanted evening, they are led out of the nest by the workers. And each princess carries, in a special pouch behind her jaws, a little hoard of fungus spores with which she will begin the economy of a new nest. You might compare it to the yeast which a pioneer bride took with her to her new home, when this continent was being settled, so that all under her roof might be given their daily bread. Now the princess spreads her fairy wings and takes off into the wide air. The males follow; they have enormous eyes, their wings are built for speed, like a pursuit plane's, and eventually the princess is overtaken somewhere high in the warm dusk. Once the mating is done, the life of the males is also finished. They fall to earth and die.

But the female, now sufficiently fertilized for the rest of her life, descends purposefully to earth. And of all of the strange sights I have seen in the insect world, the oddest is a young queen wrenching off her own iridescent wings—as if an angel should decide to become a woman. Then she runs around nervously, like a cat looking for a place to have kittens; when she finds a cranny under a stone or log, or a crack in the earth, she scurries in and begins excavating still farther. Never again will she see the light of day.

Here in the new nest the queen ejects from her mouth the pellets of fungus spores she has brought from the old. She prunes the first crop as it grows, and licks it to keep it moist. At the same time she starts to lay her first eggs. As the eggs hatch into little larvae the queen feeds them on the kohlrabies. As soon as the first adult ants emerge, they find there are jobs waiting for them. The fungus gardens must be tended; leaves must be brought in for compost. The nest must be guarded, the babies washed and fed, and the new subterranean quarters enlarged till the domelike mushroom cellars, connected by a system of corridors as complex as a big-city subway, grow to the size of a man's head.

Now the workers, who are all female-neuters (maiden aunts, you might say), make all the decisions and give out the rations which will determine the caste of each ant. A precious prisoner in the dark, perpetually pregnant, the queen is just a big egg-laying machine, zealously fed on kohlrabies by the workers, who will die in her defense. Thus, forever completing their cycle, the ant society fulfills every law of a blind, tyrannical instinct. Not for the ants the light of reason by which we humans make our mistakes and find our freedom.

PART 2

THEIR FATE AND DESTINY

*Certain species of the Earth—whether insect
or bird or mammal—share an unusual fortune
or misfortune. Some have been living
together on the Earth from earliest times.
Some have perished, even at their fullest tide of
life. Some live at great heights, at great depths,
or in other climes formidable to man.*

Chapter one

THE VANISHED AND
THE VANISHING

Each year in this modern era one more wild animal passes into oblivion as man continues to hunt, bulldoze marshes, pave woodlands and disregard the needs of wildlife. Since the birth of Christ, 106 kinds of mammal have become extinct, almost a third of them in the last 50 years. But our abuse gathers momentum, and 600 more mammals are threatened. There are no replacements: not one new animal is known to have evolved in the past million years.

The extermination of the modern beasts usually begins with the actions of man. He hunts or traps an animal until its numbers are reduced to a thin margin of life. The pert little heath hen, the passenger pigeon—their stories are the same. At first there were many. Then by hunting them during the breeding season and not limiting the kill, man plunged their populations so low that other killing forces could move in. Predatory enemies, fire, the hazards of weather cut them down further—to that mystical threshold where there are too few individuals to make an enduring animal society. Soon they were gone from the Earth.

Other beasts are facing the same fate: the whooping crane, the grizzly bear, the gorilla, the bison, the green turtle—on and on down the list of 600. Some, such as the great beasts of Africa, can be saved if we plan quickly enough. Others, however, cannot be pulled back. Their extinction is only a matter of time.

THE RACE TO SAVE THE WHOOPING CRANE

Peter Farb

Hunched in a blind on the Platte River in central Nebraska, two hunters scanned the gray October skies. As two targets appeared on the horizon, the men raised their guns. Then their fingers froze on the triggers, and they gazed in wonder. The great birds soaring overhead were snowy white except for jet-black wing tips and carmine heads. Their powerful, broad wings had a seven-foot spread; their necks and heads stretched forward like spears cutting through the air. As the birds came to earth, a buglelike call resembling an Indian war whoop burst from the windpipe of the male.

The hunters knew at once that these were migrating whooping cranes—the rarest and one of the largest, most magnificent of all birds to spread their wings over North America. The two men rushed to a nearby farmhouse to call their game warden and report the sighting. At once the "whooper network" spread the word to other wardens and sportsmen farther south on the migration flyway. Newspapers, radio and television stations swung into action, warning hunters not to molest the great birds.

Today there are only 39 whooping cranes left, eight of them in captivity in zoos. The species has been living on the edge of extinction for many years. Now it is inching its way back. Each fall these rare birds are "convoyed" on their migration of 2500 miles from their nesting grounds in the wilderness of northern Canada to their winter sanctuary at the Aransas Refuge on the Texas Gulf Coast. And there each November they are counted, in the hope that once again they will have gained in their dramatic comeback.

At one time whooping cranes ranged over almost our entire continent and bred throughout a 1000-mile swath of the American heartland from Illinois to the Dakotas and into Canada. But as the birds were shot for food and sport, and their nesting grounds on the prairies turned into cropland, their numbers declined steadily. The few that survived did so in remote wilderness areas. As early as 1912 the naturalist E. H. Forbush pronounced them doomed to extinction. A decade later their once tremendous wintering range had shrunk to a pinpoint on the Texas coast. Finally, in 1937, to protect the few birds that had survived,

This splendid group of whooping cranes represents more than one tenth of the entire whooping-crane population.

about 47,000 acres were set aside as the Aransas National Wildlife Refuge. Despite this step, the plight of the cranes worsened: in 1943 amateur bird-watchers near the Platte River sighted only one bird.

This alarming report sparked the Coöperative Whooping Crane Project, set up by the National Audubon Society and the U.S. Fish and Wildlife Service. The late Robert Porter Allen, an energetic, cigar-chomping, rough-and-ready naturalist, was chosen to head the project. Allen served the cause of wildlife preservation well as both Sanctuary and Research Director of the National Audubon Society. He had seen whoopers only once in his life, on a camping trip in the Aransas Refuge, when three of the huge birds strode by less than 200 yards from him. He was overwhelmed by their magnificence—their man-high noble bearing, their yard-long stride, their wild trumpeting, their untamed spirit. To him, the whooper was like a great "prehistoric bird prancing over the mud flats."

The first winter of the project Allen counted 25 cranes at Aransas. Whoopers mate for life and keep each youngster with them for a year. Soon he was able to recognize various pairs and families. Giving them names like "North Family" or "Middle Pair," he plotted 14 distinct homesteads. Each family of adult birds with their brownish-red young born during the summer had staked out a territory of about 400 acres—and woe to any pair that wandered into another's territory! (When this happens, the defending male first challenges the intruder with a whoop that can be heard for more than a mile, then puts his head down and charges with his javelin beak outthrust.)

As the weather warms each March, the birds climb daily into the sky. Each day they circle higher and higher, as if tugging at the invisible stays that bind them to their winter quarters. Then one day in early April they disappear into the north. Allen felt that it was essential to trace their route to their breeding grounds, and to protect them on the way.

He headed for a major stopping-off place for the migrating birds, the area along the Platte River in Nebraska. He had studied reports of past sightings of the cranes, and now he plotted a probable migration route. All along the route a network of volunteer observers was set up to scan the skies. The birds were tracked in Oklahoma and Kansas, but in anxious weeks of waiting he saw not a single crane along the Platte. Finally a farmer called and said he was certain that he had five cranes on his property. Allen raced there in his car, but the birds had flown. He drove to the airport and found a pilot to take him up. Within ten minutes the low-flying plane was above five large patches of white on a mudbank in the river. There was no doubt—they were the North Family and the Slough Pair that Allen knew so well.

The network of sportsmen, civic groups and bird clubs continued to track the birds as far north as Saskatchewan. After that they disappeared. But Allen now had an accurate migration path, a thin line that varies no more than 50 miles. He had made an immense stride toward seeing that the birds would never again be molested on their passage across America.

All the sightings showed a straight-line route north. Allen extended the line and found that it pointed close to Regina, Saskatchewan. This seemed a logical jumping-off place to search for the birds, since the last recorded nesting of whoopers had been near there in 1922. So Allen headed for Canada. Hitching rides on U.S. Fish and Wildlife Service planes, he flew back and forth across a wilderness larger than all New England. Wherever his plane landed, he asked about the cranes. Some of the older Eskimos and Indians recollected the great white birds but told Allen they hadn't been seen in years. Finally, after two summers of hunting, he had to call off the search without finding the elusive nesting grounds.

During the following summers there were persistent reports by pilots who had seen cranes in the Northwest Territories. A pattern was beginning to emerge: all sightings occurred in the vicinity of Wood Buffalo Park, one of Canada's least-explored areas. It was now more urgent than ever that the nesting grounds be located and protected, for the 1954 breeding season had been the worst since the Coöperative Project began. Not a single young bird reached Aransas that November, and of the 24 birds that had gone north the previous spring only 21 returned.

In the spring of 1955 a Canadian Wildlife Service biologist flying out of Fort Smith in the Northwest Territories definitely identified whooping cranes with young at Wood Buffalo Park. Allen, together with a representative from the U.S. Fish and Wildlife Service and one from the Canadian Wildlife Service, set out by canoe from Fort Smith for the remote breeding grounds. But after a week of log jams, backbreaking portages and ceaseless attacks by hordes of biting insects, the weary men gave up and returned to Fort Smith.

A few days later a helicopter took them into the wilderness, but the pilot set them down in the wrong location. It took them 11 grueling days to cut their way out. Then they got another helicopter. This time they were landed in a place that looked right—a marshy land interlaced with shallow ponds and lakes. The men made camp, then fought their way through dense thickets. Suddenly there was a flash of white in front of them—a whooper! Allen had finally reached the last stronghold of the whooping cranes.

The discovery came none too soon. Even with protection in the nesting area and along the migration route, no young birds arrived in Aransas in 1962, but seven did appear in 1963. It is still too early to say that the battle to save the whooping crane is being won. As a species, it has a precarious hold on life, but it *is* holding on.

RETURN OF THE SEA OTTER

Donald Culross Peattie

The Pacific sea otter has the most beautiful and valuable fur in the world. Through greed for it hundreds of men have died and many have been cruelly enslaved. In the hunt for it the history of North America has been changed. And by the beginning of this century the peerless fur had almost cost the extinction of the gentle bearer itself.

Either a jet black or a velvety brown so deep it looks black, yet silvery at the tips, the otter's pelt is equally rich at all times of the year. The animal lives in waters enduringly cold and has no need to change its coat. The fur is warmer than sable and more durable than mink, which looks coarse beside it. Yet no amount of money can buy a coat of this fabulous pelage, for in 1911 a four-nation treaty (the United States, Russia, Japan, Great Britain) placed severe restrictions on the killing of sea otters.

In the days when the sea otter was numerous past all counting, it thrived in the spray-smoke of the ocean's endless warfare with the rocks, from the northernmost island of Japan and the Aleutians through the isles and channels of Alaska down the foggy coast of northern California all the way to Mexico, following the cold Japan Current. In the kelp beds—giant seaweeds—the playful animal found safety from man-eating sharks and killer whales, its principal enemies before man found it. Here the herds of otters were happy, loving the fury of the waves, breathing contentedly the shrouding fog. For swimming, the sea otter uses chiefly its powerful webbed hind feet in a scissors stroke. Though a true mammal, it is no relative of the barking seal or bellowing sea lion, but belongs to the order of the musk bearers, as do the river otter, the mink and the skunk. A male is four to five feet long, including the tail, used as a rudder.

The forefeet are so short that a sea otter on the shore has a sadly lumbering gait; they serve better as hands than as feet. Indeed, this is one of the few animals that can actually use a tool—a stone brought up

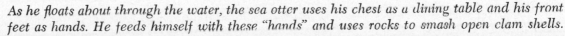

As he floats about through the water, the sea otter uses his chest as a dining table and his front feet as hands. He feeds himself with these "hands" and uses rocks to smash open clam shells.

from the deep and placed on the chest like an anvil, on which it smashes the shells of the seafood that forms its diet. Rocking peacefully on its back, the creature uses its chest as a dining table, tearing the meat from crab or mussel with those Teddy-bear fore-paws and licking its paws to finish off the meal. Then, if the light is bright and the need for a snooze comes over it, the otter may cover its eyes with those paws, the better to drowse in the wild waves.

Like human beings, otters mate in any month and have normally only one offspring at a time, though occasionally there are twins. Born in the water, otter pups do not know instinctively how to swim; they have to be taught. If a mother has to flee for her life, she clutches her pup to her breast, plunges deep and comes up again only when the little one is out of breath. If all is well, the mother spends hours playing with her child, which has a cry very like a human baby's. The animals sleep when darkness falls, wrap-ping themselves in long strands of kelp so that the ocean currents cannot bear them away.

This idyllic existence was threatened in the first half of the 18th century. The Russians, having ex-panded their empire to the shores of the Pacific, sent a Dane named Vitus Bering out looking for a vast imaginary continent in the mid-north Pacific. What he found was Alaska and the Aleutian Islands. But the top brass on his expedition insisted on keeping at sea, looking for what was not there. The party's food was spoiling when the ship struck a rock. The few who could got to shore on a desolate island.

Now the Russians had plenty of fresh meat. The sea otters were so unsuspecting that the castaways could walk among them and simply club them to death. Bering died on the island, but when spring came the survivors managed to rebuild their boat, and with a goodly lot of sea-otter skins they at last reached Kamchatka. There the furs made a sensation.

Thus the sea otter, which the Aleut Indians had taken only sparingly, entered an era of commercial exploitation. Russia had found a fur finer than its sable to exchange for China's teas and silks. In a few years sea otter became the imperial fur of China. It cloaked mandarins and their ladies as well; soft mittens of it warmed the long-nailed fingers of the wealthy. What was not sold at the Kiakhta gate to Cathay was bought at staggering prices by buyers from Europe.

Captain Cook's expedition, exploring the northern Pacific at the time of the American Revolution, took back to England word of the fabulous fur bearer and the prices brought by its pelage. After 1784, English and French, Portuguese and Americans sent otter-hunting ships into waters the Czar thought of as

Russian. But the Russians were driven by their de-manding market. At gunpoint they forced the Aleut Indians to do their otter-hunting. They sent these experts out in *baidarkas* (kayak-like canoes covered with sea-lion skin) armed with dart and rifle. As the northern herds diminished, Russian ships with Aleuts and *baidarkas* aboard hunted farther and farther south. In 1812, out of redwood timbers, the Russians built Fort Ross, still standing not far north of San Francisco.

The Yankees, more particularly called "the Boston men," had to come around Cape Horn, but no dis-tance was too great for them in any marine trade. The poor sea otter continued to fall in countless numbers until fashion entered the stage of history again. Sea-otter fur went out of style in China, and the value of the pelts sank. Losing interest, the Russians withdrew. Thereafter, when it could be found, the sea otter was still pursued until 1911, when the U.S. government passed a law to back up the four-nation treaty re-stricting otter-hunting. Even so, by 1920 some sci-entists asserted that the wondrous little animal had vanished from the shores of the Golden State.

Yet along the Monterey coast a few bobbing heads had been noted by game wardens and local residents. Then, in 1938, two Carmel residents, Mr. and Mrs. H. G. Sharpe, were testing their fine new binoculars when they saw a herd of animals floating and swim-ming on their backs in the sea. Alerted, nearby scien-tists identified the gamboling ocean-dwellers as the vanished sea otters, returned some 300 strong!

But the sea otter reproduces slowly. There arrives, it is calculated, about one pup to a dozen adults; a mother does not bear a pup every year. There is al-ways danger from sharks, which have recently been drawn much closer to shore by a warming of the Japan Current. So the sea otters are still imperiled, although their present watery haunt, from the islands off Santa Barbara northward to Carmel, has been made a sanctuary for them.

The latest census, taken by helicopter in 1958, showed that the California sea-otter population had maintained itself during the last 20 years. A larger herd, perhaps 5000, is known to exist in Alaskan waters, and even more live in the lonely Aleutians. But these "children of the sea" have been pushed so close to the vanishing point that any major disease or serious poaching could wipe them out.

The U.S. government is not conserving the sea otter so that it can be killed, as of old, for its fur. It is trying to save this appealing little fellow citizen for its own sake, that it may once more thrive in the spray and the fog, dive and float and play with its pups, and regain what it can of the idyll of its long-lost prime.

ONCE THERE WERE BILLIONS

Maitland Edey

The fate of the passenger pigeon is almost unbelievable. Just a century ago these birds were probably the most numerous on earth. Yet within a span of 50 years human beings succeeded in destroying every last one of them. Nowhere else in the long, uneven war between men and birds has the rapacity of mankind been so brutally recorded.

The passenger pigeon itself was striking, closely resembling the mourning dove but about half again as large. Its mien was alert, its general impression one of grace. It was exceptionally swift and powerful. Indeed, it had to be, for life in the great pigeon flocks was highly competitive. The flock was all-important. As long as there were pigeons at all, they tended to come together. But when the flocks were broken up and the survivors were forced to exist in small, scattered groups, they seemed incapable of doing so.

When Jacques Cartier, the first white man to report on the pigeons, came to North America from France in 1534, he saw them in infinite numbers. To the Indians the pigeons were a rich and handy food. They used a blunt-headed arrow which, when shot up through the bottom of a nest, neatly knocked out the squab sitting in it. Whole tribes would camp near a nesting, collecting squabs as long as they could. But this nibbling at the edge of a great flock caused no perceptible diminution in their numbers.

Impressed by the clouds of pigeons overhead, ornithologist Alexander Wilson one day in 1810 sat down on the bank of a creek in Kentucky to count them. They flew steadily past him at a speed he estimated to be 60 miles an hour, in closely packed columns— not less than three birds to a cubic yard of air—on a front more than a mile wide. An hour later this torrent had widened and deepened. They continued pouring by until after nightfall. Altogether, Wilson estimated the flock was 240 miles long and contained 2,230,272,000 pigeons. Incredible? John James Audubon, calculating the population of another flight in 1813, conservatively arrived at half Wilson's figure, but was left with a single flock of more than a billion.

The pigeons would cruise over the forest on the lookout for acorns and beechnuts, and when they saw a likely spot, they would settle to the ground with a rush of wings like a windstorm. As they advanced,

Martha, the last of the passenger pigeons, died in Cincinnati in September 1914. She is now mounted and can be seen at the Smithsonian Institution in Washington, D.C.

they swept the forest floor bare. Those in the rear were constantly flying over those in front and landing ahead of them, giving the illusion of an endless wheel of birds thundering among the trees. Their appetites were enormous. Studies indicate that the yearly consumption of Wilson's flock alone would have been enough to fill a warehouse 100 feet high, 100 feet wide and 25 miles long.

As with other communal creatures, the pigeons' responses were deeply grooved. When some pigeons in a flock were forced to veer suddenly from a diving hawk, following birds would blindly execute the same maneuver in the same place—long after the hawk had gone. They could fly in close formation with breathtaking skill, thousands of birds soaring and swooping as one, in and out of treetops at full speed, never touching one another, never touching a leaf. But two flocks meeting head on produced severe damage, since the birds apparently knew only how to fly alongside other pigeons, not directly at them. Buildings baffled them. They would spatter against the side of a barn like hailstones.

The pigeon flocks used certain preferred roosting places—often in swamps—and would return to them night after night, despite the fact that they sometimes had to fly 100 miles for food and would not get back until midnight. Moreover, in their roosts they were constantly dogged by predators and particularly by man. Audubon described a visit to a roost on the Green River in Kentucky. He arrived late one afternoon, just before the pigeons were due to come back:

"A great number of persons with horses and wagons, guns and ammunition had already established encampments. Two farmers had driven upward of 300 hogs to be fattened on the Pigeons. People employed in plucking and salting were sitting in the midst of large piles of birds. The dung lay several inches deep, covering the whole extent of the roosting place like snow. Suddenly there was a general cry of 'Here they come!' The noise they made reminded me of a hard gale at sea, passing through the rigging of a close-reefed vessel. . . .

"Thousands were soon knocked down by men with poles. The birds continued to pour in. Fires were lighted, and a magnificent and almost terrifying sight presented itself. The Pigeons, arriving by thousands, alighted everywhere, one above another, until solid masses as large as hogsheads were formed on the branches. Here and there the perches gave way under the weight with a crash and, falling to the ground, destroyed hundreds of the birds beneath. It was a scene of uproar and confusion; even the reports of the guns could seldom be heard. It was past midnight before I perceived a decrease in the number of those that arrived.

"Towards the approach of day, the noise in some measure subsided. The Pigeons began to move off, and at sunrise all that were able to fly had disappeared. Eagles and hawks, accompanied by a crowd of vultures, came to enjoy their share of the spoil, whilst the authors of all this devastation began their entry amongst the dead, the dying and the mangled. The Pigeons were piled in heaps, until each had as many as he could possibly dispose of, when the hogs were let loose to feed on the remainder."

The nesting sites were as concentrated as the roosts, stretching for miles along creeks or river bottoms,

with as many as 200 nests in a tree. At a certain moment, usually in April, a month or so after the migrating flocks had begun to arrive in the northern states, a site would be mysteriously agreed upon by a group of birds. Within a day or two they would be courting in great numbers. This activity, with its incessant cooing, its fluttering and flapping of wings, spread an electric message of erotic suggestion, and soon all the pigeons in the area would excitedly begin pouring in. Within a short time nest-building would start.

One egg was laid, and during incubation the parents took turns going off for food. At daybreak the males would depart as if on signal, millions rising from the trees in a giant exhalation. Then the site would remain quiet for several hours until the males came back and it was the turn of the females to go off and eat. The whole cycle of rearing young took only a month—two weeks for incubation of the eggs and two weeks for feeding the babies. At the end of the month the squabs were as fat as butter and as big as their parents. Having all been hatched within a day or two, they all matured together, and together they were abandoned, billions of helpless youngsters sitting like lardy lumps in their nests, crying for food. When they became hungry enough, they would plop to the ground on wings whose feathers were not yet fully grown. There they would scramble around as best they could, living on their body fat while they learned to fly. After a week they were as thin as shad but able to shift for themselves.

From the beginning the young betrayed the same overpowering instinct for flocking and fast flight which gripped their parents. They formed flocks of their own—weak, low-flying but headlong ones which followed the bends of watercourses or open glades. The young birds impaled themselves on twigs, they sliced themselves in two against telegraph wires, but they flew, impelled by an ungovernable urge. They *had* to fly, and the survivors soon flew superbly. By fall they had joined up with the adults and were generally indistinguishable from them.

Thus the passenger pigeon, one of the most remarkable birds that ever existed. How, then, was the species obliterated? It did not take long. All through the 18th century and the first half of the 19th the eastern section of the country was filling up with settlers. Men killed pigeons as a matter of course. They ate them fresh, dried and pickled. They rendered them into fat, and salted them down for hard times ahead. Laborers, servants and slaves often saw no other meat. Whenever the pigeons came, all hands would turn out and kill as many as they could. Their roosts and nesting sites were tracked down and plundered.

This incessant pressure the birds could not withstand. A time soon came when there was no place where they could find sanctuary, no hour of the day or night when they were not being attacked. The railroads and the telegraph sealed the pigeons' doom. Like the birds themselves, men could now travel several hundred miles in a day, the news flashing along the wires that the flocks were in Wisconsin one week, Michigan the next.

An enormous demand built up. At a single nesting in Petoskey, Michigan, no less than 2000 persons were employed in catching, killing and processing pigeons.

Squabbing was a revolting business. The quickest and most efficient method of collecting a couple of hundred squabs in a tree was to chop down the tree, if possible felling it in such a way that it would bring down the tree next to it also. Or you could set a tree on fire. A birch would go up in a sudden roar of flames, sending a cascade of half-roasted nestlings to the ground, while the adult birds would go rocketing out of the tree, feathers smoking, to fall singed and helpless miles away.

The number of pigeons shipped to market strains belief. From one nesting site after another in Pennsylvania, upper New York and Wisconsin came reports of half a million, a million, two million birds being shipped out in a few weeks. Undoubtedly an equal number never got shipped, having been burned, trampled, eaten by hogs, spoiled or never collected.

But far more important than squabs shipped or not shipped were the squabs not even born—the progeny of millions of birds given no opportunity to reproduce. By 1878 a huge nesting in Michigan probably comprised most of the remaining pigeons in the country. A decade later there were no nestings worth reporting anywhere, just a scattering of a hundred birds here, a dozen there. In another ten years even those had gone. There were no passenger pigeons at all—outside of zoos. In the zoos they clearly missed the excitement of numbers, and they bred intermittently. By 1908 the total world population of passenger pigeons was exactly seven. By August 1910 only one, a female named Martha after Martha Washington, survived.

She lived on in the Cincinnati zoo—an object, one would think, of enormous interest and national shame. But her declining years were obscure, and on a September afternoon in 1914 she was found dead in her cage. She was promptly frozen into a 300-pound ice cake and sent to the Smithsonian Institution in Washington, where she was stuffed and mounted. She may be seen today in a handsome case in the museum. Martha was said to be 29 years old when she died, a long life for a pigeon. But not nearly long enough.

THE BUFFALO THAT REFUSED TO VANISH
Robert Froman

The wildest and woolliest—and in some ways most hilarious—roundup in the history of the West started one autumn morning in 1906 in the valley south of Montana's Flathead Lake. It lasted five years, wore out scores of cowboys and Indians, and never did fully accomplish its purpose. That was to load in railroad cars for shipment to a wilderness refuge in Canada the 800 members of the last big herd of North American buffalo.

At the end of the Civil War uncounted millions of bison (the correct name) still roamed the plains from northern Mexico to northern Canada. Then began a gruesome carnage. The animal's size—bulls average 1600 pounds, cows 1000—its fearlessness and its open habitat made it the easiest of rifle targets. Ranchers, railroaders, hide-hunters and meat-hunters (who often took only the tongue) wiped out herd after herd. At times vast areas were uninhabitable because of the stench of rotting carcasses. By 1889, when zoologist William T. Hornaday made a census and found only 541 buffalo left, the species seemed doomed.

It well might have been but for Michell Pablo, a remarkable man who was half Mexican and half Blackfoot Indian. Orphaned in childhood and raised by a Scottish trader, Pablo had learned the art of buying and selling and proceeded to build a cattle fortune. In 1883 he acquired a small herd of buffalo and gave them the freedom of the range, promising drastic reprisal against anyone who hunted them. The herd increased at a rapid rate and by 1906 Pablo was ready to sell. Conservationists tried to persuade Congress to buy the herd, but without success. So Pablo accepted the Canadian government's offer of $250 for each buffalo he delivered to the railroad at Ravalli, near the southern end of that Montana valley.

Neither Pablo nor anyone else anticipated difficulty with the buffalo. As the first small bunch trotted into the railroad yard, their characteristic shambling, head-down gait made them look humble and hopeless. Then the first old bull started up the runway into a cattle car and, with scarcely a break in stride, he and his followers smashed through the stout planks, out the other side of the car and trotted back up the valley. For a long moment the spectators stared at the splintered cattle car. Then they set up a shout of mixed cheers and laughter. "Hey, Pablo," some wit yelled, "is them what you call the vanishing buffalo?"

Pablo, seeing $200,000 grow slippery in his grasp, did not join in the merriment. In spite of his 70 years, he was well suited for the contest that lay ahead. A rugged six-footer with big white handlebar mustaches, he still spent most of his waking hours in the saddle. He had a voice that could nearly match the bellow of a buffalo bull, and was accustomed to having his orders instantly obeyed. Now he halted the roundup

One of North America's most magnificent mammals, the buffalo has powerful shoulders, a shaggy, bearded head.

and settled down to a winter of preparations, building a stronger holding corral and subdividing cars into compartments just big enough for a bull or a cow and calf. To save money he built the corral against a steep cliff so that the cliff formed the fourth wall.

In May 1907 he resumed the roundup. Again his riders drove about 20 buffalo down the valley to Ravalli and into the corral. But before the massive gate had closed behind them the buffalo were already

on their way up the supposedly unclimbable cliff. Disgusted, Pablo ordered the pen wall continued along the bottom of the cliff, then led his men out again.

This time, finding a herd of 100 grazing together, the riders cut out 30 and headed them toward Ravalli. The others stampeded up the valley with a wild uproar of thundering hoofs and reverberating bellows. Hearing this, the smaller bunch turned, charged straight back through the line of riders and rejoined the main herd. Eventually the cowhands found a small group grazing alone and got them into the corral. But a big bull inserted his horns under a 2 x 12 plank, heaved, tossed it over his shoulder. Then he backed up for a short run, splintered a couple of other planks and led the bunch to freedom.

Pablo now decided to try loading only cows and calves. After repairing the corral, he led his men out after the buffalo once more. It proved the wildest fiasco so far. The chase lasted from early morning until dark, covered some 60 miles and ran down not a single buffalo.

Another man might have felt discouraged, but Pablo merely concluded that he needed more help and recruited 75 of the best riders in the state. Concentrating all his men on groups of a dozen of the calves and smaller cows, he finally succeeded in getting the loading started, and in early July he was able to send off a trainload of 215 buffalo. Another 180 of the smallest and most nearly manageable animals were loaded by October, and Pablo was convinced he could finish the operation the following year.

He was mistaken. In 1908 he failed to load a single buffalo. Of the nearly 400 that remained most were bulls, wary now and in a mood for fight. Up to this point, when cornered they had behaved in orthodox fashion, pawing the ground, digging into it with their horns, bellowing and sticking their tails straight up in the air just as they charged. Now they charged without warning. Horses were killed, riders were injured. Newspapers from coast to coast ran admiring accounts of the fight the "outlaws" were putting up.

In mid-July Pablo called a halt. If the bulls wouldn't be driven to the railroad, he'd get them there another way. To accomplish this he built in the middle of the valley a vast, elaborate trap. Two heavy log barricades were constructed, each a mile long, and a mile apart at the entrance. The barricades narrowed down to a small opening out in the swift current of the Flathead River at a point where the river entered a canyon. Across the river and 50 yards downstream was a narrow beach closed in on three sides by the sheer walls of the canyon; the one exit, a gully in the canyon wall, was closed with a barrier of heavy logs. Heavy log booms placed across the river prevented the buffalo from escaping by swimming upstream or down. The idea was to drive the animals down the V-shaped trap into the river and over onto the beach. There, one at a time, they would be lured with hay and oats into wheeled crates, each just big enough for one animal. Mule teams would haul them out through the gully to the railroad station.

The buffalo, in spite of their cussedness, coöperated with this stratagem. They were used to crossing the river, and, once isolated on the little beach, many of them seemed glad to accept the crates as a way out. By the fall of 1909 the crew had managed to load 218 more animals. Another 66 buffalo were shipped in the spring of 1910. That left only the biggest and toughest of the bulls—some 100 altogether—that refused to be trapped or, if trapped, battered their way out of the crates or smashed through the side of the cattle car. Pablo became obsessed with these holdouts. When summer began to wane without a sign of hope that more could be corralled, he issued an invitation to Canadian officials to take part in the world's last buffalo hunt, the hunters to pay $250 apiece for any they killed. When the news leaked out, the U.S. public was outraged. As a result, the Montana game commission declared the hunt illegal.

Age was beginning to catch up with Pablo, but, though he had now collected almost $170,000, he kept after the animals for two more years and managed to ship, one at a time, another dozen. In his 76th year he finally gave up. He died two years later, and the rest of his buffalo lived out their days under the protection of the nation's conscience. The last of them died a natural death in 1917. But, thanks largely to the public sympathy won by their fierce resistance, Congress in the summer of 1908 established the 18,000-acre National Bison Range, northwest of Ravalli, and the newly formed American Bison Society stocked it with 34 buffalo. Fittingly, one of our greatest herds now roams the hills overlooking the valley where the great roundup was staged.

Today in Canada's vast Wood Buffalo National Park, a 17,300-square-mile wilderness straddling the Alberta-Northwest Territories boundary, the descendants of Pablo's herd number some 15,000. Herds on the U.S. National Bison Range, the Wichita Mountains Wildlife Refuge in Oklahoma, Yellowstone National Park, South Dakota's Custer State Park and other western ranges total more than 10,000. Seen up close, with their great, shaggy heads and powerful shoulders, they are a vision of western history. And when an old bull looses a muffled bellow, it seems to reverberate through the corridors of time.

THE STORY
OF THE STORK

Donald Culross Peattie

No youngster of today believes that the stork brings babies. Some may even call the stork a humbug. For not even in the zoo can you easily find the knowing old fellow of the birth-announcement cards, with his snow-white plumage, black wing coverts and red bill.

Yet this fabulous creature was once common in every country of Europe (except the British Isles, Norway and Finland), returning each spring from Africa in shining flocks to settle like a happy omen on a chosen roof. But now, mysteriously, the white stork has forsaken one country after another. Even in Germany, Holland and Denmark—so well adapted to stork life, with their reedy shores and thatched roofs—storks are so few that the people rejoice over every pair. In a few more human generations this beloved bird may become extinct.

I journeyed 6000 miles, from California to Copenhagen, to see storks while I still could. The search finally led to Ribe (pronounce it Reebeh), seven hours by motor from the Danish capital but hundreds of years backward in time, straight into some fairy tale by Hans Christian Andersen. Ribe is a medieval town where the low, old, half-timbered houses lean sociably toward one another, where the cathedral bells play a folk song and where, as you turn a corner, you meet the wise old bird.

He was mincing down the middle of the street, standing about waist-high to the rest of us on his long, red-stocking legs. With his plump white body and dapper black wing coverts he had an old-fashioned elegance, like a man in a cutaway and white waistcoat, strutting along, his head bobbing as if bowing to passersby. In some quarters of Denmark he has even received a human name—Peter Jensen.

From the top of the ancient cathedral tower I swept all Ribe with my binoculars, spotting nests on the clustering roofs below. A stork's nest is no ordinary cradle of a season, but a veritable round tower, jealously guarded by succeeding generations of owners, added to each year until it may become a cylinder of braided twigs six feet high, four feet broad. Such a ponderous affair, exposed to all the winds that blow, must be anchored firmly to some good substratum. A thatched roof, a flat-topped chimney stack, a medieval turret are ideal. Once, presumably, all storks built in

trees; the Bible says they nested in the cedars of Lebanon. But this most human of birds has long thrown in his lot with man, on whose roof he is protected. There has come to light a bill for repairs to a stork's nest in Thuringia dated 1592; records show it was in existence as early as the discovery of America. It was still being occupied a few years ago.

People believe not only that the presence of a stork's nest protects a roof from lightning but that the lucky homeowner is sure to live long and grow rich. To invite a nest, a Danish householder will hopefully fix a platform to his rooftree. On a school roof I saw an artificial nest, woven of twigs by children. Success had attended the children's hopes, for it contained a brooding bird.

For hours I watched a mother stork in a nest on a low roof. The great dark eye of the patient baby-sitter shone motionless over the nest's parapet. There was almost no sign of restlessness—time is nothing to a brooding stork, nor driving rain nor gale. But as the light began to fade, the bird threw back her head and, twisting her neck, scanned the heavens like an airplane spotter.

At last the male arrived. He came in on long, stiffly held pinions and swept over the nest like a plane circling a landing field. Before alighting he braced his dangling legs forward, as though putting down landing gear. Then, flapping his wings to brake his velocity, he lit on the edge of the nest, lifted his bill to the sky and clappered with it in ceremonious greeting. The female arose and went through similar antics. Those who know storks best say that if mates meet 50 times a day they still go through these politenesses. And the young, as soon as they are old enough to learn manners, stand up in the nest each time a parent returns and respectfully clapper their mandibles.

Storks talk with their bills, for their vocal cords are useless. They can only clap the two hard mandibles together like castanets, but by variations in tempo and volume they can utter all their emotions and meanings. The machine-gun rattling of a male outraged by some intruder is as eloquent as the whisper of the mandibles when, in mating, he lays his bill along the female's neck and woos her.

Usually the baby-sitter, on being relieved at the nest, will go off foraging. Sometimes, however, the two birds settle down side by side, with much ruffling and elbowing, till they sink to rest upon their eggs and prepare to spend the night in conjugal sociability.

Through the ages storks have been a symbol of faithful married love. Everyone who has witnessed their mating speaks of its singular unhurried gravity and gentleness, the male balancing himself with slow,

Each year fewer and fewer European storks return from their winter quarters in Africa to their rooftop nests in the north. Strangely enough, no one is certain why they are disappearing.

angelic motions of the wings, bringing them to touch, back to back, above his head, then letting them droop to the edge of the nest like a snowy coverlet. For it is in the ancestral freehold of the nest, not on the ground or in trees as with most other birds, that the sacred rite of perpetuating the race goes on.

Storks are proverbially devoted to their young. When a thatched roof caught fire in Denmark a few years ago, the mother bird stuck to her nest, covering her young and, as the flames rolled nearer, beating her wings violently to keep the youngsters from suffocating in the smoke. When the fire was extinguished she was black with soot, but her babies were saved.

Small wonder that the baby-bringing legend attached itself to this tender fowl. And that belief is not so silly as it sounds. For the original thought was that the stork who came to preside on the family roof embodied the soul of some ancestor and took the liveliest interest in each anticipated descendant. So he it was, people came to think, who fetched, from that well or spring the village called "the children's fountain," not the expected baby's body but its little soul.

For nourishment Peter Jensen and his wife provide their young with frogs, small snakes, snails, beetles, crickets, grasshoppers, mice, moles. They drop such prey in the center of the nest and let the youngsters squabble for it. On hot days a stork has even been seen to bring water in his bill and syringe it down the parched throats of the nestlings.

Since first Peter Jensen and his human friends began to live on opposite sides of the same rooftree, mankind has wondered where he went in winter. In the last 50 years scientific bird-banding has made the whole story clear. The young storks, who have never yet been away from home, go first, without even an oldster to show them the way. The annual round-trip migration covers some 14,000 miles. The storks from Russia, Poland, Germany, Denmark and northern Holland use an eastern flyway, winging southeast to the Holy Land, over the Sea of Galilee, over Mount Sinai, to the bulrush marshes of the Nile and down to the veld of South Africa. The birds of southern Holland, Alsace, Spain and Morocco take a westerly course. From the Strait of Gibraltar they fly over the Sahara Desert (where airmen have overtaken them cruising along at the rate of some 200 miles a day), cross the Congo rain forests and arrive in South Africa, where they meet those from the eastern flyway.

The life of the storks in Africa is the opposite of their European domesticity. They rarely mate or nest there, never gather on the roofs. They sleep in small flocks on riverbanks and hunt singly on the grassland of the veld. In Afrikaans they are called "locust birds"

because of the quantities of this insect they consume. When there is a plague of locusts the storks gather by the hundreds to rout the dreaded hordes.

But as autumn comes to the veld, in February, the white storks of Europe feel the pull of the north. They spiral up and up, on lifting air currents, into the beckoning sky, each bird returning on the traceless airway by which he came. Most return to the same region where they were hatched and often find their way to the identical neighborhood.

But each year more of the waiting nests are left empty. Peter Jensen's many friends would gladly cry "Save the storks!"—if anyone knew just what to save them from. Certain dangers are clear. Many storks are electrocuted on high-tension wires. Others are shot by the heartless. In South Africa fierce hailstorms sometimes cause havoc among them; and the arsenical sprays used to combat the locusts there are believed to poison them indirectly.

But long before modern perils the storks began mysteriously to lessen. Pliny, the Roman naturalist, writing 2000 years ago, called the white stork common; then within 400 years it ceased to nest in Italy. In the last century, under no particular persecution, it forsook Belgium. It is possible that the species has outlived its best days and is suffering from internal racial fatigue—some failure of fertility, perhaps.

And yet, tucking his red bill down in his soft breast, cocking a sage, dark eye at us, the stork seems to have secrets of his own. May they help him weather his troubles, whatever they are, to live on as long as his friends of the human race!

THE DINOSAUR AND THE EGG
Roy Chapman Andrews

The cartoonist's picture of a gigantic creature peeking into the second-story window with an expression of expectancy on its rather benevolent face is the popular conception of a dinosaur. *Brontosaurus*, the "thunder reptile," is the usual subject for the sketch. He was pretty big—65 feet long and weighing 30 tons—but he was a pygmy in intellect; his brain was not much larger than a man's clenched fist.

The thunder reptile was only one of the dinosaurs. The largest of all—found in the western United States and East Africa—was 100 feet in length; the smallest hardly larger than a chicken. Some were plant eaters; others ate only flesh. Some lived on land; others in

The Age of Reptiles, when dinosaurs ruled the Earth, lasted for more than 130 million years. Some of the earlier forms, shown here, were the plant-eating Edaphosaurus *and the flesh-eating* Dimetrodon *with huge crests billowing from their spines; short-legged, long-tailed* Plateo-saurus, *eating the tree; and in front of it* Cynognathus, *which resembles the earliest mammals. In the foreground at the right is* Camptosaurus, *which ranged in size from 5 to 15 feet.*

water. Some walked upright on two legs; others crawled on all fours. They dominated every continent during the Age of Reptiles—a period which lasted about 200 million years—then completely disappeared from the Earth.

There are several theories to account for their extinction. Among the least complex is the explanation that *Brontosaurus* and his relative *Diplodocus* floundered along the shores of lakes seeking the several hundred pounds of vegetable food a day needed to nourish their gigantic bodies. When the lakes dried up they died. With their tons of flesh, small heads and feeble teeth they could not adapt themselves to even a slight change in the world about them.

Another theory is that the dinosaurs exterminated themselves. When the Central Asiatic Expeditions, under my leadership, discovered the first dinosaur eggs in the Gobi Desert, we found the skeleton of a small toothless dinosaur right on top of the nest of eggs. There is every reason to believe that it lived by sucking the eggs of other dinosaurs. Possibly it was in the very act of digging up these eggs when it was

overwhelmed by a sandstorm. This group of toothless dinosaurs may have become so numerous that they actually exterminated their relatives by eating the eggs as fast as they were laid.

The first mammals were tiny creatures no larger than rats. Close to the spot where the first eggs were collected we found skeletons of these little mammals. This discovery gives rise to the theory that they aided the toothless dinosaurs in their work of extermination by eating the eggs.

From the well-preserved skeletons of many dinosaur species it has been a simple matter for anatomists to represent accurately their appearance in life. Remains found in the sandstone of Montana even show what the skin of *Trachodon*, the 25-foot duck-bill dinosaur, was like. When these animals died, they apparently were covered with wind-blown sand before decomposition set in, so that the impression of the skin is perfectly preserved. Widely distributed in Europe, Asia and America, they fed on lush vegetation in a semitropical climate. This we know from the impressions of fossil plants found with the skeletons.

Dinosaurs varied in shape and in size—some were no bigger than chickens, others grew to be 100 feet long. The giants here are the thick-necked Allosaurus, *the spiked, plated* Stegosaurus, *the long-necked* Brontosaurus. *Far in the background are another* Brontosaurus *and* Allosaurus. *The small dinosaur in the foreground is* Camptosaurus, *the flying reptile is* Rhamphorhynchus.

The greatest engine of destruction that ever lived was *Tyrannosaurus rex,* "king of tyrant reptiles." The late Dr. Barnum Brown discovered a perfect skull of this huge beast and a fairly complete skeleton, now to be seen in The American Museum of Natural History in New York City. When erect on his two hind feet he was 18 feet high. The small forelimbs were equipped with large talons. The great mouth opened a yard wide and was armed with double-edged daggerlike teeth six inches long. Its food was the flesh of other dinosaurs, and at The American Museum there is a skeleton of a thunder reptile plainly showing the teeth marks of these gigantic cannibals.

No other creature that lived was a match for the tyrant reptile, unless it was the three-horned *Triceratops.* He was a massive beast, 20 feet long, weighing perhaps 10 tons and with a skull which projected backward over the neck like a fireman's helmet. When *Triceratops* threw up his head, bringing into fighting position the three great horns, it also brought the helmet down on the neck—probably the most vulnerable spot on his body—like a shield. Dozens of other types of these nightmare creatures leaped, ran or wad-

dled over the Earth in that incredibly ancient period.

There seems to be an idea that all a scientist needs is a single bone to reconstruct a complete skeleton. But until practically complete skeletons of dinosaurs representing different groups had been discovered it was impossible to do much reconstructing of imperfect specimens. Now, given an imperfect skeleton, we first determine what were its nearest relatives among the many already known forms. Then, because the general anatomical structure of related animals is similar, the skeleton can be assembled without much fear of going wrong except in details.

Such great collections of fossils now exist that it is seldom a specimen is discovered which does not show a definite relationship to known forms. In the case of the *Baluchitherium,* C. Forster Cooper of England found the first remains in Baluchistan in 1911. They consisted of only a few bones, including one foot bone and two neck vertebrae. Yet from those few bones he concluded that they belonged to the largest mammal that ever existed and that the beast was probably an aberrant rhinoceros. Thus the matter rested for 11 years, until our

Dinosaurs disappeared 70 million years ago; man, who evolved a million years ago, never knew them. Left, an armored Ankylosaurus *and, behind it, a duck-billed* Anatosaurus. *In the center,* Tyrannosaurus, *the most powerful land dweller of all time. At the right, two horned dinosaurs:* Triceratops *and, behind it,* Ornithomimus, *the ostrich dinosaur. The flier is* Pteranodon.

expedition discovered the skull and part of the skeleton of a similar individual in Mongolia. Cooper was proved right on all the deductions he had made from these few bones. Incidentally, the skull we found was in 600 pieces, which had to be assembled like a jigsaw puzzle. One man worked seven months until all had been placed. It was done so accurately that, although two other skulls have since been discovered, it has not been necessary to make more than minor readjustments in the original specimen.

Sometimes only a few of the important bones give us a great deal of information about the animal. If a leg bone is solid, it means a sluggish creature or one of more or less aquatic habits. If hollow, it indicates an active land animal. If the hind legs are disproportionately long, the inference is that the beast walked erect. Even one tooth or claw will tell a lot: a sharp-pointed tooth could not be used for eating grass — therefore the animal must have been carnivorous; a blunt claw is not adapted for rending flesh—it suggests a herbivorous diet.

Dinosaur tracks left in the mud of some ancient lake, river or sea bottom help us to pose dinosaurs.

The finest dinosaur footprints in America are from the Connecticut Valley, which was subject to great fluctuations of water level. During dry periods dinosaurs wandered along the muddy shores, leaving hundreds of tracks. Strangely enough, they all lead from west to east as if the animals were following a well-defined route to their feeding grounds. Some of the tracks show clearly where a dinosaur squatted down to rest or walked slowly on all fours, touching just the toes of the front feet to the ground like a kangaroo.

In Belgium, where a great number of skeletons related to the duck-bill have been found, the prints show that those dinosaurs walked like birds, on the toes alone. Moreover, they must have carried their tails well up from the ground, counterbalancing the body, for otherwise there would have been a continuous furrow between the footprints. On the other hand, where some of the short-limbed dinosaurs waddled along, the tail furrow shows clearly between the imprints of the feet.

Every time a new creature is discovered it adds a few more words to the history of life upon Earth which we are endeavoring to translate for all to read.

A rare sight today—wild horses of Wyoming's Red Desert. In 1865 more than two million of these mustangs ranged from the Columbia River to the mouth of the Rio Grande.

GHOSTLY HOOFS ON THE PRAIRIE

Herbert Ravenel Sass

Fling your mind back 3000 years to the plains of Arabia and of Barbary, famous throughout the ancient world for their swift, high-mettled horses. Phoenician galleys are sailing to Spain. They take with them iron, dyes, spices, fruits; and take with them, also, horses of these fiery-hearted desert strains. Long centuries pass; and the lithe, sinewy Arab-Barb horse has become the horse of the Spaniard.

Now come to North America, to the American West. In all respects but one it is the West of song and story, the West of the buffalo, the antelope, the grizzly bear and the Plains Indian. But throughout the length and breadth of the land there is not so much as one horse, and the Plains Indians—Pawnee, Comanche, Sioux and all the others—move ploddingly on foot.

Drop the curtain; then lift it and look at the West as it was when the early American frontiersmen saw it. A miracle has happened! The plains are alive with droves of wild horses, in places almost rivaling the buffalo in numbers. The Indian nations of the plains, just now earthbound footmen, are nations of mounted

warriors, perhaps the finest cavalry in the world.

How did this miracle happen? It was one of the most dramatic and most momentous transformations that ever took place in any land under the sun. For out of it came the whole splendid drama of the West.

In 1519 the Spanish conqueror Hernando Cortez landed in Mexico, bringing with him the first modern horses that ever set foot on the continent of North America. In 1540 Francisco Vásquez Coronado rode northward across the Rio Grande with some 260 mounted men, exploring the unknown West as far as Kansas. From these expeditions horses were lost, and it may have been these strays that became the first of the wild horses of the West.

If the horse—a kind of horse able to survive—had not come to the West and established itself there in great numbers before the American frontiersman and settler came to it, the West could not have been what it was. Most of what it was economically, and what it has become in literature and art, springs from the horse—the horse that came to America with the Spaniard and conquered an empire that the Spaniard was never able to win.

This was the desert horse of the Phoenician and the Arab, but little changed. Of fine Arab-Barb blood, this hard and sinewy creature, thrown on its own resources in the hot, dry, waterless wilderness of the American Southwest, became at once the most enduring and the most beautiful of all the horses of the world, thriving amazingly where the big, bulky northern breeds would have perished. The increase of the wild droves was astonishingly rapid. Zebulon Pike saw vast numbers in Texas and all the northern Mexican provinces, while Victor Shawe speaks of such multitudes between the Columbia River and the high desert country that "a single band traveled from dawn until dusk in passing a given point."

And along with this increase came a spreading awakening over the West, as nation after nation of red men, plodding footmen for hundreds of centuries, dropped the fetters that had bound them to earth. Nothing illustrates this revolution more dramatically than the story of the Sioux, who two centuries ago were a forest tribe living about the headwaters of the Mississippi. Unable to hold their own against the Ojibwa, or Chippewa, they were driven out upon the buffalo plains. To them presently came the first wild horses—"divine dogs," as the Sioux called them, not knowing what they were. Suddenly the Sioux were a nation on horseback; suddenly they, who had been rather ineffective footmen fleeing before less numerous enemies, became the most dreaded cavalry of the plains, a proud and powerful nation.

In the West, with the passing of generation after generation, the horse lost beauty, size and shapeliness until the later cowboy form was evolved. Again and again, however, there were individual "throwbacks," and such stallions, larger, swifter and handsomer than the common run, became famous. Most or all of these were true mustangs (the word comes from the Spanish, meaning an animal without an owner). Descendants of the original Arab-Barb horses, they had no such admixture of other stocks as is found in the range horse today.

Some 10,000 to 20,000 wild horses, a mere remnant, still survive in the West. There is some mustang blood in these "fuzz-tails," of course. They live in bands of six to 60, chiefly in Nevada, Wyoming, Arizona, Utah, eastern Washington, Oregon, western Colorado and Montana.

The real mustang—the wild horse that transformed a continent has gone forever from the plains. He vanished with the buffalo, whose doom he helped to seal. But it is only just that we should not forget him —for he gave us the splendid West, with all that it has meant to the lives and minds of men.

THE TURKEY, WILD AGAIN
John Stuart Martin

Autumnal dusk was gathering as my wife and I neared the New York–Pennsylvania border. Off a thickly timbered hill beside the Delaware River a huge bird flew across the highway ahead of us. It had a long neck, and its wide pinions beat short, crisp strokes between stretches of gliding—the unmistakable straight-line flight of a wild turkey. As the great bird winged away to roost in the river's bottomland, a second followed. We watched, breathless, until ten had passed. Not for years had we seen that sight and never so far north, though we had heard that Pennsylvania was bringing back the wild turkey.

When spring came I visited Pennsylvania again to learn how the miracle was wrought. Johnny Spencer, the game protector stationed at Mount Pocono, took me in his pickup truck into a vast sanctuary on the wild ridges above Cresco, one of several such areas which the state maintains. As he unlocked a barway across the road Johnny warned me, "Look sharp, now. The critters travel everywhere up here. Mostly they're shy as schoolgirls, but they can be bolder than bulls."

Suddenly, as we topped a rise, four lordly shapes

from Daniel Boone's day marched calmly across the road ahead of us! In the spring sunlight their heavy wattles flamed scarlet below their bluish heads. Glints of green and fire and cerulean flashed from their iridescent bodies. We could see the bronzed tips of their tail feathers and their coral-pink legs, which distinguish the wild bird from his white-tipped, black-legged tame cousins. Johnny whispered, "That's a bachelors' club which hasn't broke up yet for mating."

To me the wild turkey symbolizes our primal wilderness as the white settlers first found it. Indigenous only to this continent, these gobblers were the feathered emperors not only of the South's dismal swamps but also of the northeastern forests. They roved so boldly that the Pilgrim Fathers could take them with a blunderbuss. But by the 1920's they were almost extinct above the Mason-Dixon line, their disappearance caused as much by the leveling of tall timber by axe and fire as by shooting and trapping.

Two generations ago Pennsylvania's game managers foresaw that in nature's regular cycle the big woods would eventually rise again, their canopy shading out the underbrush which hampers turkeys, and that there would be mast from oaks, beeches and wild cherries. To prepare for that day, they began trying as early as 1929 to propagate wild turkeys for restocking. West and south of the Susquehanna River some native turkeys still survived deep in the mountains. But when a few wild gobblers from this area were live-trapped and put in with semi-wild game-farm hens, they would neither breed nor eat. An obvious solution was to take captive hens to native gobblers in the woods, but when a tom turkey is ready to confer his favors, he chooses a strutting ground and puts on a powerful act to attract a harem. He puffs out his breast, drags his outspread wings, extends his high tail fan, shakes his inflamed jowls and imperatively gobble-obble-oobles. It is not for him to go running among the trees seeking mates; they must come meekly, admiringly to him.

Near known gobbling grounds the game-farm men built ten-acre enclosures of eight-foot wire, topped by electrified strands to repel predators. Into these nuptial pens were put wing-clipped turkey hens. When the haughty toms gobbled nearby, the hens started dutifully toward them—but were stopped by the wire. Their responsive cluckings brought the gobblers up to the fence. There the toms strutted and gobbled furiously, but remained too proud to fly over the wire themselves. At this point the game-farm men built wooden ramps leading up from the outside to 'coon-proof trapdoors in the wire. By day the doors were lowered inward to make platforms four feet

The North American gobbler the Pilgrims found had bronze plumage and a tufted breast (shown here). The smaller Thanksgiving bird we know came originally from Mexico.

off the ground, too high for the hens to hop without wing-lift but low enough for any gobbler who deigned to strut up the ramp. In time, love conquered pride, and the gobblers not only jumped down from the platforms but learned to fly over the wire.

Finding fertilized eggs inside the enclosures without disturbing the mated birds was work for sharp eyes and stealthy feet. A turkey hen makes her nest simply by shuffling a depression in dead leaves so that they will hide her clutch when she slips away. The men sought only the first month's eggs, leaving later ones to hatch into wild broods. The four-ounce, yellow-white eggs with rusty speckles were put into incubators at the turkey farm. There, after 28 days, they yielded chicks known to be at least half wild. Females of this strain were reared to maturity and offered in the pens the following spring. After repeating this process for several years the state had a strain of bird so wild it was almost unmanageable.

Pennsylvania's present wild-turkey population is some 45,000, and its techniques of culture have now spread far. The birds have been restored to so many areas—throughout the Middle West and as far as the St. Lawrence—that it is impossible to know how many or where they are.

Chapter two

LIVING FOSSILS

In our midst are creatures which should have been extinct aeons ago.
The horseshoe crab, some snails, a few of the spiders and cockroaches and
all of the snow fleas have remained unchanged by evolution over millions of
years. Most of the ancient creatures eventually succumbed to invading seas,
glaciers and the rise of new species of enemies. But the "living fossils"
persisted. They were designed for survival so perfectly that nature could not
improve— or destroy—them.

Some ancient creatures are still living today for a completely different
reason. Their homeland, Australia, became separated from Asia,
and the mammals of more recent times never reached their shores to
kill them off. And so the monotremes (the platypus and echidna) and the
marsupials (the kangaroo and his relatives) flourish in Australia.
As they did millions of years ago, the monotremes are still laying eggs,
the marsupials nestling their babies—hardly more than embryos—
in outside pockets. In the United States only one of the ancient marsupials,
the opossum, still lives on. His secret for survival may be, in part, his ability
to play dead, as his enemies—the foxes and other carnivores—rarely
touch a carcass.

Most amazing of all the living fossils is one that is alive today for
no apparent reason— the coelacanth, a fish dating back almost 300 million
years. His skeleton is almost identical with the limestone fossils of his
ancestors. When we look at him, life seems miraculously tenacious.

Fossil of a coelacanth (above), dating from about 150 million years ago. It was thought to have been long extinct until 1938, when one was caught off the coast of South Africa. Below, a cast of the 1938 fish. The coelacanth may be a link between land and sea creatures.

THE FISH THAT COULDN'T BE

James Dugan

On December 22, 1938, at East London, a port in southeast Africa, Miss M. Courtenay-Latimer, the inquisitive curator of the local museum, was examining some sharks brought in by a trawler. Among them she found the mauled body of a surpassing strange fish more than five feet long and weighing 127 pounds. It was steel-blue, with heavy scales, a powerful jaw and padded fins that stuck out like limbs. "It was so peculiar," she said, "that I felt it had to be preserved."

Miss Latimer hauled the "heavy, dirty and oily" fish to the museum and there tried to identify it. Unsuccessful, she made a sketch and sent it to Professor J. L. B. Smith, the famous fish expert, of Rhodes University College at Grahamstown, South Africa.

Professor Smith, who has discovered and named more than 100 species of fish in his career, looked at this one with something like shock. "My surprise would have been little greater if I had seen a dinosaur walking down the street." For this fish was one thought to have died out with the dinosaurs! It was known to scientists only from fossil impressions in rocks laid down millions of years ago. Here was a creature unchanged in more than 60 million years.

"Though it was difficult to believe so incredible a thing," says Professor Smith, "I identified the fish as a coelacanth"—pronounced see-la-kanth—"and named it Latimeria in appreciation of what Miss Latimer had done." Given the species name chalumnae (for the Chalumna River, at whose mouth the creature was caught) and the name of the identifier as the usual appendix, the fish became Latimeria chalumnae Smith, or L. c. Smith. "Here," said Professor Smith, "is the closest living relative of the long-extinct fish that is accepted as the ancestor of all land animals. He is almost in the direct line of man's ancestry."

The news of L. c. Smith made an international sensation. The professor wanted to find other specimens. Thinking that the big, rough-hided creature looked like a fish of rocky ledges, he decided that it lived "somewhere about Madagascar." Having no means to organize an expedition, he printed and distributed a descriptive leaflet in English, French and Portuguese, with a photo of the fish and offering $400 for another coelacanth. World War II blacked out his search, but afterward he and his wife hunted

on, tramping the coast, sailing on fishing boats and distributing the leaflets. Years passed without a clue.

In 1952, in Zanzibar, Mrs. Smith gave some leaflets to an English sea captain, Eric Hunt, who ran a trading schooner in the Indian Ocean. The day before Christmas the Smiths got a cable from Captain Hunt: HAVE COELACANTH IN COMORO ISLANDS. COME AND FETCH IT. The fish was 2000 miles away, this was the peak of the Southern Hemisphere summer (would the fish decay?) and the professor had no money to charter a plane. He appealed to Prime Minister Daniel F. Malan. The Prime Minister loaned him a military transport plane. "To my unspeakable relief," says Professor Smith, "the fish turned out to be a true coelacanth."

The fish had been dead nine days, but had been embalmed on the fourth day by Captain Hunt. It had been caught off Anjouan Island in about 650 feet of water by a fisherman who had taken it to market. There a schoolteacher recognized it from Smith's leaflet and sent it by bearers 25 miles over mountain trails to Hunt.

As news wires chattered with the story, the administrator of the Comoro Islands received an astrin-

Professor J. L. B. Smith of Grahamstown, South Africa, is shown with the ship's crew that brought in a coelacanth in 1953. This specimen was the first to be preserved intact.

gent signal from the Ministry of Overseas Territories in Paris, asking if he had been in siesta while foreigners brazenly flew in and lifted a scientific treasure of France. Whereupon Professor Jacques Millot of the Paris Museum of Natural History, who had entered the big fossil chase, designated the Scientific Research Institute of Madagascar responsible for all coelacanths taken henceforth in French territory. The Institute duplicated Smith's reward, scattered a ton of reward leaflets and set up fish-embalming stations at strategic ports.

A third coelacanth was taken September 24, 1953, by Houmadi Hassani, a fisherman, off Anjouan Island. Leaving his wife to guard the big fish, he ran for Dr. Georges Garrouste, who had one of the embalming kits. The doctor had been roused many a night by people who said they had captured *le poisson* but actually had not, so he interrogated Hassani. Hassani said he had a big brown fish with white spots and phosphorescent eyes. Dr. Garrouste had seen Professor Smith's No. 2 fish, a steel-blue monster whose eyes were notable only for chill and size. He told Hassani to run along. The fisherman persisted. Finally the doctor went with him. He recognized a genuine coelacanth even though it *was* brown with white spots and *did* have phosphorescent eyes.

Professor Millot, waiting in Tananarive, Madagascar, got a virtually undamaged specimen with limblike fins developed differently from those of each previous coelacanth. Millot concluded that all were of the same species, and that the fish has an extraordinary capacity for individual variety. His contention has since been borne out.

Administrator Georges Savignac of Great Comoro Island was roused at midnight on January 29, 1954, by the arrival of *L. c.* Smith No. 4. "It was very exciting," he said later, "rushing to get it ready. We were finishing up at four a.m. when a man staggered in with an even bigger coelacanth. We went to work on it, and loaded the two boxes on the plane. Two days later a third coelacanth was brought in. We were getting tired of fish." The administrator, figuring he was in for a busy season, ordered a big stock of formaldehyde. No more were caught for eight months.

The fish taken so far, 28 in number, have come from depths ranging from 650 to 2000 feet in a period from September to February. The largest weighed 209 pounds, the smallest 43 pounds.

In his studies of the specimens at the Paris Museum, Millot has been struck by the variations in the pectoral or side fins. "The orientation of these fins varies completely from one specimen to another. This sheds fresh light on the all-important anatomical problem of how the fins of primitive fish were able to develop into the limbs of the terrestrial vertebrate, of which the human arm is one derivative." Professor Millot also finds that the heart of *L. c.* Smith is a living example of an early stage of heart evolution. The tissue of the fish is "remarkable for its ordinariness. Any competent medical student could probably identify at first glance in the microscope most of the organs, the cells being disposed as in our own bodies."

The experts have reached no conclusions yet about how the fish survived the extinction of all known forms of its period. Millot has found wide variation in the water temperatures in which coelacanths have been caught and says they owe their survival, at least partly, to their ability to live in different temperatures, as well as to "their great anatomical robustness and the great depth of their habitat."

The climactic coelacanth sensation came with the eighth specimen, captured at Anjouan at two a.m. on November 12, 1954. The fish was brought in alive, and it was a female. Almost all previous specimens had been males. "Ah, the female!" Professor Millot had said earlier. "If we find one with fertilized eggs, the embryos may reveal life forms receding to unimaginable epochs!"

Put in a water-filled whaleboat, *L. c.* Smith No. 8 seemed to have survived her 840-foot ascent to the surface very well. But after daybreak the light of the sun appeared to upset the animal. She tried to conceal herself in the darkest corners of the whaleboat. Professor Millot arrived at noon after a dashing flight from Madagascar. He noted, "At 1445 hours it was still swimming feebly; but at 1530 hours it had its belly in the air and only the fins and gill covers were making agonized movements." Millot thinks the fish died from photophobia, or sensitiveness to strong light. "The sunlight seemed literally to hurt it." Unfortunately, the female carried no fertilized eggs, nor did a second female, caught January 1, 1960.

Millot is hunting for a living *baby* coelacanth. That baby, he thinks, may be a miniature history of evolution. "In youth," he says, "the embryo changes physically, casting off vestigial characteristics from day to day, which will perhaps permit us knowledge of the life form millions of years before the mother."

Meanwhile Professor Smith continues *his* search for more coelacanths. To him Professor Millot has paid high tribute. In an article in the London *Times*, Millot wrote: "The capture of the coelacanth, with which the name of Professor J. L. B. Smith will always be linked, has been rightly described as 'the most amazing event of the century in the realm of natural history.' "

THE TRIUMPH OF ARCHY THE COCKROACH

J. D. Ratcliff

Dozens of times you have seen him and probably not realized that he is a creature more remarkable than anything in a zoo. He is one of Earth's oldest inhabitants, and a long pageant of life has passed before his small, sharp eyes. He was present to greet the arrival of dinosaurs 170 million years ago, and to bid them good-bye more than 100 million years later. He saw the Rockies, Alps and Appalachians push their way upward. He traveled the land bridge that several times connected the British Isles with the Continent. He was already an old-timer when Texas oil and West Virginia coal were formed. Express his 350-million-year tenure on Earth in terms of a calendar year. The year was nearly over—December 30—when he welcomed the late arrival, man.

We are speaking of the lowly cockroach.

At a time when our very survival on Earth is in jeopardy we might do well to observe Archy—so indelibly christened by Don Marquis in his *archy and mehitabel*. The cockroach has learned more about survival than has any other creature. A living fossil, he has some extraordinary attributes. He lives anywhere, from the middle of the Sahara to military kitchens in Labrador. Cockroaches have been found comfortably ensconced in cash registers and market scales, and have lately acquired a new home in TV sets, where the parts provide warmth—plus wax and paraffin, an acceptable if not epicurean diet. But less than one percent of the 3500 known species prefer the home of man to other environments. Some live in the burrows of ground squirrels. Others prefer the forest.

A large part of Archy's ability to survive undoubtedly traces to the catholicity of his food tastes. He has been known to eat everything from orchid buds to shoes to the glue that holds cartons together. He sips beer, chews through gravy spots on neckties, nibbles at paint, relishes soap. He even eats his own cast-off skin and, if sufficiently hard-pressed, dines on the eggs of his own species. Like his cousin the termite, one species of cockroach has minute organisms in his digestive tract which convert any wood he consumes into utilizable nutrients. He survives periods of starvation that few other creatures could tolerate. Without visible ill effects he can live about a month without any food or water, two months on

The durable cockroach, 350 million years older than man, has developed many ways to resist all enemies. Represented by a variety of species, it has circled the globe.

water alone, five months on dry food but no water.

We think of cockroaches as filthy because of their fetid odor. The odor traces to scent glands much like those of the skunk. This is another of Archy's protections; because of his aroma many potential predators refuse to eat him. Actually he is quite fastidious, spending hours washing feet, legs and antennae.

Get a close-up of the Blattidae—that's Archy's family name. Some forest-dwelling tropical species are nearly as large as hummingbirds—2½-inch bodies, 7-inch wingspans. Others are smaller than grains of rice. Color is usually in the brown-to-black range, although some are as resplendent as rainbows. Nearly all have wings—even household species can fly when other means of escape fail—but main reliance is placed on six long, powerful, fleet legs. The cockroach's two antennae are his most remarkable equipment. Longer than Archy himself, they help him feel his way in the dark. Containing olfactory cells, they detect food and water and play a key role in reproduction. Archy strokes his lady's antennae to arouse sexual interest.

His nocturnal habits have helped ensure his place on Earth. In the sanctuary of darkness he avoids many potential enemies. He has two superbly sensitive compound eyes and three "simple" eyes on top of his head. He has a wide range of vision. Even when blinded he somehow recognizes light as danger and scurries for cover when the kitchen light is switched on.

Archy is far tougher than the 35-ton dinosaurs he once rubbed elbows with. Step on him and his hard, compressible body often saves him—he skitters away when pressure is removed. A contortionist, he can get through cracks that appear impossible to negotiate. Freeze him and he walks away when thawed.

He is also a prolific breeder: females have produced as many as 180 offspring in 303 days. Given favorable circumstances, the population leaps ahead in fantastic spurts. Russian entomologists collected 475,000 dead cockroaches from a single fumigated barracks.

The female is generally a good mother. Some species hatch eggs within their bodies to produce live young. But most species carry 12 to 40 eggs in a neat little purse-shaped sac protruding from the end of the abdomen. As with other females, the purse is occasionally mislaid. The eggs hatch anyway, the newborn being able to survive a week without food. Usually, however, the female drops the sac near a source of food, camouflaging it with debris.

Cockroaches are inveterate travelers. Almost surely, European cockroaches arrived in America aboard the *Mayflower;* now they are headed for space. Studies at the U.S. Department of Agriculture indicate that the Madeira species may be the astronaut supreme. He withstands over 100 times the radiation that man can endure. The same is true with gravity pull. Man blacks out at 12 g's, and severe structural damage begins at 18. The cockroach has withstood 126 g's for four hours and gone nonchalantly about his business. A capsule has been prepared for Archy's first journey into space—a beer can. Electrodes have been devised to check his nervous and muscular responses. All this is expected to yield information translatable to man.

Because of hardiness and rapid breeding, cockroaches are valuable in cancer and heart-disease research and in nutrition studies. Many species serve man by consuming dead vegetation that would otherwise clog forests.

Useful fellow though he may be, most of us prefer not to have Archy around. But chances of getting rid of him are virtually nil. "If we can hold our own against roaches, that is about the best we can hope for," says Dr. Philip Spear of the National Pest Control Association. New roach-killers come from research laboratories in a steady stream. Most are effective at first. But, given time, Archy learns to live with them —as he has learned to live with everything else. Scrupulous cleanliness is about the best weapon the homeowner has against cockroaches.

Some insects are known for their pedagogical achievements. Ants teach thrift and planning, bees the virtues of industry, grasshoppers the pure joy of living. Archy? Nothing in particular—unless it is that living quietly and tending to one's own business seem to pay off over the course of 350 million years.

OLD SLOWPOKE
Lewis Nordyke

Zoologists say that the opossum is the stupidest and least aggressive of animals. But Old Slowpoke continues to lumber leisurely through our woods, even extending his range and increasing his numbers. Strictly an American animal, he is our only survivor of the maternal-pouched ancient marsupials. Fossilized skulls found in Montana prove that he lived during the days of the dinosaurs—ferocious monsters that couldn't adapt themselves to changing conditions.

When the sun goes down and darkness and silence come to woodlands and streams of the Americas from southern Ontario to Argentina, the opossum stirs in his leafy nest in the hollow of a tree. With mouth open in a silly grin, he lazily pokes his long snout through the opening of the hollow and peers out at the world with berry-bright eyes. He crawls along a limb on legs so short that the belly seems almost to drag; the back arches slightly, and his long, hairless tail clamps around a branch. He is ready for his nightly prowl in search of food.

Br'er 'Possum looks something like a woolly pig. He is the size of a large house cat; he has grizzled, grayish fur and small, naked ears. When full grown he weighs about nine pounds. He once snuggled warmly in his mother's fur-lined marsupial pouch, a four-inch expandable pocket that runs lengthwise down the mother's abdomen. Not until he was a month old did he see any part of the world outside that pocket. How he got into the pouch and lived there is one of the strangest of animal stories.

The gestation period of the opossum is from 14 to 17 days, a shorter time than that for other mammals. At birth Old Slowpoke was a pink, shapeless thing less than an inch long. Only his mouth and front legs were developed, and he had no eyes, yet the helpless mite squirmed to the maternal pocket. Even then he had no assurance of survival, for the maternal pocket usually has no more than 13 teats, and often as many as 16 young arrive. The unfortunate that can't find food must die; there is no taking turns, because the teat, once found, swells in the baby's mouth until he can't turn it loose.

The suckling in the dark goes on for more than a month, until one night the baby realizes he can get loose from the teat. As big as a mouse now, and covered with soft down, he eases his head out of the pouch and discovers that he can see. Soon he ventures out to crawl over his mother's fur. When she goes on her nightly prowls her youngsters clamber onto her back and entwine their slick little tails about her long tail, which she obligingly holds over her back like an overhead handrail on a bus.

Before long the mother is getting her pouch ready for a refill. In the mild climate of the southern states, three litters a year are not unusual. When the second litter arrives, the first batch remains in the vicinity, frequently in the nest, for about two months, then strays away. Young 'possums never know their father. The male has no responsibility after the breeding.

Along his unhurried way, Old Slowpoke occasionally noses into danger. Eagles, hawks and large predatory cats seek his flesh; dogs and men hunt him. Tooth, claw, speed, cunning, horns, quills, armor, offensive secretion and savage noise—all these have been given to other animals for their defense. But Old Slowpoke received none of these. His sole defense, other than to climb a tree, is to feign death.

A pack of hounds attacks him; he curls into a dead-looking heap, his exposed teeth protecting his vulnerable throat. The dogs chew and shake; the opossum unflinchingly hits the ground with the limpness of death. The dogs sniff and depart. Long afterward the wounded opossum may get up and walk away. Leading naturalists believe that he does not deliberately adopt this method of self-defense; they suspect that the presence of danger is too much for his nervous system and that fear causes temporary paralysis. This may be true, but many hunters have been severely wounded by an opossum suddenly "come alive."

The opossum eats almost anything—fruits, vegetables, grain, tender roots, birds, eggs, rodents, insects, fish, frogs. He has learned to make his way to the poultry yard for a good meal. He is so stupid, however, that he starts eating his warm kill in the hen house even though the surviving chickens raise a rumpus and arouse the irate farmer.

The opossum was named by the Indians of Virginia, where he was first seen by colonists, and he is practically the official animal of Dixie, where 'possum hunting is a favorite sport. High-bred hounds are carefully trained for it. Boys earn pocket money by trapping opossums and selling the skins at from a dime to a dollar. 'Possum pelts make up no little part of the annual fur harvest of the United States and roast 'possum is popular in the South. Even so, out in the woods and the river bottoms Old Slowpoke continues to survive, bungling along as he has done for ages. Apparently there will always be a 'possum.

The 'possum is the only pouched mammal to survive in North America. His skill in wrapping his long tail around a branch permits him to avoid enemies by hanging.

SNAIL FOLK
William Beebe

On my laboratory table in Bermuda was a snail in a glass dish, deep within his shell and with his door shut tight. I filled his dish with salt water, and, tight though his brown mahogany swirl of a door seemed to be, yet knowledge of the change in the outer element trickled through. The lid lifted—a dark finger of a tentacle wavered tentatively, an eye glinted in the portico and out came the owner. His ancestors, like mine, unquestionably came from the sea.

Shortening the level of my outlook to his, little by little, I tried to pry as deep as I possibly could into his molluscan soul. Somewhere, far back in the dim early ages of Earth life, there lived some creature which, today, snail and I can call *our* ancestor. But the changes which have intervened in the meantime are immeasurably divergent. As my line stretches back, my brain contracts, my muscles expand, I drop down on all fours, sprout a tail, develop long ears and snout, my teeth simplify and insects satisfy my hunger; reptilian characters accrue, my ribs increase; I slip into the water and, looking for the last time upon the land, I sink beneath the surface. Gills mark my rhythm of breath, limbs shrink to fins and even these vanish, while my backbone, last hold upon the higher life, dissolves to a notochord. At one end of my evolution I am considered superior to every other kind of creature—millions of years earlier any passing worm might have hailed me as brother.

My little snail has meanwhile glided about unchanged through the ages. When a race of creatures develops an ability to clothe itself in impregnable marble palaces, immune to a host of dangers which threaten less armored brethren, there is little need of its changing to meet new conditions.

As yet we know nothing definite about the very early ancestors of our snail, but even in the early aeons of the sea he had achieved a shell, and when he crawled shoreward and out upon primeval mud flats, it was as if he dragged with him a bit of the unchanging deeps. As long as food was at hand and no danger threatened, he crept slowly along, peering safely from a narrow crevice between earth and shell, and at the first hint of trouble he withdrew within his mineral castle. Such a procedure made for individual safety, but cramped the style of progress.

In the course of time the architecture might vary—spines and pillars might be added, pigment of the whole spectrum, or an elaborate hinged entrance. To such unimportant lengths of variation, but no further, might a mollusk go without endangering precedent. No wonder we find these creatures dominant as fossils—when in life they are little else, born in a ready-made, rocky sarcophagus.

With the slogan of "eternally conservative" the ancient snails spread along all the shores of the sea, clambering to the farthest spray of high tide. While they were content to munch old fragments of algae and cringe to all the cosmos, their neighbors fought and died and, through their changed offspring, lived again. Landward crept the pioneers—fish, crabs, worms and even lowly single-cellers, all changing, altering every portion of their beings to cope with the new conditions. And along with this host quietly glided the same old snails. Today I see cousins of this sea snail in full sunlight, creeping upon leaves high over my head, far from their original home, yet with almost no external adjustments to the new life.

All the time I am writing, our snail is steadily placing the inches behind him. He turns neither to right nor left, and his pace is unchanged whether over glass, cedar, blotting paper or manuscript. When he reaches the freshly written preceding paragraph, he smudges a line of the inky writing as he passes over it. The smudge is made by a fluid that he pours out in front, thus oiling his path in advance, smoothing the boulders of dust and killing any unpleasant feel or taste of inks and other alien fluids in his way. It is as if a sleigh were provided with a pair of ice machines in the front runners. This fluid also brings a snail clean and fresh to the end of its journey, whereas otherwise it would be coated and choked with dust.

I now begin my detective work, which is all that real science consists of, and first of all hold a stopwatch on my snail. I find that on the straightaway a snail can make three inches in one minute. That means a yard in 12 minutes and a mile in 15 days. I find from other experiments that a snail weighs one and a quarter grams, his house two grams and his thin, horny operculum (the "lid" attached to his body) only seven thousandths of a gram. We have a corresponding figure in a man weighing 125 pounds, carrying a shed of 200 pounds and a door of about half a pound in weight.

The shellfish that have ensconced themselves in their armor have a defense which seems well-nigh impregnable. Yet one of the most dramatic things is the way others have learned to pierce these marble

Periwinkles, shore-dwelling snails, found all over the world. These were photographed in the Hawaiian Islands.

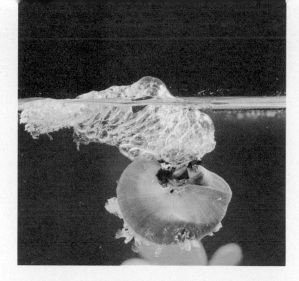

Purple sea snail, laying eggs. This creature floats about in the sea and gives off a purple fluid when it is disturbed. Photographed off one of the Florida Keys.

SNAIL SHELLS: They are the most beautiful of all animal structures, especially the highly colored ones found in tropical areas. Many, such as the periwinkle and cowry, have been used by man as money. Snails have a distinct head and foot which are withdrawn inside the shell when danger threatens. There is one group of snails, the slugs, which have only embryonic shells or no shells at all.

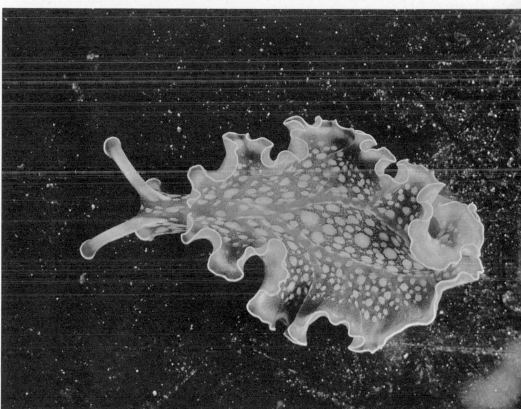

Above: garden snail, common throughout North America. Below: the cowry, one of a group of tropical water snails and a favorite of collectors. This was photographed in Hawaii.

Shell-less sea slug, colored like algae, its food. Photographed in Florida.

Flamingo tongue, a marine snail found from North Carolina to Florida and in the West Indies, where this was photographed on Tobago. It often lives on coral in shallow waters.

forts. Please visualize now a limpet that has attained adult snailhood unharmed by elements. He is crouched in his perfect-fitting form, perhaps peering out through the merest crack at his two-plane world, when he feels the touch of a tentacle on his shell. Instantly he draws tightly down and adjusts everything that a limpet has in the way of bolts, bars, portcullis, blinds and vizors. Still his sensitive shell transmits the shifting play of a delicate touch. Then a heavy weight presses down, and for a time nothing more happens. Finally, grind, grind, grind comes a new and different sound—we might liken it to an endless filing or scraping of sandpaper.

A great snail, the moon snail, with a rounded shell and a large amount of fleshy foot has climbed upon the tent roof and is busy with some nefarious work. We perceive a whole kit of tools—burglars' or executioners', or what you will. A narrow band covered with thousands of minute sharp teeth, like an ever moving file, is working swiftly upon a small section of the limpet's shell. Soon a small, round well is bored through—the shell is perforated. Then a most horridly ingenious tool comes into play, a living pair of shears on the end of a long, mobile proboscis. This is pushed down upon the unfortunate limpet and actually begins to cut and hack it into small pieces. One by one these are sucked upward through the hole, and when the moon snail packs up its outfit and moves away, the shell is cleaned of every particle of the former owner.

As we watch the moon snail glide smoothly on its way, we observe that the long tentacles are never still —they forever ply here and there in the path to come. We look for eyes and suddenly realize that the moon snail is blind.

My first memory of any snail is of long lines and curves of conch shells along the walks and around the flower beds belonging to my grandmother. It was a conch that led to my most cruel disillusionment. I used secretly to grub up one of the garden conchs, hold it to my ear and listen ecstatically to the sound of distant surf in the heart of the shell. The double joy of this was totally destroyed by some practical-minded gardener who showed me that a teacup gave forth identical moanings of the ancient seas. But as I near the end of this account of snails, I hear in the distance, over the water, a low, sweet tone, swelling to penetrative power. Far away I see a fisherman holding a conch shell to his lips. And now my last sense of disappointment passes—I no longer regret my juvenile hopes, for the conch has yielded a sound more intimately its own than any pseudo-roar of the surf could ever be.

The horseshoe crab, once called the horse-foot crab, resembles a horse's hoof (above) as well as a horseshoe (below). It is a relative of the scorpion, not of the crab.

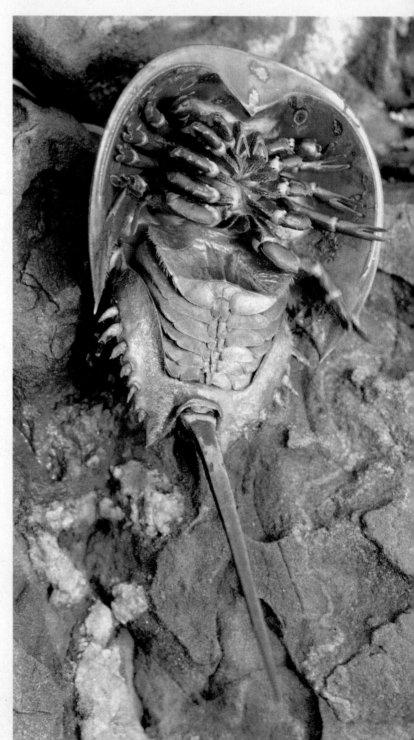

THE CREATURE
TIME FORGOT
Lorus J. and Margery J. Milne

In 1557 one of the early explorers of the East Indies brought back from the Molucca Strait a sea animal the like of which had never been seen in Europe. A careful description of its armored shell and low, bulging eyes was published the following year. Half a century later Sir Walter Raleigh led an expedition to the New World and on the coast of North Carolina met an almost identical creature—the horseshoe crab. Local Indians called it the "see-ekanauk" and used its six-inch tail spine to make a stiff point for their fish spears.

Gradually the naturalists of the world realized that these animals were an ancient form of life that had survived with relatively little change. Fossils of almost identical crabs have been found in the rock record dating back over the last 190 million years. Probably the habits of horseshoe crabs are as unchanged as their bodies.

From the Bay of Fundy to the shores of Yucatan on the Gulf of Mexico, horseshoe crabs approach the Atlantic coast of North America each spring. When time and tide are right, they clamber up the beaches and bulldoze through the mud flats to lay their eggs. As the water recedes, pairs may be seen at the edge, looking like combat helmets. In front is the "cow" crab, usually older than her mate and measuring as much as 14 inches across. Clinging to her shell with a peculiar claw on each of his front walking legs is the smaller "bull" crab. He is ready to fertilize her eggs as she deposits them in a depression scooped in the beach.

During the rest of the year horseshoe crabs scavenge in deeper water, feeding on mussels and marine worms. These are chewed, although the crabs have no jaws of any kind. Instead the mouth is hidden between the spiny bases of the five pairs of legs, and these "shoulders" grind together to masticate the food. The mouth and legs lie below the horseshoe-shaped (or, more strictly speaking, hoof-shaped) front part of the animal's body. Hinged to the hind part is the smaller abdomen, tapering to the sturdy, sharp-pointed tail spine. Underneath the abdomen are six pairs of overlapping gill plates.

The horseshoe crab runs along the sea bottom with a curious bobbing gait. Waves of motion pass backward, affecting leg after leg and then the gill plates. At the beginning of each wave the crab nose-dives toward the sand. But as later legs take up the movements the shell tilts upward.

Particularly vigorous running raises the animal almost clear of the bottom. For a moment the tail spine drags. Then the creature performs a half-loop, to angle toward the surface. Or it may swim horizontally with back downward, its paired legs and gill plates beating rhythmically. When it finally settles to the bottom, the tail spine is used to turn the body right-side-up.

Horseshoe crabs are not true crabs or even crustaceans. Their nearest living relatives—spiders and scorpions, creatures of the land—are only distant cousins. The great group to which these living fossils belong (scientists call it Xiphosura) has been distinct from all other forms of life since that early period in the Earth's history known as the Devonian, about 350 million years ago. Of their many near relatives in those ancient times, all are extinct now. Only the horseshoe crabs found the formula for survival.

THE 50-MILLION-YEAR-
OLD PLATYPUS
Robert S. Strother

Back in 1797, Lieutenant Colonel David Collins wrote for scientific colleagues in far-off London a description of a strange animal he had encountered near the Hawkesbury River in New South Wales, Australia. After telling of the webbed feet and beaverlike tail of the little fur-bearing creature, Collins went on to say: "But the most extraordinary circumstance observed in its structure was its having, instead of the mouth of an animal, the upper and lower mandibles of a duck. . . . Its webbed feet enabled it to swim, while on shore its long sharp claws were employed in burrowing. Nature thus provided for its double or amphibian character."

This account was strictly accurate as far as it went, and it could have gone a great deal further without exhausting the remarkable list of oddities which distinguish the mixed-up animal known today as the duck-billed platypus. But, incomplete as it was, the description created a sensation in scientific circles in London and on the Continent. Most of the savants suspected a "monstrous imposture" and with good reason—sailors prowling in remote corners of the planet were forever sending back for public exhibit artfully contrived specimens of such wholly fabulous beings as mermaids and unicorns. Moreover, Australia had only recently been the source of a wild variety of unheard-of creatures: wombats, phalangers, echidnas and even a marsupial carnivorous wolverine bearing the label of Tasmanian Devil.

The furore touched off by the written description of the platypus was revived and amplified a few years later when the British Museum received a pair of pickled specimens sent in a cask of spirits by Governor James Hunter of New South Wales. Dried skins had been received before, but these were the first actual platypuses ever to be seen outside the Antipodes. They were turned over to Everard Home, a distinguished anatomist, for dissection. Dr. Home's report left the members of the Royal Society in a state of stunned incredulity. He pronounced this egg-laying aquatic mammal outrageous but genuine, and thus touched off a controversy that was not cleared up for nearly a century.

Most zoologists found it hard to credit the notion that a mammal could lay eggs and then suckle its young, but visitors to Australia, impressed by the aborigines' accounts of the habits of the "mallangong," as they called the platypus, were inclined to take the oviparous, or egg-laying, side of the controversy. Finally, in 1884, Dr. W. H. Caldwell, a Cambridge zoologist, was sent to Australia by the British Museum with the mission of finding a platypus egg, if any existed. After a strenuous search, he found two. They proved to be about one half by three quarters of an inch in size, with soft shells like lizard eggs.

While he was at it, Dr. Caldwell also looked into the confirmed reports that a sort of cousin of the platypus also wore hair and laid eggs. This was the echidna, or spiny anteater, which looks like a pint-size porcupine and is known in some circles today as the "egg-laying hedgehog." The echidna and the platypus make up a zoological classification called monotremes. The discoverer forthwith excitedly cabled the British Association for the Advancement of Science: MONOTREMES OVIPAROUS.

Today Australia is known to zoologists as an "evolutionary deep freeze" where a number of species that

The egg-laying platypus is not half mammal and half bird, although he looks it. His outlandish features are even more unbelievable to the scientist than to the rest of us.

have long since vanished from other parts of the globe continue to flourish. The platypus can boast of 50 million years of existence as a species and is considered a link between reptiles and mammals. The name "platypus" was selected by Dr. George Shaw, who was the lucky recipient of a dried skin in 1798. The name is Greek for "flat foot," and while its feet are indeed flat, some critics have suggested that one or another of the animal's more notable peculiarities might have served better as the basis for its name.

As people became better acquainted with the platypus, the list of its distinctive features was steadily enlarged. It has capacious pouches in its cheeks for storing sand and gravel used presumably for grinding worms, small crustaceans and other delicacies, and it possesses a facial furrow that simultaneously closes both eye and ear orifices when the animal submerges. It has a unique method for nursing its platykittens, of which there usually are two. The mother platypus exudes milk from her abdomen, and the baby licks it off her fur.

Platypuses are sometimes playful. They also can be mean, and to assist them in defense the males make adept use of poison spurs on their rear ankles. Although there are no deaths from platypus poisoning on record, trout fishermen who have accidentally caught platypuses have been painfully poisoned in attempting to remove the hook.

Neatness is one of the winning characteristics of platypuses. They groom themselves carefully on emerging from the water, using their rear claws like a comb for this purpose. Their rear hips are equipped with ball-and-socket joints, and this, combined with their "India rubber" flexibility, enables them to reach all parts of their bodies.

Although they weigh only two or three pounds and measure no more than 20 inches in length, platypuses put away enormous amounts of food. They won't feed until dusk or early morning. Then they swim around with their eyes shut, resembling as much as anything else fur-bearing hot-water bottles. They zero in on their food, guided by their sensitive bills. They surface before chewing their rations, and although exceedingly particular about the kinds of worm they will accept, they don't mind swallowing a lot of dirt as long as there are proper worms inside. Their sense of hearing is amazingly acute, but they can't see straight ahead, only outward and upward. For that reason platypuses that wander away from the water usually get lost.

David Fleay of Brisbane, Australia, was the first man to breed a platypus in captivity, and it is thanks largely to his knowledge that the Bronx Zoo in New York was able to keep two of them in good health for more than ten years—the longest time that any have ever survived outside Australia. Named Cecil and Penelope, they thrived on a diet of 25,000 worms a month, supplemented by crayfish, frogs and egg custard. "The platypuses are the most expensive guests in our zoo," a curator said at the time. "The enormous quantity of worms cost more than the feed for the elephants." Every year during the decade they were the costly guests of New York, high hopes were entertained that they might achieve parenthood. Certain actions interpreted by their hosts as amorous were observed on various occasions. Once Penelope, after ardent courtship, went into seclusion within her burrow. The curators of the zoo began counting the days, their anxiety mounting steadily as the gestation period came to an end. At last, with winter rushing in, they decided they must dig out Penelope and her supposed offspring for transfer to winter quarters. Penelope was uncovered intact, but there were no platykittens, and no sign that she had expected any.

In the summer of 1957, when Cecil was again decidedly attentive, Penelope received his advances coldly and managed to escape from the platypusary. Her keepers had no hope she could find the needed quantity of earthworms and were obliged after a few days to conclude that Penelope was dead. She was never found. Cecil died two years later.

The maximum life-span of a platypus in captivity so far is 17 years, and supposedly it is about that in the wild state. Black rats and a rapacious variety of river cod are the animal's main natural enemies. Rabbits, a plague of Australia introduced from Europe, have riddled the riverbanks, making the platypus' natural haunts unfit to live in. Fish traps set for the cod often used to capture and drown platypuses, but today these traps are forbidden under the rigorous laws by which Australia is successfully protecting this strange little animal.

Formerly thousands of platypuses were killed for their fur, which is the most durable to be found in Australia. It is reddish in color, without pronounced marks except for a yellowish spot under the eye. The underfur is very soft; the outer coat is coarser, with glistening silver tips. About 60 pelts were used to make a single rug. Nowadays even the possession of a platypus pelt is forbidden by law.

With their ancient ancestry assuring their natural capacity to survive and with their numbers on the increase under Australia's conservation laws, chances are that platypuses—recently near extinction—will manage to stick around a few more centuries. Their prospects seem at least as good as our own.

Chapter three

CREATURES OF THE EXTREME

Give nature an environment, even an extreme one, and she will shape
a beast to fit it. To live on high mountains, animals require large lungs
to breathe the thin air. They must be able to withstand extremes of
cold, drought and burning sun. Their feet must grip ice and rock.
These attributes characterize the chamois and the conies.

In the polar regions, creatures must have bulky bodies to retain body heat.
They need keen noses and night eyes for the long, dark winter; they must
be rugged, able to keep going day after day in the hunt for the scarce prey.
A polar bear or arctic fox fits these requirements ideally.

Camels must have broad feet to walk the shifting sands of the desert—
as well as the ability to raise their temperature to accord with the rising heat
of the midday sun. In the humidity of the hot rain forest, some animals
move slowly. They must be able to stay motionless until coolness returns. So
there are the sloths, toucans, pythons and parrots.

The ocean presents still other situations for life to adapt to: the crowding of
too many creatures in agreeable places, or great pressure, or inky
darkness or isolation in the deeps. Hence, some animals develop camouflage
or swiftness to evade enemies, others produce phosphorescence to
illuminate the darkness, and special bladders and blubber to
resist pressure.

In these rugged, forbidding environments, least hospitable to man,
live some of the world's most fascinating and perfectly evolved creatures.

THE CAMEL—
DISCONTENTED SHIP OF THE DESERT

Arthur Weigall

All camels are discontented. They hate being camels, but they would hate to be anything else, because in their opinion all other living creatures are beneath contempt, especially human beings. The expression upon their faces when they pass you on the road indicates that they regard you as a bad smell.

They nurse a perpetual grievance against mankind and ruminate upon their wrongs until they groan aloud. When you go to them to find out what is the matter they give you no hint of any specific trouble, but merely look at you with sad, reproachful eyes and groan more loudly. In certain cases when their sense of unbearable insult is overwhelming, they try rather halfheartedly to bite you.

The fact that a camel has yellow teeth, a harelip, a hump, corns and halitosis places the poor creature beyond the range of ordinary sympathy. People never put their arms around camels or stroke or kiss them, and yet their sorrowful eyes, fringed with long, languishing lashes, are beautiful, and their whimpering is heartbreaking. But camels do not ask for love or pity. They make no response whatsoever to overtures of that sort. They have no hope, and they make no friends. When they are being ridden they do not attempt to coöperate with their riders, and when they are being used as beasts of burden they try their best to make you feel a cad.

In the days when I was Inspector General of Antiquities in Egypt, I had a horse, a donkey and a camel: the horse for ordinary riding; the donkey—one of those big white Egyptian donkeys which are almost the size of a mule—for making my daily rounds among the temples and excavations in my charge; and the camel for desert work. The camel's name was Laura, but she neither knew nor cared.

Laura proved to be one of the strongest runners of her kind. I rode her on several long expeditions into the Egyptian desert, and on one of these trips she carried me 200 miles in four days without drinking. But that is nothing remarkable, for camels can go ten days without water and can keep up an average pace of eight to ten miles an hour for six or eight hours during the first three or four days. When properly watered, they can run 100 miles a day, though 60 is generally considered a good, hard journey.

Like all camels, Laura was supremely stupid. For instance, she could never be taught that she must remain crouched until her rider was in the saddle, and must not scramble to her feet just at the moment when he was mounting. A camel's saddle is a sagging square of leather covered with a thick sheepskin, supported on a high, padded framework which fits around the hump and is fastened by a girth under the animal's body. You sit on this lofty throne with your legs crossed in front of you on the curve of the camel's neck, which is your footstool. Once you are up, you cannot get off again until you have made certain strange noises with your tongue, the signal for the camel to kneel. Then down go the awkward creature's front legs, and you hang forward over its neck. After that the hind legs double up, jerking you straight again. You can then slide gracefully to the ground—unless the camel suddenly decides to get up, in which case your descent is more spectacular.

Laura always watched me out of the corner of her eye until she caught me at a disadvantage. When I swore at her she only gazed at me sorrowfully and uttered her inconsolable grumbles. A camel, by the way, can do more than look at you out of the corner of an eye. It can turn its head completely round and stare at you full in the face with both eyes. I know of nothing more disconcerting.

There are two kinds of camel. One is the Bactrian, which has two humps and long, shaggy hair; but the kind used in Egypt is the Arabian, which has only one hump and short, sandy-colored or whitish hair. The hump is a store of fatty flesh which can be reabsorbed into the general system. When the camel is well fed, the hump is hard and big. When food is scarce, it sags and looks empty. Because a camel's fat is concentrated in one place (other mammals have an even layer of fat over their entire bodies), there is no insulation between flesh and skin. Thus the camel's body can cool more rapidly than a man's, for example.

The hump, then, is one of the reasons why the camel can survive great desert heat. Two other factors are important, too: the camel can raise and lower its body temperature and it can tolerate dehydration. Camels show themselves to be desert creatures in additional ways: their flat, padded feet are designed for treading on soft sand or hard rocks, and they can close their nostrils during a sandstorm.

It is not customary to allow a riding-camel to walk, because the motion is rolling and you lurch from side to side in a sickly manner which suggests a reason for calling the camel the "ship of the desert." A quick jog trot is the usual gait; you simply bump up and down in the saddle like a cavalry trooper, the bumps becoming bigger and better as the pace increases to a gallop. Laura used to add to the fun by occasionally jumping over low rocks, but she never fell. In fact, I have never heard of a camel falling.

Laura became a mother when she was about ten. In the spring the male camels attract the attention of the females by making gurgling noises, like water running out of the bath, and inflating their tongues until they hang out of their mouths like pink balloons. Laura could not resist the blandishments of a magnificently disdainful he-camel who hailed from down Suez way and was in the transport business. As she appeared to be all wrought up in her own melancholy fashion, we arranged a rendezvous. Although Laura was not a large animal as camels go, the resulting foal stood three feet high when it was a week old.

I have sometimes heard it said that camels are delicate and difficult to rear, but in my experience camel health is often remarkably good considering the poor food they usually get. The birth of Laura's foal gave her no trouble, and the foal itself was healthy enough. Friends of mine in the army have told me that the camels used in desert warfare do not seem much distressed when they are hit by bullets, and recover rapidly from wounds. I suppose this depends on the camel. Even with good food and care, Laura had colic sometimes, and in winter she would catch cold and mope about with her nose running. As for pain, she nearly wrecked our hospital at Luxor when an abscess in her hump was lanced.

Laura's various expressions of loathing, together with endless groans and complaining, made you think she could not possibly be in good health. I used to watch her *teaching* her foal to grumble. When she saw me coming she would start bleating and bubbling, putting her head close to her infant's as she did so, in order that the sounds might be imitated.

Heaven knows I treated her and her offspring with kindness, but I never saw the light of love for me in the eyes of either of them. Laura did love her foal for the first few months of its awkward, leggy little life, yet in the end she gave it a nip and the small creature kicked her in the ribs in return. After that they went their separate, dreary ways with their noses in the air and their hearts full of their grievances.

One of the oldest beasts of burden, the camel dislikes its working life on the desert. But it is efficiently equipped for enduring heat and sand. Its first home was probably North America.

Like the gull, the polar bear divides his time between cold waters and frosty ice floes. In winter the female holes up in a den to bear the young; the male roams through the arctic night.

THE GREAT WHITE BEAR

Jack Denton Scott

Cruising the Arctic Ocean in the late summer of 1960 aboard the Norwegian ketch *Havella,* we spotted a V-shaped wave far off to our left. Something was swimming in this roughest of the world's seas. Alf Olsen, the mate, came out of the pilothouse, and I pointed. "Polar bear!" he said.

We were so far from land that we could no longer see even its distant outlines. Yet we overhauled an enormous bear. He was swimming gracefully, using only his front feet, his rear legs hanging straight out like a rudder. We estimated that he was making about three miles an hour. I remarked that it was amazing to see a bear out that far. "That isn't far for ice bear," Olsen said. "Two years ago I saw an old she-bear and two half-grown cubs in open water 200 miles north of Greenland, apparently headed for the ice pack another 100 miles north."

The polar bear, found only in the arctic, is one of the largest and strongest carnivorous animals on Earth. When mature, he weighs up to 1600 pounds. With his elongated body, narrow head, slender limbs, long neck, and rump rising higher than his shoulders, he looks awkward, but his agility is remarkable. He can travel 25 miles an hour across ice. In the water he has been clocked at six miles an hour and can make sudden forward plunges of 15 feet.

One day when we were anchored in a quiet fiord, I saw a white bear swim into a flock of eider ducks, among the most talented divers in feathers. He swam slowly, scarcely rippling the surface, only the top of his head visible. Suddenly he was among them, and they dived. So did he. After a while he came surging to the top, a flapping eider in his mouth. Although the bear seemed to be under the water a long time, a glance at my watch showed that it had been less than a minute. F. J. De Gisbert, who spent many years in the arctic studying bears and capturing them alive for zoos, claimed that despite their almost unbelievable strength they can't swim underwater for more than 50 yards.

Most animals have to paddle vigorously to stay afloat, but the polar bear can lie motionless for long periods with consummate ease—air spaces in his fur, oil glands in the skin and a thick layer of fat support him. His legs are jointed so they can swing in a wide circle, an aid in swimming and maneuverability. He has special arctic sunglasses: a membranous third eyelid, which protects his eyes from ice glare and snow blindness. His toes are partially webbed, and he has hair on the bottom of his feet, suiting them equally well for swimming and for walking on slippery ice.

His unretractable claws, cat-sharp, are precision instruments used for hooking seals out of their air holes in the ice. He hisses like a cat when annoyed, will roar when wounded, but usually is as silent as the surrounding snow. I had one get within 15 yards of me over ice before I knew he was there. And I was standing in a boat carefully watching for him. I spotted him only by his black nose.

Knowing that his nose is a telltale mark, the polar bear usually hides it when awaiting game or stalking. A noted arctic hunter once watched two bears sitting on ice near the sea, their black noses carefully covered with their paws. Presently a seal popped out of the water. One bear put his paw under it and flipped the 500 pounds of flesh out onto the ice in a single, simple swish.

With the polar bear's tremendous physical power goes a marvelous sense of smell. He scents seal blubber at 20 miles—sometimes to his destruction, for hunters entice him to his death by burning it. Olsen told me of a party that had gone out in the summer of 1960 to photograph polar bears. They staked the *Havella* against an ice floe and then burned some blubber. After an hour they saw a bear swimming toward them. He got out of the water, walked up to the anchor rope and, using his paws like hands, pulled the boat closer to the floe. The crew placed strips of blubber on a long stick and held it over the edge of the boat. The bear stood up (he was over ten feet tall) and fetched the blubber off the stick into his mouth. This continued for about a half-hour while filming went on. But when the blubber stopped coming, the bear became annoyed, again pulled the boat closer with the anchor rope and crouched for a spring. "In a second," Alf said, "we would have had a thousand pounds of anger aboard. We didn't want to, but we had to shoot him."

Polar bears often inspire laughter instead of fear, however. Kaare Rodahl, who has spent many years in the arctic, tells of seeing a big one swim up to a seal sunning itself on a floe, hurl himself out of the water and take a swipe at the seal. The seal escaped. The bear stood upright on the floe, picked up pieces of ice and hurled them in rage. Then he flopped down, sulking.

But a polar bear is neither clown nor villain, essentially. He is a relentless hunter. Following the sun, he moves southward in the fall; in the spring he starts north again, staying on the ice belt along the arctic coast, where seals are plentiful. His wanderings (in the course of an average life-span of 25 years he is constantly on the move, sometimes traveling as much as 75 miles in a week) are linked to the movements of tiny, shrimplike sea organisms, "krills," which swarm in waters of low salinity. The krills seek spots where icebergs are melting, diluting sea water. Here fish feed on the krills, seals eat the fish, and bears hunt the seals. The polar bear likes to prowl lightly frozen cracks in ice made by tidal currents. Seals use these cracks as breathing spots, popping their heads up through the new ice. When the seal comes up for air, the waiting bear kills it.

The only living thing the polar bear fears (other than the killer whale, known to catch bears in the water) is the walrus. Three times the bear's size, it has long, sharp tusks and a hide that is almost impossible to penetrate, and it can outswim and drown the bear. But the walrus is stupid, and the bear is not. Eskimos have reported seeing a polar bear sneak up on a snoozing walrus and kill it by bashing its head with a block of ice.

Mother polar bears are among the most devoted of parents. Mating in springtime at the age of five, the female digs her lair for the January birth of one or two cubs in pressure-ice hummocks or deep snow. Unlike other bears, polar bears do not hibernate; but a mother stays in her den until late March or early April, feeding her cubs through the winter, cuddling them in the warm fur of her abdomen. She keeps them for two years, not mating again during this time, patiently teaching them the arts of hunting.

The savage white bear takes to captivity and summer heat better than most of our temperate-zone animals. His unusual appearance, amusing antics and Olympic prowess in water make him a favorite of the zoo-goer—and he knows it. A pair in a Quebec City zoo, with a diving board by their pool, never do the high-jinx act unless there is an audience. A bear in the London zoo sits erect like a proud old gentleman only when a person with a camera approaches. Even a caged polar bear is dangerous, however.

For centuries it has been the custom of anyone traveling the arctic to kill any bear he sees, but because of his inaccessibility the polar bear has survived. Now, with the advent of airplanes, fast boats and high-powered rifles, the white bear is in danger of extinction. Experts guess that the world population of polar bears is about 25,000.

The problem in protection lies in the fact that he is an international animal and each country bordering the Arctic Ocean has its own ideas about him. He also has no protection beyond the three-mile limit. Residents of Norway and most of Greenland today can kill him without restriction. He is not protected because, they say, he is ruining their sealing industry. (There is an additional reason: live cubs bring $500 in the zoo market, and skins sell to tourists for $200.) Alaska allows visiting sportsmen only one bear. The Soviet Union permits no shooting of bears. Canada protects them, claiming that the polar bear is conserving a valuable fur animal, the arctic fox. The bear leaves seal carcasses for the foxes to scavenge.

Shortly before Alaska became a state, E. L. Bartlett, then delegate from Alaska, registered a request with the Department of the Interior. Pointing out that there had been a terrific increase in polar-bear hunting, he said, "Please save our bear!" But today there is still no assurance of protection for the fabulous white hunter of the arctic.

THE REMARKABLE REINDEER

George Kent

By any standard, a reindeer is a tough and enduring animal. Cold doesn't bother it, and its coat is waterproof. A jacket of reindeer fur is a fair equivalent of a life belt because the hair is hollow and filled with air, and hence buoyant.

Reindeer will find and dig up food in what seems an absolutely barren waste of snow. Their splayed hoofs have a sharp edge which can cut through all but the hardest ice. Their chief food is the lichen of the north, often called reindeer moss, which in summer makes an ankle-deep rug of greenery. But they will eat wild mushrooms, willow leaves—in fact, almost any growing thing.

In the vast stretch of country across the top of the world—Canada, Alaska, Greenland, Scandinavia and Siberia—the reindeer and its cousin, the caribou, are the only animals of their type, with the possible exception of the musk ox, which can thrive and multiply. Late in September the mating season gets under way when the bucks begin assembling harems of 30 to 40 females. This is also the fighting season, and the air is alive with the crash of bodies and the castanet

When the sun returns to light the arctic sky, reindeer gather in great numbers to make their northward trek over land and water to a summer range in the wild tundra. The sight of a vast herd swimming a river—a forest of antlers moving over the water—is a memorable experience.

crackle of horn on horn as the bucks battle to protect their wives. At this season it is not safe to get near a cluster of reindeer. There are instances of men having been killed, and of others being stranded for days on a high rock where they had taken refuge.

Like most people, I never gave reindeer much thought, except maybe at Christmastime. I regarded them vaguely as large, good-humored beasts which hauled Santa Claus about in his high red sleigh. Then I went up beyond the Arctic Circle to Finnish Lapland, where the Lapps drive reindeer, milk reindeer, eat reindeer. The Lapps are the great reindeer raisers of western Europe, and their herds in Norway, Sweden and Finland total about 575,000.

Reindeer hair is used for mattresses. The skin makes parkas, mittens, trousers. Sinew thread is especially good for sewing canoes because it swells, making watertight seams. Knife handles and needles are contributed by the antlers. The stomach membranes (a reindeer has six stomachs) are used for packing cheese. Skin from the forehead produces a nonskid leather for shoe soles which are excellent for walking on ice and snow.

While I was in Lapland, the deer I got to know best was a morose, mangy little thing about the size of a Shetland pony. Though he was full-grown, I could have lifted him without much trouble. His coat was a frowsy brown-gray and he possessed only one horn. I have heard reports of sweet-tempered reindeer, but I did not meet any. If a Lapp wants to milk a lady deer, he has to lasso her, muzzle her with a rope and chain her to a fence or stump. The most milk he'll get is half a teacup. But it has about four times the butterfat of cow's milk, and a few drops are enough to turn coffee white. The Lapps freeze it and drop it into coffee like lumps of sugar.

Reindeer pull the Lapp version of a sleigh, which is called a pulkha, but they never pull with gusto. A wild horse can be persuaded between the shafts of a wagon in a month or two, but it takes six months to train a reindeer, and to his dying day he feels he has been unlucky.

My Lapp guide was loath to let me take a pulkha ride alone because he thought it would be too dangerous, but I insisted and got the ride of my life— a breathtaking experience, like riding at high speed in a car with no brakes. You have almost no control of the deer, which has a mind of its own; it can outrun the average horse, and its hoofs machine-gun you with pellets of snow and ice. Every few minutes the animal gets bored with the road and tries to lunge up a snowbank.

Some of the Lapp reindeer are raised as pets and allowed in the house, but most remain half wild. Strictly speaking, they are not herded but followed. The Lapps who watch over them are nomads, for their deer have to keep moving to find forage.

The United States' adventure with reindeer began in 1891 when the missionary Dr. Sheldon Jackson observed that Eskimos in Alaska were dying of starvation while other Eskimos only 56 miles away, on the other side of Bering Strait, were sleek, well fed and happy. The difference was reindeer. Dr. Jackson asked Congress for money and was refused. He raised $2000 privately to import 187 head from Siberia. These did so well that Congress relented, and about 1100 reindeer were brought to Alaska.

By 1931, Alaskan reindeer, numbering more than 500,000, were big business. There were freezing plants and slaughterhouses, and reindeer meat was appearing on many American menus. The success of the experiment was due largely to the fact that private owners were doing a fine job of herd management.

Then in 1937 the government, persuaded by well-meaning persons, appropriated $2,000,000, bought all the reindeer in Alaska not already the property of natives and turned them over to the Eskimos. But the Eskimo is primarily a hunter; he refuses to take care of a herd. The Eskimos slaughtered the reindeer by the thousands and took no care of the remainder. Today in all of North America there are only a few thousand left, some in Alaska, the rest in Canada's Mackenzie delta, where on what may be the largest ranch in the world live 7000 descendants of a herd of 3000 reindeer imported from Alaska a generation ago.

LIFE ABOVE THE TIMBERLINE
Jean George

Slashed across the tops of the tall mountains of the world lies a cruel no-man's-land where howling winds make dwarfs of trees and ice beats grass and flowers to a mat. The sun punishes; ice and rocks avalanche. This is the land above "timberline"—beautiful but harsh, dangerous, where seemingly nothing can live. And yet life has grubbed a toehold there. Not ordinary life, but creatures that have learned to live with unbelievable hardships.

I first became intrigued with the ingenuity and endurance of life beyond the trees some years ago when a mountaineer, sitting at a campfire in the West,

The whiteness of the mountain goat may not be merely protective coloration. Many biologists have come to believe that it enables the animal to hold its body heat in the cold uplands. The Rocky Mountain goat is classified as a goat-antelope because it bears the features of each.

his ice axe still on his belt, pointed to a black peak against the stars. "If a black-eyed mountain goat hadn't known that mountain better than I do, I wouldn't be here tonight," he began. "Three days ago I was crossing a glacier when I suddenly noticed a puff of dust rising like smoke—from the hanging wall just below me. I knew it was the first signal of an avalanche. I thought my time had come.

"A mountain goat, who had been feeding off to my left on a windy ridge, suddenly tensed. His big hump back quivered under his white fur. The mountain was telling him to run. He bounced to an ice wall, sized it up and sprinted out of sight. I turned and followed. At least it was a chance. I learned long ago that all animals of the high country know the mountains, but wild goats know them best. Some people think goats keep alive up there just because they can run away from avalanches and leap from enemies, but it's more than that. They know every crack and cranny. I ran to the wall, slammed my axe into the marks he had made with his hoofs and heaved up his

route. There were ledges and handgrips for me that I'd never guessed were there. Struggling over the top, I rolled onto solid rock just as an artillery explosion sounded the collapse of my trail." As he talked, I stared at the peak and wondered what other intelligent life lived in those bleak rocks, and how they made out in blizzards and storms and relentless sun.

A year later I stood at tree line in the Colorado Rockies. (It could have been the Grand Teton in Wyoming, Mount Rainier in Washington, any of the many mountains that stretch above 10,000 or 11,000 feet.) The wind that dried my face was icy cold as it funneled down a pass from a glacier. The snow still covered the northern slopes. I could see no life at all. I could hear nothing but the wind. Suddenly I realized that a big Rocky Mountain sheep was staring down on me, his pantaloons blowing. I stared in disbelief; he was fat and comfortable, standing in nothing but wind and snow. I saw no food for him. But presently he leaned down and ate, and I realized the mountaineer was right—the animals of the high country do know their mountains. The wind had swept the slope, exposing the sweet grass.

He sprinted down from his meadow and, lightly running over a talus slope, disappeared around a boulder. I followed him, remembering that the sheep, like the goats, knew the best trails. The Forest Service understood this: at the turn of the century it tossed out its own blueprints for mountain trails in favor of trails built by sheep and goats. These routes were longer but out of the wind and the sun, which is just as killing as the cold in the high country.

The first thing I learned from the ram was that knowing *where* to walk is not enough. You also have to know *how* to walk. Loose rocks went out from under my clumsy feet like a nightmare and I slid 50 yards to the bottom of a moraine. The ram walked on, up his own switchbacks, over ice and snow. He stepped to a high pinnacle, looked down at me, scratched and leaped to another pinnacle. He alighted with stiff, shockproof legs and was instantly rigid. His control was breathtaking.

Several days later I saw a group of females and lambs in a wide, high meadow. The ram was a speck above them, grazing the small, lonely grass patches that took skill and endurance to find. For the sheep, it was women and children first at the easy pasturage until November, when the ram would join them. Head down, he would drive his curling horns against those of a rival, shaking the mountains like thunder.

On all the high peaks of the world, members of this remarkable group of animals cavort and sprint on the edges of cliffs and dash along sheer precipices. The Himalayas have the shy ibex, the Andes the alpaca and llama, and in the Alps the chamois capers on boulders where lesser beasts fear to go.

The chamois is like our mountain goat. He must use environment as a shield against enemies, walking with a sheer wall rising on one side and a tremendous drop on the other. But, for all his intelligence, his mating ritual seems poorly planned. The stag lives alone until September 1, according to mountaineers. Then he leaves his hideout and follows his trail to his harem and kids. When he finds his family, the vigorous rutting begins. His horns slash open his rivals, his voice rumbles like an avalanche. He does not sleep. He does not eat. And when he turns to leave two weeks later, he is gaunt, thin and exhausted. Drifting off to his solitary hideout in poor condition, he faces the famine of winter.

After watching the goats and sheep on several trips to the timberline, I began to understand how they survived. Other animals share this ability to adjust to such rigors. The marmot is one of the most surprising. It is a hibernator. Most hibernators need long springs, summers and autumns to store up food. However, the whistling marmot (who, in his high-altitude home, actually does whistle) has only two and a half months at the most to get fat for winter. For a long time it was believed his secret was to eat from dawn to dusk without stopping. But on a camping trip to the high country I watched a marmot who spent most of his day running in and out of his den. He was seldom in his meadow feeding.

I asked a mammalogist who was with us what he made of this idleness, and he told me that the remarkable secret of the marmot's survival in the mountains is the animal's unique metabolism. "All of a sudden, toward the end of the season, these fellows can put on layers of fat in no time at all, on no more food than usual."

One of the most surprising things about the majority of the animals of the alpine tundra is that they are not massive or rugged, like the polar bear and the reindeer of the arctic. Some, like the little mountain cony, are just plain dainty and delicate.

The first time I saw a cony, bright-eyed with soft tan fur, and no bigger than a gray squirrel, I asked my ecologist brother, Frank, why the cony was running around with pretty flowers in its mouth when it ought to be working. In three leaps Frank went up a talus slope and called to me to follow. "He's a farmer," he said, "and flowers are his crop." He pointed to a pile of exotic hay under a rock in a "cony barn." It was sweet-scented and as big as a bed pillow. I could see many crops tucked under the overhangs of the boulders. We climbed higher where the snow still covered the slope. Frank got down on his stomach, twisted and peered under the snow. "A cony city," he said, and I got down to look. Rocks made tent poles and roofs for the snow, leaving alleys and main streets, silos and barns below. These cities are dim but warm, about 32° Fahrenheit all winter. And the cony's eyes are big, enabling him to run and cavort in his dark winter city under the snow and rocks.

The cony has other assets which help keep him alive during mountain blizzards. His body is round and compact, his ears are small, he has a puff for a tail. These characteristics conserve heat. There are no long appendages like upstanding ears or a tail for the wind to freeze. Like all of nature's successful creatures, he has evolved a body and habits ideally suited to his environment. At the top of the world there is no place for comfort. Animals are swiftly overtaken by rain, sleet and lightning. The sun burns. The elements deal fiercely here with all living things.

SLUGGARD OF THE JUNGLE

Lorus J. and Margery J. Milne

There is a world of eternal twilight that swelters, hot and humid, with never the touch of refreshing coolness that comes to other regions with the setting sun. This is the world of the tropical rain forest, where layer upon layer of branches reach for the sky. The rains descend at the rate of an inch a day for a month at a time, and the lush, rich foliage, shutting out the sun, prevents evaporation.

The largest rain forest in the world lies in the Amazon and Guiana valleys of South America, and one of the creatures that live out their sluggish lives in the forest's moist, hot, heavily perfumed air is the sloth, a relative of the anteater. Almost everything about the sloth is an exception to general rules. Instead of walking on its legs as most mammals do, it hangs by all four legs from the horizontal limbs of trees, having evolved powerful, hooked claws for making its way through the thickly canopied, overhead world in which it lives. Its head, of the same diameter as its neck and lacking obvious ears, seems to emerge directly from its powerful shoulders. At the other end there is no visible tail. It is often difficult to tell a sloth's front end from its rear.

Unless molested, this upside-down animal seldom moves during the day. Journeying by night through the treetops, a sloth has been known to cover as much as four miles in 48 days. It is a vegetarian, living on leaves and buds, so has no need to visit the ground. Since its legs cannot support it, it drags along at less than a tenth of a mile per hour on its rare descents.

The sloth is such a masterpiece of immobility that during the rainy season tiny green plants grow on its coarse hair. Caterpillars feed on the plants, and from the untidy covering moths may fly out! The sloth's immobility is its chief safeguard against enemies. Seen motionless, high among the dense foliage, it resembles a mass of dead leaves, a termite nest or a lump of moldy fungus. When the sloth is attacked by a hungry enemy, the shagginess of its coat, the toughness of its hide and a remarkable array of ribs (it has 23 pairs, compared to man's 12) often protect it. Even when killed, a sloth continues to cling to his branch with his curved claws. No one, perhaps not even the sloth, knows whether he is dead or alive.

The sloth's toes are an important part of its body, since it spends its life hanging from branches. Shown here is the ai, a three-toed sloth. The anau is its two-toed cousin.

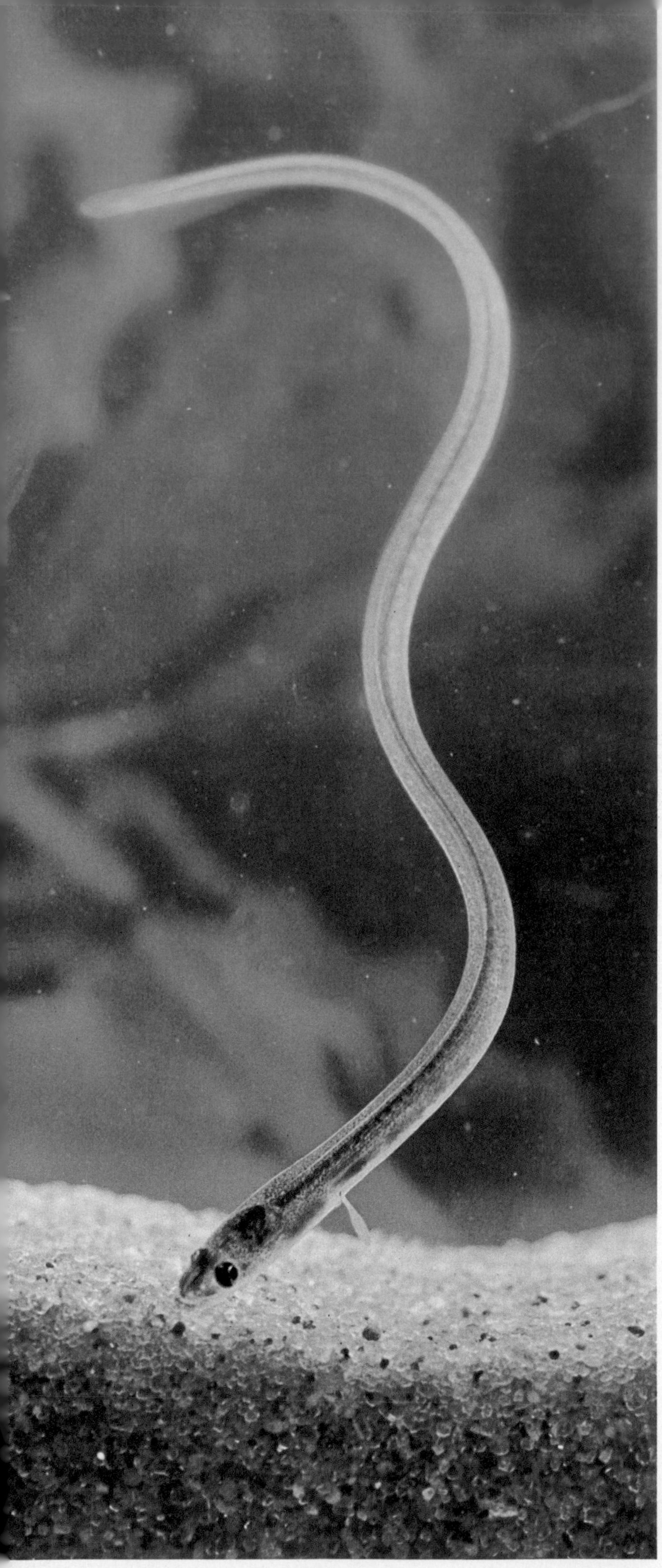

From mid-ocean, where freshwater eels breed, the larvae swim all the way to the American and European coasts, where they enter freshwater streams to grow to maturity. Shown here, an "elver," the name given the immature eel.

MAGIC IN THE OCEAN DEEPS

Jean George

The herald of spring is the robin. His spinning flight north leads the spring parade. Flowers explode, forests green, whimpering young arrive on dark den floors. But there is another spring on our planet, one that is equally awesome and exquisite. It bursts beneath the surface of the ocean, outsplendoring the one we see on the land. Spring underwater is so different in detail from the land change that it is difficult for us air-born humans to grasp its diversity. And yet its broad principles are the same. The sun, shining more fully on the Northern Hemisphere, strikes the waters at a more direct angle and penetrates deeper. Its warmth, together with more hours of more intense light, triggers the blooming of sea plants just as it flowers the land.

The first sign of oceanic spring is the northward drift of the bauble-bodied sargassum weed. This seaweed is found in the legendary Sargasso Sea, which lies in the mid-Atlantic Ocean southeast of Bermuda. When the sargassum weed moves north, the water in the shallow areas, like the land, changes color. The beautiful blue of December, January, February becomes a vibrant brown-green, a sign that plants are dividing and animals are mating and growing. The minerals in the water feed the tiny one-celled plants that are part of the plankton mass— the "pasturage" upon which sea creatures of all sizes, from the microscopic to the very largest, feed.

Among the sea grazers are the copepods. In March these creatures, about the size of pinheads, rise from the ocean floor, gallop up into the meadows and set upon the plants with insatiable hunger. Leggy things with humped backs, the copepods trail beautiful scarves of pink, purple, blue and green that set the ocean shimmering. Fishermen, seeing their colors, know where to drop nets for mackerel.

Grazing with these pinheads are sea butterflies, as delicate as paper, and lobsterlike krills, some as long as an inch and a half, with heads which are almost all black eyes. The krills swirl down on the plants with a rotary mouthpiece that devours like a garbage-disposing unit. When touched or excited they blaze into light; biologists have read at night by the glow of six krills in a jar. They are food for every fish that can find them, and fishermen can keep track of the big food fish by following the flash of annoyed krills.

The bigger sea animals time the arrival of their young to the blooming of spring's great food supply. But mating is not always as simple in the ocean as it often is ashore. Common blue crabs, for instance, have a most hazardous union on the ocean floor some 300 feet down. Encased in coats of armor, they must wait until the female molts before they can join. Eventually her shell cracks and she slides each antenna and claw out of its confining case. Now vulnerable to fish, turtle and porpoise, she peers through her stalk eyes, seeking a mate before her shell hardens.

When its creatures have mated, there comes a pause under the sea which corresponds to the moment on land when birds sing less and mammals are hard to find: the young are being born, most to be mothered by the heaving waters of the deep. The startling thing about these billions and trillions of babies is that few bear any resemblance to their parents. A baby crab, for example, has a long beak, feathery scarves, a delicate tail, a sword on its back and big, soulful eyes.

The spring growing-up period is full of surprises. For several weeks the young of the flatfishes—the soles and the flounders—have eyes on either side of their heads, and fins and tails all lined up correctly. Then one eye begins to move slowly over the top of the head until it reaches the same side as the other. Now the little fish has two eyes on one cheek. He can no longer swim in a vertical position. As he lists to the side, he sinks to the bottom and his side begins to look like a back. There at a depth of as much as 600 feet this cockeyed adult stares quietly up into the shimmering ocean.

Spring in the northern Atlantic and Pacific oceans, like spring on land, is marked by great migrations northward. Herring, cod, bluefish, whales, tuna, all start north when the waters warm. Like birds, they seek richer food supplies.

Eels are the champion migrants. In the spring, after hatching in the Sargasso Sea, the infants look like transparent willow leaves. Milling together are American eels and European eels. After several weeks they miraculously sort themselves out and take the right current to the right continent (no one has ever reported an American eel in Europe or a European eel in America). Riding the Gulf Stream, the American eels make the trip to the mouths of the North American rivers in one year. The European eels have a longer trip; it takes them two years. But—one year or two—when the eels arrive at the rivers they change from willow leaves to elvers and all start upstream, to dwell in fresh water until the urge to spawn sends them scurrying off back to the Sargasso Sea.

Recently another kind of sea migration has been discovered—that of the shrimp. Shrimp fishermen knew that the tasty delicacies they caught in the Gulf of Mexico off the Dry Tortugas, southwest of Florida, mated in deep water. They also knew that the young stayed in this birthplace for several weeks—then suddenly disappeared. Finally a scientist from the University of Miami clamped bright green tags on some 500 shrimp he captured in the muddy waters of Florida's mangrove swamps. About eight months later one of them was caught near the Tortugas, and further study solved the shrimp's secret. When two weeks old the young shrimp gather at night at the surface of the water and, rowing and sculling, race over the Gulf to the rich, muddy swamplands. Here they stuff themselves for six to nine months. Then on a special night they come to the top of the water and scull back to their breeding grounds in the Gulf. This knowledge has made Florida planners take a new look at their useless mangrove swamps. They realize the swamps must not be bulldozed for real estate if there are still to be shrimp in sufficient numbers.

Still deeper in the ocean, where pressures mount to a ton per square inch a mile below the surface, spring comes with less of a show, for there are fewer beasts. But what does occur is unbelievably strange. The eggs of the angler fish hatch in that lonely world. Somehow these tiny fry know that it will not be long before they are scattered among the watery mountains and valleys, and that years may pass before they meet another angler of the opposite sex. So while they are all together a male finds a female and gently takes her side in his mouth. He never lets go, but holds tight while the female eats and grows. Gradually he becomes part of her and is fused into her body. His head and eyes disappear, his gills and front fins vanish, and all that remains is his back fin and tail—growing from her side. In the dark abyss of the sea—light disappears below 1000 feet—this strange union assures the anglers that there will always be a spring, even in such forsaken depths.

Another strange lover in the deep sea is the electric eel. He finds his mate by bouncing electric charges off rocks and stones, fish, caves—and mates. When a special buzz comes back, he has found his female! However, this way of life has its penalties. The electric eel is eventually made blind by his own electricity. But he does not give up. He switches to another sense—pits on his head receive his reflected voltage and guide him among the craters of the sea. Springtime for an old electric eel is darkness—made lovely by a "jolt" from his mate.

PART 3

A COLLECTION OF WONDERS

Man has always been fascinated by the unusual, whether it appears in his backyard or on the other side of the world.

Chapter one

COMMONPLACE MIRACLES

Some time ago scientists in a Baltimore, Maryland, laboratory undertook
a project to learn how the firefly makes cold light and duplicate it.
Today, after years of concentrated effort, they still do not know the secret
of the enzyme that enables the firefly to create its marvel.

Miracles of nature surround us. Within the beehive lies the mystery of
the bee itself. These insects use polarized light to tell their fellow workers
where the cherished nectar lies hidden. They also "talk" to one another,
giving directions for finding flowers in meadows and fields.

A spider weaves its web with almost incredible artistry. Recently a
scientist revealed that to create its intricate pattern, the spider employs
the principles of logarithms. It has been using them for millions of years.

Even the common monarch butterfly has baffled man's intelligence.
Until recently no one knew where its eggs were laid in winter or where its
pupae developed. Now that we know the secret of the remarkable migration
of this wisp of life, we can only wonder all the more.

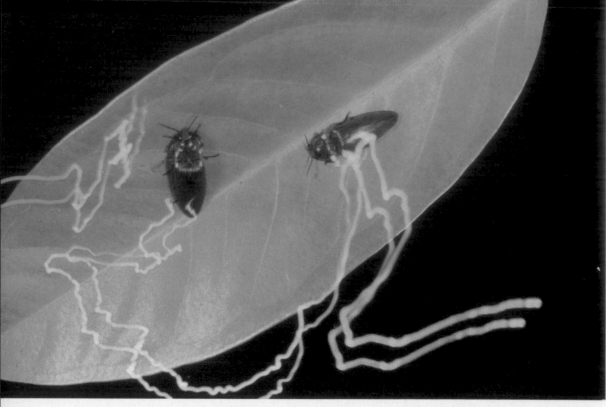

Only a few insects use their eyes when seeking a mate. The firefly is one, the males locating the females by following the flashing of their lights. The females of one species are known to flash their lights to lure males of other species and, instead of mating, eat them.

THE MAGIC OF THE FIREFLY

Donald Culross Peattie

The summer sunset drains out of the sky. The thrush's hymn to the evening star has ended. Playing children slip deeper into the shadows so as not to hear the voices calling them to bed. Then over the evening a wand is waved, and Fairyland takes charge. In shrubbery and trees, over dew-wet lawns, through woods and meadows the first fireflies of the year begin to flash. In a brief interval dusk has deepened by a scarcely perceptible shade, yet that faint difference is critical. Only when the temperature is warm enough will the fireflies illumine their lanterns, and only when the light is exactly dim enough can we see them.

Whenever such perfect conditions arise, from the Atlantic shores to the west coast, from southern Canada to deep in the tropics, the tiny magicians begin to spangle the velvet of the enfolding night. In the West Indies, barefoot natives are tying the big, brilliant fireflies called *cucuyo* to their toes to light a way through the jungle paths. Girls of Brazil are tangling the little lovelights in their hair. In Japan, during the Firefly Festival, thousands raised in cages are carried out by boat on the lake near Kyoto and released by laughing crowds, to rival the very stars.

The light of the firefly is one of nature's great miracles. It is light with almost no heat—perfect illumination, something that men still have not been able to achieve. The firefly is eerily cooler than the air of the summer night which it illumines.

Fireflies are not true flies at all, but beetles. You may know this by the shell-like wing cases that meet in a line down the middle of the back and are lifted in flight when the true wings are spread out from under them. Grayish or brownish or blackish, narrow and flat, there is nothing striking about these beetles when you see them by day.

In the common North American species of firefly called *pyralis* the little wink of light is a signal between the sexes. The males fly slowly along near the ground, searching for hidden females. They flash on an average of every 5.8 seconds—a bit more often if it is a hot evening, and less frequently when it is chillier. From the grass the female signals answer, and never does a male mistake it for the light of another male, though there is no difference in color. The female's signal is much weaker and she answers the male's signal exactly 2.1 seconds after she sees it. So he flies toward her, signaling again and guiding himself by her answers, till in the dusk he finds her. You may be able to decoy the males to you. Place a flashlight in the grass and signal every two seconds in answer to each flash in the air above. It will make no difference what the color of the flash you give, or whether it lasts one second or one fiftieth of a second, so long as you time the interval of response correctly.

If you hold a firefly in your cupped hands, you will note a continuous subdued glow in the luminous organs situated in the last segments of the abdomen.

Then, like the flash from a revolving beacon, the light leaps up brightly; it lasts but a second's fraction, and is renewed again at the precise rhythmic interval. But if the firefly is hurt, the interval is shortened and the flashes become almost continuous, just as our hearts beat faster when we are excited.

The luminous organs consist of two layers of tissue. Near the surface is a layer of granules, and back of it a layer of crystal cells which act as reflectors. The granules are the source of the light. Through them runs a network of air tubes and nerves. When the firefly flashes, probably the air tubes open, oxygen rushes over the granules and they flare up, as an ember brightens when you blow on it. If those light-producing granules are dissected out of the insect and dropped into pure oxygen, they will glow continuously until something, it seems, is all used up. That something must contain the secret of the light. Biological chemists tell us that the luminous organs contain an oxidizable, or combustible, substance called luciferin. However, it will combine with oxygen (and thus glow) only in the presence of an enzyme called luciferase, also found in the granules. But this luciferase has a double power over the luciferin—it can deoxidize it, too (as though you unrusted rusty iron), so that it can be used over and over.

If you ask what the light is for, most species of firefly give you a baffling wink. A signal between the sexes it certainly is, in our common North American fireflies. Yet some kinds do not carry the torch in the adult stage but are luminous in the larval stage, so the glow cannot be a mating signal. To deepen the mystery, some fireflies even lay luminous eggs, and other varieties mate in the daytime. The little lantern cannot be used to show the beetle his way, since it is in his tail. Nor can it scare off his enemies; on the contrary, it must enable them to find him more easily—tropical frogs have been noted which have eaten so many fireflies that their insides were revealed as if by a fluoroscope!

Different firefly species differ in interval and brilliance of flash. Some in the West Indies shine like a first-magnitude star seen with the naked eye. When American troops were fighting in Cuba in 1898, the great Dr. William C. Gorgas was operating on a soldier when his lamp went out. By the light of a bottleful of *cucuyos* he successfully finished the operation.

The greatest firefly show in the world is that put on during summer evenings in Thailand. There the males cluster on the *ton lampoo* trees, a kind of mangrove lining the rivers. Flashing 120 times a minute, they synchronize on the same interval, so that one instant there is blackness, the next every tree, every boat on the river is revealed as by lightning; then blackness, then brilliant light again.

Our firefly season lasts from about the middle of June to the middle of August in the latitude of northern Illinois. And what becomes of our fireflies then? When the dog days come, their little lights vanish. But not before they have laid their eggs in rotting logs and so left us promise of another summer's nights filled with eerie and inexplicable beauty.

NATURE'S ENGINEER EXTRAORDINARY
Leicester Hemingway

The spider clan—an ancient group called Araneida—are some of the most uncommon creatures ever to evolve on Earth. They are also among the most numerous. Naturalist W. S. Bristowe took a spider census on a grassy plot in England which showed that 2,265,000 of them were living on and under a single acre of land.

Spiders, though not generally popular, are true friends of man, and some scientists believe that human life could not exist without them. For a spider's entire life is devoted to snaring and devouring insects which might otherwise multiply and desolate the Earth. (It has been estimated that each year the spiders in England and Wales destroy insects more than equal in weight to the entire human population of that area.)

No climate is too rugged for the clan Araneida. They live at an altitude of 22,000 feet on Mount Everest—5000 feet above the vegetation line—and they have been found in caves 2000 feet below the Earth's surface. Pioneers among creatures leaving the sea to forge new lives on land, they have highly developed nervous systems, brains capable of memory, and remarkable engineering abilities.

The spider's talent for spinning silk and making nets is one of the most common miracles of nature. With a tensile strength far greater than steel and second only to fused quartz, spider silk can be stretched a fifth of its length before it breaks. A strand that can be seen with the naked eye is usually a cable composed of several tiny threads. A single thread may be only a millionth of an inch thick. Some molecules are wider. All spiders have nipple-like spinnerets—usually three pairs—located near the end of the abdomen. On each spinneret are a number of minute orifices through which the secretion of the silk glands

is expelled. In spinning a web, the tips of the spinnerets are brought together so that the streams of secretion unite in a single thread.

The most impressive spider web is the orb web, that symmetrical masterpiece which ornaments every backyard and garden. The first line of silk strung up, known as the bridge, is suspended more or less horizontally. The weaver may attach a strand to a blade of tall grass or a stump, drop down with it and then climb up to another high spot and pull the line taut. Or she may simply tilt up her abdomen and spin out silk into the breeze, much as a small boy would reel out kite string. When the silk catches on to something, the spider fixes the free end. You often see webs stretched across creeks; this is how such obstacles are spanned. Once the bridge is up, the orb weaver drops a plumb line from one end, a lower bridge is built, and a second plumb line fixed on the other end to form an aerial framework. Within the frame the spider strings radii, and at the center spins a mesh known as the hub. Around·this she spins a temporary inner spiral to give her footing while she constructs the sticky outer spiral, which catches insects. As the great naturalist Henri Fabre said, "What refinement of art for a mess of flies!"

Now the spider may want a safe retreat near the completed orb. For this she rolls a leaf and spins a silken nest inside. Finally she strings a "telegraph" line from the center of the web to the nest. And then she goes home and waits. Twang! The "telegraph" signals that something has landed on the web. The spider hurries out to examine the visitor. If it is not too formidable, it is eaten on the spot or quickly trussed up and carried back to the den. When the prey is much larger than the spider, the approach is cautious. Having poor eyesight, the spider may tap the gyrating monster to find out what it is. When it is a deadly foe, it may be cut loose. But if the enemy is judged manageable—a wasp or hornet, perhaps—the spider can squirt her silk from as much as an inch away to avoid close contact. Otherwise the spider grabs some of the captive's legs and turns it over and over while combing strong silk around it. If the hapless insect struggles violently, a bit of poison may be administered. When the spider dines, she bathes the prey in digestive juices, for she must take her food in liquid form.

The web of the common house spider is an irregular maze that brings out the wrath and the brooms of housewives. But it is an ingenious booby trap that catches more than dust. When an insect flutters against one of the taut guy lines which support the web, the line snaps like a rubber band and jerks the victim into the maze. For a heavy catch, the spider pulls and tightens some threads and spins out more strands, hoisting her prey nearer and nearer. Amazingly, she has been seen to lift mice and small snakes, although she herself is seldom larger than a pea.

In addition to their hunting prowess, many spiders are masters of camouflage, making themselves resemble buds, nuts or seeds. One species of crab spider that is white when nestled down in a white flower turns yellow when she migrates to the goldenrod and is almost invisible within the nodding blossom. For theatrical ability the ant-mimics outrank all other spiders. Some of these spiders run in the zigzag motion of ants, holding their forelegs up like antennae. Because ants are shunned by many of the spider's natural enemies, the mimics thus gain protection.

All spiders are air-breathing, but one Eurasian species actually lives underwater. She is a drab, dark-brown creature on land, but once submerged she resembles a shining globule of quicksilver, for she carries a bubble of air with her. In the spring she spins a tight, waterproof sheet of silk between the stems of water plants a few inches below the surface. Then she swims up, flops down on a large air bubble and carries it under the sheet. After many trips she has made a tiny diving bell, her home until autumn. In the mating season a male builds a smaller bell close by and spins a silken tunnel to connect the two homes. When the young hatch, they live in the bell until they are ready to swim off with their own tiny air bubbles to spin new nests.

For most male spiders courtship is a perilous and complicated procedure. Some crafty males spin bridal veils for the ladies of their choice. With this thin web a female is strapped down, unable to kill her mate. One species carefully gift-wraps an insect and presents it to his prospective mate. With her hunger satisfied, she shows little interest in attacking him. When the mating urge is upon him, the male spins a tiny, close-knit web. On this he deposits his sperm. Touching it with his pedipalpi—small, leglike appendages on each side of his head—he draws the sperm into his palpi and is ready to wander in search of a mate. Many male spiders are so tiny that they can crawl over the female unnoticed. In a few species the male is little more than a spermatophore, a thousand times smaller than the female.

The number of eggs produced during one season varies greatly from species to species. Some females lay only one or two at a time; others produce up to 3000. Egg sacs are often camouflaged with bits of mud and leaves, and some smart web weavers place their eggs in several baskets so that at least a percent-

A golden orb-weaver spider at the center of an orb web, constructed on a spoked, wheel-like frame. Spiders may wait for prey at the center of the web, as here, or hide off to one side.

age will be safe. Some spider mothers carry their egg sacs in their mouths or attached to their spinnerets.

During the sunny days of spring and fall the tiny spiderlings venture forth from their snug nurseries. Many types perform the astonishing feat known as "ballooning." When they are no larger than pinheads, the spiderlings will climb a stem of grass, tilt up their abdomens and spin out lines of silk until a breeze catches their silken chutes and wafts them to new territory. Sometimes, however, a wrong wind flattens their minute threads across the ground, and when the setting sun glints across a field you can see a virtual sea of silk. Most spiderlings, it is estimated, float along at heights not over 200 feet, but some have been found as high as 14,000 feet. Baby spiders have descended on the rigging of ships 200 miles from shore, and scientists believe many species have spread to foreign lands by ballooning.

Spiders are among the most universally feared creatures on earth, yet almost all of them are harmless. Most are reluctant to bite, and when they do, it hurts a human no more than a pinprick. However, a few spiders, including the "black widow," have a strong poison. The black widow's venom is about 15 times as potent as that of a rattlesnake, but the spider's supply is so small that it is rarely lethal. If your first reaction to a spider is to kill it, think before you act. In stamping out its life you would kill an architect of marvelous talent and one of man's most potent allies in his unceasing war against harmful insects.

THE MYSTERY OF THE MONARCH

Peter Farb

Wherever flowers bloom in the United States and southern Canada, those large, bright orange-and-black butterflies known as monarchs flit gracefully about in gardens all summer. Then, each September they congregate by the thousands. Clinging to the leaves and branch tips of trees on their overnight roosts, actually bending them down by their weight, they have assembled for their long journey southward, one of the most extensive and remarkable mass movements of any living thing.

Late in the month these tiny aerial wayfarers span the continent, some of them passing from eastern Canada to southern Mexico, a distance well over 2000 miles. At a cruising speed of 11 miles an hour, flying usually 15 feet above the ground, they circumvent the Great Lakes, assault the winding valleys of the Rockies, cross baking deserts. Flying doggedly through storms and winds, these frail creatures weighing little more than a downy bird feather may travel up to 80 miles during a single day. Finally they gather in huge concentrations along the Gulf Coast, and in California from Pacific Grove southward nearly to Los Angeles.

The monarch flocks that arrive in late October at Pacific Grove have long been famous. All winter an estimated two million cover the branches of about six acres of pines. Year after year they find the same trees and mass on the sides that protect them from the prevailing winds. On warm, sunny days they flutter to nearby gardens, feed upon nectar of flowers, then return to the trees. Pacific Grove is proud of its monarchs, and the whole town is a sanctuary for them. "It is the duty of every citizen to protect the butterflies," states a town ordinance. Thousands of tourists come each year to see them; street signs direct visitors to the butterfly trees. Schoolchildren stage a colorful parade to celebrate the monarchs' annual return.

Butterflies are short-lived, and no monarch could possibly last long enough to make the round trip twice. How, then, without leader or guideposts, do these swarms find their way over such great distances? This mystery is being solved by a mild-mannered Canadian scientist, Dr. Fred Urquhart, professor of zoology at the University of Toronto. No one has seen more monarchs or knows more about them. Because of his enthusiasm and perseverance, and the coöperation of hundreds of amateurs from every state and province, much of the remarkable story of the monarch has been unraveled.

Urquhart began collecting monarchs as a boy in the 1920's. At that time it was believed that these butterflies hibernated like bears or woodchucks, waiting out the winter asleep. Young Urquhart combed the winter woods looking for them. In vain he turned over stones and logs, climbed trees to look into holes, inspected the bark. The question of what happened to the monarchs during the winter plagued him through college and graduate school; when he joined the staff of the Royal Ontario Museum, he continued his investigations. Experiments proved that the monarchs could not exist where the temperature stayed below freezing for several consecutive days. Obviously the butterflies had to move southward.

To find where, Dr. Urquhart began to tag them in 1938. But the paper labels glued to the wings fell off or made the butterfly aerodynamically unstable, so that none of the banded monarchs were ever seen again. Then, as a meteorological officer in the Royal Canadian Air Force during World War II, Dr. Urquhart learned things about aircraft aerodynamics that led to an effective tag. He folded a thin paper label over the leading edge of the insect's wing, close to the body where it would not interfere with flight. And he devised a method of printing in this tiny space an identifying number together with directions on where to send the specimen when recaptured. With this method he got his first significant recovery —a butterfly tagged near Toronto and captured several weeks later in Virginia.

As word about his tagging program began to spread, thousands of letters poured in from people whose imagination was captured by his work with these beautiful creatures. Dr. Urquhart selected several hundred of the most qualified "coöperators," gave them labels, told them how to tag the insects and keep records on them. To date, some 50,000 monarchs have been fitted with the new tags. Lawyers and housewives, businessmen and scientists all over the continent are taking part in the "Monarch Watch." "Without the help of my coöperators," says Dr. Urquhart, "the life of the monarch would still be largely unknown." (Anyone spotting a monarch with a tag should place it in a small box or envelope with a slip of paper telling where it was captured and when, and mail to University of Toronto, Department of Zoology, Toronto 5, Ontario.)

Even with such a far-reaching organization of volunteers, recoveries are hard to come by, for the number of monarchs tagged is minuscule compared with the entire population. And the few which are tagged must survive storms and winds, predators, disease and other hazards to provide useful information. Finally, they must be captured by someone who will take the trouble to return the specimen. Nevertheless, enough recoveries have been arriving at Dr. Urquhart's office so that many of the bits and pieces of the monarch's mysterious life have begun to fall into place.

Monarchs reach the height of their abundance in the autumn. Only the late generations produced in the summer migrate. (The earlier ones die before autumn.) The migrating hordes fly approximate southwesterly paths to their wintering places. In the spring the survivors of the original multitudes must face the hazards of the long trip north again. On tattered wings, their colors faded, they make the return flight, scarcely noticed because of their reduced numbers. They rarely pause in gardens to sip nectar; they are hurried on by the eggs developing in their abdomens.

They lay their eggs—each exquisitely faceted like a diamond—on milkweed and only milkweed, for this

Monarchs select certain trees for swarming—the same each year—as they prepare for their migratory flight.

abundant weed of roadside and pasture forms the sole diet of the caterpillars. In about two weeks each caterpillar encases itself in a beautiful green, gold-speckled pupa; in about another two weeks the butterfly emerges. These butterflies may themselves produce one or two more generations before summer's end, resulting in the hordes that leave the breeding grounds to spend the winter in warmer climates.

One monarch mystery is how they navigate. Dr. Urquhart once thought that their routes followed definite aerial highways. Now he has learned that the route is like a river joined by smaller streams along the way until the flow of the monarchs in the autumn becomes a great wide path heading southwestward. Feeble-sighted, the butterflies could not use landmarks, nor would any landmarks exist across the maze of mountain valleys. Their only landmarks may be in the sky—the sun acting as a compass.

In still air the monarchs can fly about 650 miles without alighting. Riding a following wind, they can traverse the seas as well as the continents. Their indomitable energy, with help from tailwinds and hitch-hikes on ships, has enabled specimens to visit all around the globe. The first monarch was captured in Britain in 1876, and hundreds have been netted in the Azores, Canary Islands and western Europe. Since milkweed does not grow in these places, the monarchs cannot reproduce successfully there. But milkweed does flourish in many areas in the Pacific, and the monarch, island-hopping from North America, is now established as a fairly common butterfly in Hawaii, Australia, New Zealand and the Philippines.

The most spectacular feature of the autumn migration is the gathering on "butterfly trees," those special trees that year after year are hosts to hordes of migrating monarchs on their overnight stops. It was once thought that the monarchs selected the same trees year after year because the males covered them with a long-lasting scent from special glands. But *nothing* links these trees to the butterflies from year to year. Certain tree species are always chosen; the butterflies' feet can cling only to pine needles, the narrow petioles of willows, the deeply notched margins of maples. Then, from among these preferred species the butterflies select the ones which offer the best protection against prevailing winds. Invariably, Dr. Urquhart has found, each new crop of monarchs chooses the same trees out of the hundreds or thousands in the vicinity.

If, one September day, you discover a tree ablaze with the color of thousands of butterflies festooning its branches, you should pause a few moments to admire it. For you will be seeing one of nature's rare and glorious displays.

THE WORM THAT TURNED

W. Gilhespy

There was once a worm that turned—into an explorer. His ancestral home, a field by a brook, had been ideal long ago. The soil had been porous and full of worm food—humus, warm and moist, though never wet. Then the farmer who owned the land moved; ditches filled, the land was flooded and many worms drowned. In winter the whole was frozen into a solid block of ice; few earthworms survived. But one of the survivors was a pioneer. He left his birthplace and settled on land to the west. Since he was not anxious to make a breakfast for the early bird, he had to sink his new shaft and be well out of sight before dawn. The surface of his new home was a combination of sand, clay and fine gravel. Untouched for years, soaked by winter rains and baked by summer heat, it was like concrete. But the worm had to get in it or die.

So he pushed out his nose till its needlelike point found an entrance between the hard-packed grains of sand. It was not easy. Another push and another—he kept on till he had gone down half an inch. Then the ground was too hard for pushing; he had to *eat* his way down. Soil and sand went down his gullet to a crop that was lined with skin like hard leather. Grit in the crop acted like tiny grinding mills which crushed the sand to paste, the process being facilitated by digestive juices which turned particles of decayed vegetable matter into body-building material. The rest passed through his body in the form of "worm casts," excellent fertilizing material for the soil.

The explorer did not rest for one moment all night. Even so, half his five inches remained above ground when the birds began to twitter ominously. Then the worm struck luck in the form of a long, straight root of red clover. That root had been slowly disintegrating the mineral matter around it by the gases of its decomposition. The result was a narrow shaft, lightly packed with soft matter. The nose-needle found its way into that—to safety.

The rest was easy, but only for a worm. He was stronger, in proportion to his size, than any creature which walks, swims or flies. For ribs he had 200 rings which encircled his mighty little frame; the lower edges acted as feet. Contracting the ribs in front, he expanded those behind till they had a firm grip on the sides of the tunnel. Then he pushed and kept on pushing, contracting and expanding his ribs, widening and smoothing the tunnel at each move forward. Drawing upon his own chemical laboratory, he enameled the sides of his tunnel as he completed it.

Though he was sightless, his skin was sensitive to light, so he did not go up to the surface till nightfall. Then he emerged, partly for a change of diet, also to drink the dew and bathe in it. With his wonderfully sensitive nose point, he found microscopically minute portions of withered leaves and shriveled roots which he turned into nutritious food, no matter how decomposed they were. Just before dawn, he was alarmed by a tiny shrew. So sensitive is the worm to soil vibration that the tread of those wee feet sent him back to his burrow. He retired tail first, pausing only to drag a scrap of dead turf over the mouth of his hole, partly to hide it and partly to prevent evaporation.

He had work to do down there. Though there was food around him, he always kept a storehouse—hoarded scraps of dead leaves and roots. Each was carefully coated with digestive juice and packed away neatly. That first vertical shaft had been only the beginning of his mining; he needed tunnels in every direction. Each led to further supplies of food, admitted air to improve that food and provided avenues of escape from the centipedes and slugs which would follow him. There was not much to fear from moles,

at first. Later more worms would come into the new land and make the soil porous. Then the mole, driving his tunnel with comparative ease, would eat many of them. But, on the other hand, when the mole drives his tunnel close to the surface, he gathers far more foes of the worm than worms themselves.

The explorer was not alone for long. The conditions which had driven him to the higher ground sent other worms after him, and in due time the pioneer found a mate. Reproduction was slow, and there probably were not more than 100 worms to the acre that first year. They had no communal activities; each drove himself endless tunnels. But the more each aerated the subsoil, the more he benefited his neighbors.

Formerly the rain had been held near the surface till it evaporated, souring and packing the earth so hard that no air and little moisture reached the depths. Now tunnels admitted both, their reaction freeing potash, lime, nitrogen, phosphates and other plant food. What had been barren land was now rich with herbage, providing in turn more food for more worms—more little grinding mills to crush inorganic matter into fertilizing materials. So arose beauty and wealth from desolation. The worm knows nothing of the incalculable benefits he confers on mankind—that unless he worked, man would soon starve. He is no boaster; he can only work miracles.

The earthworm belongs to a group of creatures called "bristle-footed," and it is these bristles, four pairs on each segment of the body, that enable it to grip the soil and move about. In one year of burrowing on one acre of land, worms turn over some two to three tons of earth.

THE QUEEN'S STORY

Charles D. Stewart

A queen bee, although she differs from a worker bee in size, shape, function and a whole set of instincts, is hatched from the same sort of egg as the worker. The difference is wholly due to feeding. Nurse bees will take any one of the recently hatched female larvae, and simply by giving it a different diet will cause it to become a queen bee instead of a worker. In fact, any beekeeper can make this change. Among those who raise queen bees for the market it is a matter of everyday practice. The operation consists in transferring a young larva from one of the small worker cells into a very large special one, a queen cell, which the beekeeper makes artificially. The nurse bees bring up the little larva as a queen.

Honeycomb is made up of cells of two sizes, other than the queen's. The larger are used for the raising of drones, which are male, while the rest serve for the smaller and more numerous workers. These,

though practically neuter, are essentially female, and it is from among them that the queen is chosen.

As each variety of cell affords just enough room to accommodate a full-grown grub of the sex for which it is intended, it is necessary for each to receive an egg according to its kind; and in this the queen makes no mistake. She lays a male egg in each of the larger cells, and a female in each of the smaller.

That an animal can produce one sex or the other in conformity with some outer circumstance is rather hard to believe, and when we patiently look into other facts in hope of explaining this one, we find new wonders. A virgin queen—one that has by no possible chance become impregnated—can lay eggs and produce young quite as readily as an insect that has become a mother in the usual way. But her eggs will produce only drones, or males. After her eggs have been fertilized, she can lay either kind.

The queen differs profoundly from the female workers in several ways. On each of the hind legs of the worker bee is a brush for gathering pollen and a basket for carrying it home. On the legs of the queen bee these tools are lacking. On the abdomen of the worker bee are pockets which extrude the plates of building wax; the queen possesses no such device. The workers have but the vestige of their sex, while the queen is sexually complete.

But it is in the mechanism of the sting that we find the most surprising contrast. The worker bee has a straight sting which appears to be a solid shaft. Actually it consists of a stiletto above and two barbed lances below. These pieces, somewhat concave inside, fit closely together and form the channel through which the poison flows. When the worker stings, the shaft is thrust into the unlucky victim and the barbed lances are pumped alternately deeper into the wound. This action drives the stiletto farther while the venom is expelled through the canal. The sting of a worker bee takes such strong hold that it usually resists the bee's best efforts to extract it, and when it pulls out of the bee's body it is likely to bring the tip of the abdomen with it. The bee dies. A queen bee, on the other hand, has a sting that is curved like a scimitar and is easily removed from the wound. It is never lost and may be used repeatedly. But, though she has this formidable-looking weapon, a queen may be handled without fear. The sole function of her weapon is to kill rival queens. She is not a defender of the hive, and so she generally lacks the instinct of stinging.

When a queen is about a week out of the cell in which she started life, she may leave the hive briefly and acquaint herself with the landmarks nearby. Shortly after, she takes a "wedding flight," high in the

Some chambers of the comb are used by honeybees to store multicolored beebread—a mixture of pollen and honey on which young bees live. Here worker bees are placing it in the comb.

Left: enlarged close-up of a worker bee's hind leg, showing the bristles on which it collects pollen. Right: a bee with a load of beebread, about to take off to carry it back to the hive.

air. In this swift flight she is pursued by drone bees until one catches her for a momentary union. Sometimes they sail to the ground, where the queen disengages herself and rises again to be chased by other males. Other times the couple separate in the air, the male alone dropping to the earth. In either event the drone always dies, while the queen may mate with as many as a dozen males before she returns to the hive. Within several days she will usually depart again on one or, occasionally, several mating excursions. In a very brief time she acquires the spermatozoa necessary to produce all the female progeny she will engender during her life. A queen usually remains active until some time in her fourth year, and at the height of a season she can lay more than 2000 eggs a day—most of which will develop into female workers.

Bees must do the year's work while the flowers are in bloom. If there is not a great multitude of these short-lived workers in May and June, there will not be enough honey to carry the clustered swarm through the dark months of winter. Also, there must be a surplus of young bees so that migrating swarms may go out and increase the number of colonies. This is fundamental not only to bees but to the economy of nature and man. As grain, nuts, fruit and vegetables must all be fertilized before they can bear, the pollen transfer is most important.

Until quite recently not one fact was ever discovered regarding the sex of bees. And yet the mysteries of bee life were a continual source of speculation. Virgil represented the bees as having no sex at all, and thought the young were somehow generated from the inner material of flowers. In fact, from Aristotle to Shakespeare the principal bee of the swarm, catching the eye by its distinctive size, was known as the King Bee. The plain truth is that the principal bee is simply the mother of the whole lot. If a gold-banded Italian queen, for instance, is put into a colony of German or black bees in place of their own queen, it will be but two months before the whole swarm will consist of purebred Italian bees and there will not be a black bee left. It was by such experiments that we have been able to determine the maximum length of life of a bee during the working season.

When we consider that for centuries before cane sugar came into use the beehive constituted the sugar factory of the world, we naturally wonder why all the beekeepers of the past discovered so little about them. But the hive—whether artificially made or established by the bees themselves—was a place of inner darkness. The invention of the observation hive and the modern microscope revealed in a few years what the ages had been unable to discover.

MR. BIG NOISE
Donald Culross Peattie

If you wake some morning in May or June to a sound coming from the trees as if a saw were going through their protesting trunks . . . if you find the underbrush weighted down with thousands of heavy-bodied, flopping insects bearing on their clear wings a little brown *w* made by the intersection of veins . . . then you will know you are in the midst of an outbreak of the cicada, or "17-year locust."

This fantastic bug, an inch and a half long with a three-inch wingspread, belongs to the underground of the insect world. For 17 years he leads a subterranean existence, emerging at a sudden but predictable moment to rend the morning with his strange and insistent din.

The male is the performer: like many an opera tenor, fat in the middle and short of leg. But he is floated on fairy wings—a long pair in front, a shorter one behind—clear as mica and exquisitely veined. His two big compound eyes have a gleam of fire in their red. On each side of his abdomen he has a corrugated membrane like a little drum, and powerful muscles set these to vibrating. Moreover, he can amplify this noise by means of two little disks which shine on his body like flecks of isinglass—these act as sounding boards. For a long time it was thought the females had no ears, but specialists finally found them —under their bellies.

We can't say why this species should have such a long interval between appearances. But it keeps up its numbers well enough with a honeymoon once every 17 years, thanks to its industrious fertility. Systematically the mother cicada, with her long ovipositor (miscalled a "sting"), punctures the twigs of shrubs and trees, especially oaks. When her 200 to 600 eggs are deposited, she dies, as the male does even sooner, when he has mated. In a few weeks the eggs hatch; the little antlike nymphs emerge, drop and burrow down into the ground. Now begin those 17 years of solitary confinement.

The nymph makes itself a tiny chamber, from six inches to four feet underground, conveniently situated near rootlets on which it can feed by sucking juices now and then. From these rootlets it does not move, summer or winter, year in, year out. It grows by going through six molts. Before emergence it becomes a

True to its name, the 17-year cicada spends 17 years underground as a nymph, emerging in the spring for a summer-long life above ground. It climbs to a tree to shed its skin (as it has just done in the photograph at the right), grows strong and brightly colored, then mates and dies.

pupalike nymph—a stage vaguely corresponding to human adolescence, when an adult body, complete with wings and sex organs, forms inside the childish shell of its past. Then, on some appointed date (varied only by extremes of weather), all the nymphs of the region come up out of the ground simultaneously, generally at night. As many as 25 of their little escape turrets are commonly found on one square foot of ground, and 9000 of these burrow exits have been counted under a single tree.

The nymph clambers onto a twig and its skin casing splits down the back. Out of it the pallid, wet, weak adult can be seen struggling clumsily. The pale empty casing is left clinging to the bush. In an hour or two its body hardens; then its wings, at first folded, rooflike, over the back, spread glitteringly; powerful muscles move them, and off the creature flies. Soon the world is resounding to its love song. At this point public alarm begins. Telephone calls jam the offices of agricultural bureaus, health departments, tree surgeons. Excitable newspapers carry stories about an "invasion" by "17-year locusts." This is, however, no locust but a cicada. And there's a big difference. For true locusts, on the rampage, may migrate from state to state. So busy are they laying waste that all the noise they make is the leathern whirring of their wings, the costly champing of their jaws on wheat and corn, alfalfa and grass.

But cicadas are not remotely related to locusts and have none of their habits. The 17-year species has no jaws; it bites not, neither does it chew. Its mouth, like a mosquito's, is adapted only to piercing and sucking —in this case, plant juices, especially those of oaks. It never migrates, but flies, mates and dies within a short distance of the spot where it emerged as a nymph.

The only damage wrought by periodical cicadas comes after the song has ceased and people have forgotten the whole outbreak. For the silent females in laying their eggs may cut the plant tissues so deeply as to kill the twigs. This does wild trees no permanent harm, though the leaves may wither prematurely. But where there are fruit orchards or nursery stock abutting directly on woodland the damage may be so great as to kill young trees.

In its brief four weeks of aerial life the periodical cicada is attacked by a host of enemies. I remember well thousands of birds arriving at a sudden banquet in the great outbreak of 1928; warblers and grackles, sparrows and even hawks gorged themselves on cicadas. Hogs and dogs picked them up wherever they flopped on the ground. Furthermore, there is a fungus disease that spreads among cicadas with fatal swiftness in the crowded conditions of swarming.

The early colonists were terrified by their first encounters with this unknown creature. Wrote Nathaniel Morton, in *New England's Memoriall,* "There was a numerous company of Flies, which were like for bigness unto Wasps or Bumble-Bees, they came out of little holes in the ground, and made such a constant yelling noise as made all the woods ring with them, and ready to deaf the hearers." The descendants of that very brood of Mayflower times are still sounding off. It is officially known as Brood XIV—for government entomologists have charted every known outbreak—and when last heard, in 1957, the Plymouth cicadas were as uproarious as ever. This Pilgrim Father batch will strike up again in 1974; members of the same band will be heard on Long Island and from Pennsylvania to Tennessee and Illinois.

Most other parts of the eastern United States will not have a cicada visitation that year. For the creature does not emerge simultaneously all over its wide range (east of the Missouri, south of the coniferous "North Woods" and north of Florida). There are 17 broods of the 17-year type of cicada, each appearing one year later than the numbered brood before it. Thus Brood I, a small swarm whose center is in the mountains of Virginia, appeared in 1927, 1944 and 1961. Brood II, which swarms from Connecticut to the piedmont of North Carolina, appeared a year later in each case.

The year 1951 witnessed the swarming of Brood VIII, which has headquarters in adjacent parts of West Virginia, Pennsylvania and Ohio, with branch offices as far east as Martha's Vineyard.

Brood XIX also appeared that year, and it was a whopper: it ranged through most of Illinois, Missouri and Arkansas, and extended south to Mobile, west in a scattering way to Oklahoma and east to coastal Virginia—where the Jamestown colonists may have heard it in 1608. This brood, like most of those in the Deep South, emerges every 13 rather than 17 years. Thus the District of Columbia and vicinity, with five broods, in recent years has heard the cicadas in 1953, 1957, 1961 and 1962, and will experience them again in 1966.

In some regions there is an overlap in area between two or more broods, with resulting outbreaks more frequently than 17 years. But as the cities spread and the tractor passes over more and more land where once the forests stood, the cry of the cicada must diminish. The broods already small or weak will vanish entirely; those now mighty will be increasingly decimated. And I am sorry. I rate the cicada's din with the yelling from the bleachers when all bases are full—as typically American as hickory, as corn pone or a Memorial Day parade.

Chapter two

ZOO'S WHO

As far back as history records, man has delighted in marveling at animals exhibited in zoos—or, more properly, zoological gardens. A Chinese emperor entertained guests in his "garden" in the 12th century B.C. Henry I of England had his own royal menagerie, and so did Louis XIV at Versailles.

But until the 19th century, zoos existed almost exclusively for the enjoyment of royalty and the very wealthy. Today men, women and children all over the world can gape at elephants and giraffes, and they do—in increasing numbers. Zoos from Tokyo to London draw millions of visitors each year.

The wonder of a zoo or circus never quite wears off. Even on the fiftieth trip to his cage, the sight of the giraffe's melancholy eyes, extraordinary neck and intricately shaded spots is still an exciting experience. The lions, the bears, the tigers, the monkeys, the kangaroos, the hippopotamuses, the rhinoceroses are featured in all the zoos of the world and wherever circuses travel.

For most visitors the exotic appearance of these beasts is enough. It is wondrous just to see the swinging trunk, the great jaws, the regal carriage. However, in recent decades another dimension has been added to the zoo, and that is knowledge. Scientists have been studying the animals at close hand, learning more and more about their natural habits. The result is that today we know why a giraffe's neck is long, why the kangaroo lives only in Australia and how dainty the grizzly bear really is.

ELEPHANTS ARE HUMAN—ALMOST

Brian O'Brien

At Queen Elizabeth National Park in Uganda, Warden R. C. Bere and I were driving across a plain one afternoon when we observed a group of elephant cows with their calves. They looked around, flapped their ears and ignored us, so Bere pulled up to let me take photographs. Suddenly the largest cow spread her ears, shook her head wickedly and, screaming deafeningly, charged. She pulled up not six yards from us.

"What brought that on?" I asked. "She was peaceful enough before."

"Maybe she was sick of the sight of safari cars," Bere answered. "Or maybe she ate something that disagreed with her. Maybe it was mosquitoes; they drive elephants crazy sometimes. With elephants, you never can be sure. They're unpredictable—like people."

Bill Ryan, a senior hunter for Ker & Downey, the famous safari-organizing firm in Nairobi, Kenya, has studied elephants for more than 40 years. "They figure things out, like people," he told me. "And sometimes they outsmart them. At one of our permanent camps a herd of elephants used to raid the garden. We put up a fence. They pushed through it. So we connected a new fence with the generator and electrified it. It took those beasts only a few nights to reason that when our lights went out the juice was turned off in the fence—so down it went again. We kept the generator running all night. But those brutes hung around fooling with the wire until one of them found that his tusks were nonconductive. Finally we had to put out rangers with shotguns to keep them away."

When the lodges for visitors to Murchison Falls National Park were being built at Paraa, Uganda, carpenters were repeatedly chased off the job by a 3½-ton bull known as the Lord Mayor of Paraa. He seemed to regard the area as his private domain and even after the lodges were finished he continued his patrol, pausing obligingly to be photographed. One wonderful night he smelled *pombe*, a native beer made from fermented bananas, and tore the roof off a hut to get at some banana mash. Soon he began searching for bananas in every car that came into Paraa. If it was a convertible, he tore the top off to get at the fruit; if a sedan, he reached in the windows or picked the car up and shook it.

Near Amboseli, one of Kenya's national reserves, lived an elephant with a sense of humor. He liked to lurk around a tight bend in the road until an automobile appeared. Then he would rush out, ears spread, with a deafening screech. Satisfied that he had terrified everyone in the car, he would back off and watch them pass, with an obvious twinkle in his sly little eyes.

At Queen Elizabeth National Park, where thousands of elephants can be watched by visitors in perfect safety as long as they obey park rules, I've seen elephant love in bloom. With Warden Bere I was observing a herd feeding on a slope above Lake Edward one day, when a handsome young bull stepped out of cover 200 yards from the group. At once a cow left the herd, turning her head shyly from side to side as she moved toward him. When they met, he took her trunk in his and their heads lifted, trunks entwined, until their mouths met in an unmistakable kiss. Then she butted him playfully. He pulled up a tussock of grass with his trunk, beat the dirt off it against his knees and offered it to her. She tucked it into her mouth as they moved off, shoulders touching, stopping often to exchange kisses, until they disappeared into a stand of trees. "They've been going steady for over a week," Bere said. "Courtship continues until the female comes into season. Then, in a remote forest glade—for elephants, like humans, prefer privacy for their lovemaking—she responds eagerly to his fondling."

The pair keeps company near the herd all day, then slips into the forest to continue lovemaking at night, until the female becomes pregnant and loses interest in her mate. A few months later the female seeks the company of an older cow who will stand by her when the baby comes; the gestation period is about 21 months. The "auntie" stays on guard, charging viciously anything that comes near while the calf is being born. The calf weighs about 200 pounds, can stand on its wobbly legs in a few minutes. The affection of elephants for their young is touchingly human.

A giant African bull elephant may weigh as much as seven tons. His tusks are his front teeth; they grow all his life and become too heavy for even so large a beast if not worn down.

They support them when crossing water, tear down green branches that are too high for them and, when necessary, discipline them for disobedience.

One afternoon Bere and I were watching a herd of four cows and five calves beside the Kasinga Channel connecting lakes Edward and George. When a small, fat calf wandered down to the channel bank, one of the cows screamed a warning to him. He ignored her, shuffling along the bank like a small boy seeing how close he could get to the edge. Suddenly the earth gave way under him and, with a terrified shriek, he fell into the water.

The cows whirled, ears cocked, then thundered down to the channel, reaching out with urgent trunks. But the calf, wallowing out of his depth, was too panicky to reach for them. Two cows knelt on the bank, rumps in air, while the other two lowered themselves carefully into the water. Between them, grunting encouragement to the spluttering calf, the latter two got their tusks under him and lifted him until the two on the bank could drag him to safety. One cow, obviously the mother, drew him close, chirruping and squeaking as she anxiously felt all over him with her trunk while he huddled against her, whining and blowing water. Then, when she was satisfied that he had come to no harm, she fetched him a tremendous wallop with her trunk and, screeching with anger, chased him away from the water.

A pathetic instance of mother grief was reported in Murchison Falls National Park a while ago. Colonel C. D. Trimmer, the warden, sighted a cow carrying a newborn calf on her tusks, holding it in place with her trunk. The calf was dead. For three days the mother carried the little carcass, laying it on the ground only when she had to drink. Later she was seen without the calf, standing beside a tree. She stayed there for several days, eating nothing and charging anyone who approached. Finally she went away. Later, Trimmer found that she had scraped a grave under the tree and buried her calf there.

The protective instinct is characteristic, it seems, of almost all elephants. A bull grown too old for breeding will leave the herd, possibly because he has become too slow to keep up on the long marches. One or two young bulls may go with him. The young guards will urge him away from danger, shoving him gently into cover, then rush back to challenge the enemy. The youngsters frequently stay with him until he dies, which may be at about 60.

Contrary to popular belief, these giant animals are not clumsy. They can step on a coconut with a delicacy that cracks the shell without crushing the meat, and they can turn sweet potatoes from the ground without breaking the skin. They are inclined to be right- or left-"handed"; sweet-potato digging, for example, is always done with the same tusk.

Elephants are among the finest swimmers of all land animals. There is record of a train of 79 Asian working elephants crossing tidal stretches of the Ganges where they had to swim for six hours without touching bottom. Asian elephants, which have much smaller ears than their African brothers, are often domesticated and used as work animals.

An elephant needs very little sleep—about half as much as a human being—and this is just as well since he must spend most of his time gathering food. To browse the 1000 pounds of leaves and grass that make his daily ration he must feed 16 hours out of the 24. Also, he must continually search for water, since he needs 30 to 50 gallons a day.

It is true that an elephant never forgets. One thing always remembered is the scent of man. Observers claim that, once hunted, the tusker can detect with his trunk the difference between the scent of white man and African at a distance of two miles. Sydney Downey told of a solitary bull he followed for years in northern Kenya: "He fed in loops, straying off to left and right but always coming back to cross his trail. There he'd stop, sniff the ground with his trunk, and if there was no scent he'd move on. If he scented a native foot on his trail, he would back into cover and watch until he was sure all was safe. If he scented a white man, he'd trample the ground in a rage and take off in a straight line for 50 miles or more. He knew what kind of weapons whites carry."

Colonel Bruce-Smith, a well-known Kenya settler, maintained that elephants remember kindness as well as danger. He once captured a small elephant with a bad sore on one of its hind legs. Bruce-Smith had the elephant put in stocks, a chamber of thick logs too narrow to permit him to move, while he dressed the wound. At the first bite of the antiseptic, the elephant screeched with pain and rage, almost breaking out of the stocks. But Bruce-Smith finished the job and made the animal comfortable. After three or four dressings the elephant accepted treatment with patience, but he had to be confined in order to prevent him from pulling off the dressing. Finally he was released. From then until the animal was shipped to Nairobi, he would run to Bruce-Smith every time he saw him, take his hand in his trunk and guide it to the now-healed wound.

The great elephant herds are being depleted. But in Africa's national parks visitors can still see for themselves that these unpredictable animals do indeed frequently behave like the beings who watch them.

THE FIERY TIGER

Jack Denton Scott

A big, shaggy, black water buffalo came clumping up the jungle road below my tree blind, his hoofs sending up little smoky spirals of dust. In the lowering Indian sun his horns gleamed like a pair of polished ivory tusks. From the carefree way he ambled, I knew that this was a domestic animal strayed from a herd, probably heading homeward to the village three miles away.

As I watched from the pipal tree, which I had climbed to photograph peacocks that frequented this area, there was a wind-whisper of movement in the pale grass 20 feet from the road. With a motion that came as quickly and startlingly as a bad dream, a tiger thrust his whiskered, orange-white head out of the grass and watched the buffalo plod past. He was so close to me that I could see the wet gleam in his hard eyes and could count the five stripes that crossed his forehead.

Twisting out of the cover as sinuously as a snake, he stood in the road in breathtaking beauty. His coat was a delicate golden rust, with stripes so vividly black and well defined that they looked freshly painted. Not a muscle quivered in that superb ninefoot body, but I could sense the deep reserves of strength. Graceful as a run of water, the cat flowed down the road after the buffalo, his marvelous control a terrifying thing to watch. He stopped, motionless as marble. Now I could see his muscles bunch. Then a few bounds and a sudden 30-foot leap, frightening in its fury of motion, catapulted him upon the back of the buffalo. Lurching and staggering, the enormous animal never knew what had hit it. The tiger sank the claws of one front paw into the buffalo's shoulder, plunged his long canine teeth into the back of its neck, and hooked his other front paw in the nose, drawing the head down. With the bull plunging forward in panic, the cat tripped it with his hind feet. As the buffalo fell, its neck was broken instantly. I remember thinking: If this is the way death in the jungle must come, I'm glad it's so swift, so surgically skillful.

I was able to witness the tiger's kill because of the only weakness I have discovered in this magnificent predator—his inferior sense of smell. The buffalo's murderer didn't know I was there. But a tiger's hearing, sight, strength, speed, agility and cunning combine to make him lord of everything he surveys.

Many training sessions, from the time he is a tiny cub, perfect the tiger's adult skills. After a 15-week gestation period, the terror of the jungle is born into a litter of from two to six, in late fall or early spring; he is the size of a small house cat, fuzzy but with a full complement of stripes. Promptly after the mating his father leaves, and his mother finds an isolated place near water and shade (often in an abandoned temple) where other tigers can't molest her offspring. Adult males may kill any cub they see.

At about the age of two months the cubs leave the den for brief periods but don't follow their mother until two months later, when they are about the size of cocker spaniels. At five months the cubs are no longer satisfied by their mother's milk, and she begins to kill small game for them—mouse deer, jungle fowl, peacock, pig—which they mangle in play and learn to eat. When they are a year old, she cripples game and introduces the litter to their lifetime of killing—and survival. Rao Naidu, one of India's foremost hunters, once watched a tigress show her three cubs how to stalk a barking deer that she had evidently disabled for her students.

At 18 months, young tigers begin making their own kills and are taught the arts of hunting silently, utilizing cover, using their remarkable eyes and ears and their poor noses. Learning to approach their prey from downwind is important, for tigers have a strong, musky odor that betrays them to horned game. They are also taught to swim: unlike most felines, they are fond of water. Many a tigress has been seen up to her neck in a stream with cubs splashing nearby.

Ready to mate again, the tigress deserts her offspring when they are about two years old, but the cubs may remain together, aiding one another in the hunt, until they get their own reproductive urge. Maturing at five, they become solitary stalkers and killers (except when mating) for the rest of their 30-year life-span. Males grow to be from eight to nine feet long and weigh up to 500 pounds. Females are considerably smaller, but otherwise the sexes look much alike, although the female is more lithe and elegant and has a narrower head. She is also fiercer, the one who never falters in her charge.

English sportsman F. C. Hicks was attacked by a tigress who charged out of the grass and leaped on his elephant's hindquarters to get at him. He shot her; she circled and again leaped on the elephant, clawing and biting the huge beast till Hicks fired a second shot that ended her life. The elephant, which was ten times the size of the tigress, trembled and trumpeted in terror throughout the attack.

Breathtaking in its power and beauty is the tiger. Except for the exterior, it is almost identical physically with the lion, and cross-breeding does occur. The hybrids are called tigons and ligers.

Many consider the tiger the true king of cats. More than three times the weight of a leopard, he has the smaller cat's agility and can actually jump 18 feet straight up or leap a 40-foot gorge without any seeming effort. I also think the tiger is fiercer than the lion. The Masai and other African tribes successfully hunt lions with spears. Indian aboriginals have as much courage as the Africans, yet the tiger is never hunted by their tribal groups—with *any* weapon, even guns. The tribes respect and fear the giant cat too much to go after him in his own territory, where he usually dictates his own terms.

There is an air of mystery about the tiger that the other cats don't seem to have. He always appears suddenly, dramatically, then melts away into cover as secretly as he came. Perhaps this is why he inspires fear throughout his vast range: Siberia, the Caucasus, northern Iran, central Asia, Manchuria, Mongolia, China, Korea, Burma, the Malay Peninsula, India and Pakistan. Other animals may be as dangerous and as powerful, but the tiger has always been synonymous with terror.

I admit that one of the varying emotions the tiger arouses in me is fear. That feeling was born one sunlit afternoon when my wife and I were walking with Rao Naidu through a ringal jungle of young, gold-stemmed, feathery bamboo toward an enormous fan of vultures unfurling in a cloudless delft sky. We found the remains of a gaur, India's giant wild ox, and saw that a big cat had been at it. As I was wondering aloud how even a tiger could pull down this animal that must have weighed nearly a ton, Rao nudged me. I looked where he was looking. The wheat-brown grass rose hip-high. Less than 100 yards away, head above it, was a huge black-and-gold tiger. He stood sculpturesquely still, glaring at us, fearful symmetry without motion except for the white tip of his tail twitching like a hovering bird behind him. Tense, in a block of fear, I thought suddenly of Kipling, who knew the tiger and the jungle, and who described fear unforgettably:

"Do you know what fear is? Not ordinary fear of insult, injury or death, but abject quivering dread . . . a fear that dries the inside of the mouth and half of the throat, fear that makes you sweat on the palms of the hands, and gulp in order to keep the uvula at work. This is a fine Fear—a great cowardice, and must be felt to be appreciated. . . ."

Gulping and sweating, I was feeling Mr. Kipling's great cowardice now. Then the tiger moaned, a deep *ahhh-hhh*, turned in a graceful movement and vanished in the golden grass.

We ran for the nearest tree and went up it, fear making us as agile as monkeys. While we sat, carefully searching the terrain, I learned from one of the world's cat experts about two more of the tiger's characteristics: the sounds he makes and his incredible strength.

Sher, as the Indian tiger is called, moans when he is disappointed or displeased; also to warn animals that he is approaching (either to avoid tangling with an irritable old wild boar or to herd weaker animals into a trap). He also barks sharply, "pooking," to call to another tiger; coughs to frighten animals away from a kill; and makes a hissing, bellows-like sound when blowing on a carcass to dislodge stinging insects. Rao claims to have heard him make a distinct whistle, which Rao believes is used to call a mate. A tiger roars to express either good spirits or anger; the two sounds are easy to distinguish—one bold and buglelike, the other merely peevish. His most frightening sounds are a series of insane roars which he emits when he is about to charge, tail lashing from side to side.

Old jungle hands say that the big cats imitate the call of the sambar stag, enticing that elklike animal near. They will even splash their paws in a pool to attract the curious creature. George Hogan Knowles' *In the Grip of the Jungles* describes a tiger luring a wild bull buffalo. Crouching in high grass, it imitated the bellow of a bull spoiling for a fight. The clever cat even set the scene by scratching the earth and making dust rise, much as the hoofs of a mad bull would. When the bull gave a responding bellow, the tiger challenged from his ambush again until the angry animal came thundering up—to sudden death.

The tiger's strength is remarkable. One hunter found the carcass of a 1200-pound bull which the striped cat had moved a quarter of a mile over rough terrain. Another tiger leaped a seven-foot stockade, killed a man and, with the body in his mouth, sailed easily over the fence again.

When a tiger turns man-killer, he does it with a vengeance. One tigress in the province of Scindia killed 127 people, stopping all use of the main roads for months. The Indian man-eater of Champawat killed 436 people; another brought such terror that 13 villages were abandoned and 250 square miles of agricultural land were left uncultivated until the beast was hunted down. In a single year for which records were kept, tigers killed 22,000 people and 80,000 domestic cattle throughout India.

Those who know tigers best, *shikaris* like Rao Naidu, Vidya Shukla and Bobby Kooka, believe that the magnificent cat wants to ignore man—is, in fact, afraid of him. A well-known taxidermist of Mysore who collects the skulls of man-eaters told me that, without exception, all of his man-eaters had been wounded, or were crippled or badly incapacitated by old age; of his 50-odd skulls, 40 carried severe bullet wounds. He believes that most man-eaters are man-made.

There are occasional cases of man-eaters who appear for a while, then apparently return to the normal pattern. Rao Naidu is one who believes that these are females with young. His theory is that tigresses with cubs must stay in areas where there are no other tigers and, thus, little natural food. Forced to feed on anything she can find, the tigress often has to resort to man until the cubs are large and strong enough to move back into the jungle where wild game is plentiful.

Another factor drives tigers toward man and his cattle: in India many of the jungle people own firearms and their poaching is rapidly thinning out wildlife, thus destroying the tiger's normal food supply. In retaliation against tiger attacks, villagers are placing massive doses of fast-acting poisons in the carcasses of slain cattle, killing large numbers of tigers. They claim that they do this as a simple matter of protection, but tiger skins are becoming increasingly valuable, and other parts of the big cat, such as whiskers and claws, are used for everything from aphrodisiacs to a supposed cure for rheumatism. If the Indian government doesn't face the problem soon, the tiger may not be able to hold his own much longer. And if he goes, one of India's most precious possessions will go with him.

Awesome is probably the one word to describe the tiger. Anyone who has sat in a tree in the Indian jungle at night and watched this magnificent animal walking along a cart road in the white moonlight knows what I mean. So beautiful and perfectly proportioned that he seems cast in gold-bronze, the tiger is a living sculptural masterpiece. He is so suddenly gigantic there beneath you that he doesn't seem real; so lordly and graceful as he glides that I liken his movement to moonlight itself.

Picture the most handsome, well-brushed, coat-gleaming, pedigreed house cat you have ever seen. Make it 100 times larger, place it in a wild place where moonlight and shadow meet dense jungle, then examine your emotional reaction. If it includes admiration, surprise, awe, fear, even frozen wonder, then you have an admixture of what I feel every time I see a wild tiger in his own land. I am strongly in favor of forever keeping the tiger burning bright in his forests of the night.

THE BOUNDER WITH THE BUILT-IN POCKET

Alan Devoe

In 1770 the explorer Captain James Cook sent men ashore from his ship, the *Endeavour*, to scout for food in the unknown Australian bush. They came back goggle-eyed, bringing with them an animal that resembled nothing they had ever seen on land or sea. A good five feet high, the beast had a delicately shaped head and deerlike neck, but these graceful upper parts sloped down to huge, heavily muscled hindquarters like the rear of an overdeveloped mule, to which was appended a thick, heavy, four-foot tail. The animal had big, soft eyes, a twinkly little nose, lips like a rabbit's, hands like a man's, and low on its stomach, for a final impossibility, it had a capacious fur-lined pocket. When Captain Cook's mariners questioned the natives about this fabulous creature, they spread their hands eloquently, shrugged and murmured, "Kangaroo!" Freely translated, that means: "It would be hopeless to try to tell you!"

The zoologists of Europe, after years of debate, including a serious surmise that the kangaroo might be a species of nightmare-sized mouse, finally put it down as the chief of a strange zoological order called the marsupials—*marsupium* is Latin for pouch.

The kangaroo is found nowhere in the world but in Australasia. Ages ago, when that part of our Earth was cut off from the Asian mainland, this fantastic animal from nature's long-ago was also isolated. There are some 50 living species distributed through Australia, southward to Tasmania and northward to New Guinea and some neighboring islands. Some are no bigger than rabbits; some can climb trees. They are known by a variety of picturesque names: wallabies, wallaroos, potoroos, boongaries and pademelons. But *the* kangaroo—the one that is Australia's national symbol—is the great gray kangaroo of the plains, admiringly known throughout the island continent as the Old Man, and also as Boomer, Forester and Man of the Woods. His smaller mate, in Australian talk, is a "flyer." Their baby is known as Joey.

A full-grown kangaroo stands taller than a man and commonly weighs 200 pounds. Even when he sits in his favorite position, reposing on his massive haunches and tilting back on the propping support of his "third leg"—his tail—the head is five feet or more above ground. His huge hind legs, with steel-spring

A double rarity. Albino kangaroos seldom appear, as they are easy victims and few survive.
Usually only one Joey is raised, probably because most pockets aren't big enough for two.

power, can send him sailing over a nine-foot fence with ease, or in a fight can beat off a dozen dogs. A twitch of his tail can break a man's leg like a matchstick. Yet this king of the plains starts life as a baby so tiny that he and two like him could be held in a teaspoon.

A newborn kangaroo is less than an inch long— about the size of a bee. Its body is semitransparent, like an earthworm's. The only part of the baby that is fully developed is its little "hands." Gripping his mother's fur, Joey hitches his way toward her protective pouch, ordinarily making the trip entirely on his own. On the rare occasions when he needs help, his mother takes him gently in her lips and tucks him away in the pouch, which is usually all Joey's, for in most instances there is only one baby kangaroo in a birth.

As soon as he is installed, Joey takes hold of a milk gland and hangs on with an inseparable grip. He isn't strong enough to feed himself by sucking, so nature provides the mother with special muscles by which she pumps milk into him. How he breathes during this process was a puzzle until naturalists found that while Joey is a nursling an elongated part of his larynx connects with the back part of his nasal passages, so that air passes directly into his lungs. Thus he can keep up his milk-drinking all the while, and never choke.

By the time he is four months old, Joey has grown a fur coat, detached himself from his mother's milk supply and taken to peeking out of the pouch in the pose dear to cartoonists. When his mother halts to graze, he hops to the ground and does some grass-nibbling on his own. At any sign of danger he scampers back into the pouch and is whisked away on a bouncing flight to safety. But if a mother kangaroo is run down and captured, there's never a little Joey in her pouch. The mother's favorite strategy when chased is to hide her baby in the bush, retrieving him when she has tired out her pursuers.

At adulthood Joey becomes a member of a group. Kangaroos are gregarious and live in bands of 20 to 50. They are entirely vegetarian and do most of their browsing in the early morning, at dusk or by moonlight; midday is given to rest and play. Their favorite and most famous sport is boxing. A big Boomer's five-fingered hands are very much like a man's. When two kangaroos spar off, each holds his hands close to his chest in a tight guard, steadies his body with his heavy tail and then begins feinting. Presently there is a flurry of brisk clouts, and then the boxing Boomers step back and pause for the end of Round One. Kangaroos rarely lose their tempers, and naturalists have been astonished to see how scrupulously they observe a rhythm of rounds and rests, even when boxing for hours. They aren't fighting to win, but just for the sport of it.

Anyone who has seen a kangaroo in sparring exhibitions with a human partner probably has assumed that it has undergone a long period of training. Actually the chief problem is to teach a kangaroo not to use its terrible kick. A kangaroo's hind foot has four toes, but nature has modified three of them to such trivial size that they don't count. Instead one toe has become tremendously long and strong, like a huge spur with a curving, razor-sharp tip. Ordinarily of gentle spirit, when the Old Man is cornered he can turn into a murderously dangerous animal. Bracing himself with his tail, his fists clenched close to his chest, he kicks out with one of his spurred hind legs. One kick can easily kill a powerful dog or a man.

A Boomer seldom resorts to this defense: he can get away from nearly anything else on legs, and he prefers flight. A kangaroo in a hurry makes nothing of a broad jump of 25 feet, and he can lope along for miles in continuous gliding bounds of 15 or 20 feet. He has been known to hit close to 25 miles an hour in straightaways. Even if pursued by "kangaroo dogs," specially bred in Australia for hunting old Boomer, he rarely stages a hind-leg defense. He just bounds into a shallow watercourse, wades out until he is waist-deep, then waits. As the dogs come thrashing out to him, he grabs them and holds their heads under water. A strong old kangaroo has been known to drown half a dozen attacking dogs, one by one.

Kangaroos love nothing better than to sit by the hour in the tall, sun-bleached grass, like so many rabbits in a meadow, dozing and nibbling and wrinkling their noses. Like king-sized rabbits, too, they play a game of bounding rigmaroles that resembles tag.

Kangaroos have meant many things to Australia. They were a chief food supply for the aborigines—who brought down old Boomer, of course, with a boomerang—and they were equally important in furnishing food to the early colonists. Kangaroo meat is gamey and coarse, but kangaroo-tail soup is held to be better than oxtail. Australia exports it to gourmets all over the world.

Today civilization has driven the kangaroos to the vast plains of the Outback. There they live and breed in great numbers. In drought years they are a menace to grazing lands and water supplies; a sheepman once counted 2000 of them in an hour—each capable of consuming more forage than a sheep. Kangaroo-shooting is a lively business in some districts; more than a million skins are brought to market every year. They make excellent glove and boot leather and the fur is a valuable export. Kangaroos also provide an endless supply of tall tales, and the beauty of tall tales about the kangaroo is that they can be almost as tall as you please and still be close to fact.

AFRICA'S UGLY PRIMA DONNA

Reed Millard

A train rumbling along the tracks in Kenya came to a sudden crashing stop, then plunged off the rails. While the stunned passengers crawled out, the cause of it all shook herself and calmly walked away. The train had been derailed by the charge of an angry lady rhinoceros. By this surprising feat, she proved not only the savage power in her two-ton bulk, but also the right of the mighty rhino to be called the most temperamental beast on Earth—a distinction shared by male and female alike.

Sometimes friendly and docile, these ponderous denizens of Africa, second largest land animal in the world, will for no apparent reason go into a mad charge, hurling themselves against anything momentarily considered an enemy. Rhinos have thus attacked trucks, bands of elephants and even, on one occasion, an artillery detachment, upsetting and trampling field guns.

For sheer all-around ugliness, the rhino is unsurpassed by any other beast. His hideous face, outlandish horns, rough skin and ungainly body, too big for his tiny feet, make him seem to belong among the monstrosities from Earth's biological past. Nature appears to have slipped up badly in designing the rhino's skin, which looks as if it had been cast off from some still larger creature, for it hangs in great sagging folds.

The rhinoceros is equipped with a most fearsome weapon, a large central horn. This anatomical marvel reaches awesome proportions. The record horn of a black rhino actually measured 53½ inches, and a white rhino topped even that with a horn that was five feet long! A rhino's horn does not grow out of his skull but out of his scalp. And, oddly enough, it is not made of bone, but of tightly compressed hairs. Nevertheless, it is hard enough to remain unbroken even in a charge against a solid object.

Surprisingly, though, the horn has an odd weakness. If a bullet hits it, the rhino goes down, knocked out cold for a few seconds. Zoologists explain that

The rhino unpredictable, agile and stupid, has a love of charging full-steam, even though he can't see what he is after. When he is going at top speed, all four feet may be off the ground.

such a hard, sharp blow is transmitted directly to his brain, with the resultant knockout. Harder but less sharp blows are somehow absorbed by the horn.

Though it is his most effective weapon, the rhino's horn has led to the near extinction of the breed. For this curious feature has, over the centuries, been credited with marvelous medicinal powers. European monarchs once prized it when made into a drinking cup, since they believed that it would ward off the effects of poisons.

For all his massive build and great weight, the rhino is surprisingly agile, and his speed, together with his wicked horn, would make him a formidable opponent even if he behaved like other beasts, which he doesn't. For hours the leaf-eating rhino will graze peacefully; then, with no warning and without visible provocation, he will suddenly charge a zebra or a giraffe with which he has just been on the best of terms. If this quarry gets away, he may turn upon any other that happens to be within reach. Such a sudden rhino attack looks like an explosion, as animals scatter wildly in all directions. A few hours later they may drift back together again and the rhino will move peaceably among them, showing no sign of his former belligerence.

Many experts agree that nothing is so likely to send a rhino into a charge as to have something get between him and a waterhole. Hunters have seen thirsty rhinos lunge into herds of elephants when they stood in the way.

A bull rhino is a fearsome pursuer, but a mother rhino may be worse. The mother tends her baby with unusual affection long after he is perfectly capable of fending for himself. If any danger, real or fancied, appears, she hurries to put herself between it and her offspring. With total disregard for consequences, she will charge any menace.

The rhino's most startling display of prima-donna temperament often is shown after he has begun a charge. Scientists and hunters have reported rhinos driven off by tossed stones or the beam of a flashlight. One rhino charging a man suddenly stopped and stood pawing the ground in front of a large bush. Lowering his head, the animal charged the bush and trampled it underfoot. After looking at it blearily for a moment, he trotted off with the air of a conqueror.

Almost beyond explanation is the curious behavior of a rhino chasing a hunter whose gun and gunbearer were nowhere in sight. Suddenly the earth-shaking sounds of pursuit ceased, and the hunter, hiding behind a bush, stole a glance, then stared in disbelief. His mighty pursuer stood stock still, head drooping—sound asleep!

BRUIN, THE BIG BRUISER
David M. Newell

Whoever coined the phrase "strong as a bear" knew what he was talking about. No animal of equal size is more powerful than the common North American black bear. He can crush the skull of a steer with a single blow. In Florida I trailed one which had killed a 150-pound hog and carried it a quarter of a mile—evidently in its forepaws, since there were no marks of the pig's being dragged. This bruin had also broken down scrub oaks 20 feet tall to get acorns. Once I followed the trail of a bear which had been caught in a trap. The animal had simply walked off, dragging the 300-pound log to which the trap was fastened.

Bruin's great strength stands him in good stead, for he has to forage for a living under all kinds of conditions. He is omnivorous, eating berries, nuts, roots, insects, fish and any small animal he happens to catch. I opened the stomach of one bear I had shot and found in it two quarts of yellow jackets. He had swallowed those stinging demons whole! Bears love honey, and will raid a wild-bee tree or a farmer's hives. They have even climbed telegraph poles and torn the wires down because they mistook their hum for the droning of bees. It is amusing to watch one of the hulking beasts catch ants. When he locates an ants' nest he sticks his paw into the place and waits for the angry insects to swarm over it; then he sits down and licks them off with great gusto.

Bears do things that often seem inspired by mischievousness or downright malice. A trapper in Ontario told me of one that completely wrecked his cabin. Bruin had smashed every food container; on the floor was a hideous mixture of flour, molasses, sugar, rice, beans and coffee. Scattered through it were clothes and broken dishes. The animal had bitten open several dozen cans of fruits and vegetables, just to be sure he hadn't missed anything. Such depredations are common. I believe they are caused by the bear's temper, for Bruin flies into a great rage when his desires are thwarted. A locked cabin or food in a box or can irritates him into a frenzy.

He can change from a playful mood to hot anger with no warning. Many serious accidents have occurred because of this, particularly in the national parks, where black bears become quite tame. One tourist, getting out of his car to take pictures of a

The black bear, smallest of the North American bears, is inquisitive and usually playful. He becomes ferocious when food is offered and then withheld, or when defending his young.

big one, tried to make the animal stand on its hind legs by pretending to hold up some food. Enraged at being fooled, the animal suddenly lashed out with its forepaw and nearly tore off the man's scalp.

Contrary to popular belief, a bear does not hug his quarry and thus squeeze it to death; he merely holds it in order to bite it. I once saw a black bear seize a 60-pound pig in his forearms, bite into its neck and tear the pig's head from its body. And, as my guide said, "That pig's head was put on there good, too!"

Though they appear to be slow and cumbersome, bears are capable of great speed. For a short distance they can travel nearly 30 miles an hour. Three hundred pounds is a good average weight for a large male. He may be nearly three feet high at the shoulder when on all fours, and over six feet tall when he stands up like a man. His color may be black, cinnamon, chocolate or light brown; he has a tan muzzle and occasionally a gray or white patch on the breast.

Of all North American bears, the black is by far the most numerous and widely distributed. I have followed its tracks along Alaska salmon streams, through Arizona canyons, through the laurel thickets of the Great Smokies and across muddy cypress stands in the Florida Everglades. The animal shows an amazing ability to adapt itself to the variations in climate, topography and food conditions found in this huge area. In northern regions the black bear hibernates in a cave, or under the butt end of a large fallen tree. He holes up not because of the cold, but because he can no longer find enough food. During the fall he puts on a thick layer of fat which sees him through his long sleep from November until April.

Black bears mate in the summer. The two or three cubs are born late in the winter while the mother is still in hibernation. Blind and almost hairless, they weigh less than a pound at birth. Nature seems to have made the cubs extremely small so that they will require little food, for the mother is dependent for her nourishment on her stored-up fat. The cubs nurse and sleep for the first month or so. On leaving the den at the age of about two months they are the size of adult raccoons. The cubs love to climb into the top of a sapling until the tree bends with their weight; then they swing out as far as they can and jump off— immediately scrambling up the tree again to repeat the performance. By fall the youngsters are as large as shepherd dogs and can fend for themselves.

The black bear is in no danger of annihilation. Even in such thickly populated states as Pennsylvania, black bears are increasing. In spite of occasional depredations, the smart old strong man of the woods is generally harmless to human beings.

NATURE'S SKYSCRAPERS
George G. Goodwin

It was along a trail leading east from Voi in Kenya, East Africa, that I first got acquainted with the giraffe. Four big fellows were browsing leisurely on the branches of an acacia tree. Of course, I'd seen giraffes before in zoos, but this was different. There were no iron bars or display windows here. I was a little man alongside the tallest creatures on Earth.

Only the heads of these giants could be seen, rising a foot or more above the tops of the trees. I was so close I could watch the long black tongues dart out and reach for leaves and shoots, the slender tip wrapping around a twig, daintily plucking it and drawing it into the extended lips. But what held my attention longest was the giraffes' enormous dark brown eyes, shaded by surprisingly long black lashes. Not only were they the biggest eyes I had ever seen, but they had a liquid, sorrowful expression that was unique.

The giraffe is found only on the African veld, and nowhere else in the world is there an animal even remotely like it. Its only living relative is the okapi, of the Congo, a somewhat similar beast with sloping back and slightly elongated neck.

Not only is the giraffe the tallest, but it is among the four largest land animals. Full-grown bulls are often 19 feet high, some even taller. A large portion of the height is neck, in which the seven vertebrae (the same number as in man and other mammals) are greatly elongated. A shoulder height of 12 feet is not unusual; a man can even stand upright between the front legs of a bull giraffe. Most large bulls weigh a ton to a ton and a half, some as much as two tons.

The giraffe's lips are long, prehensile and quite hairy—a protection against the stabbing thorns of its favorite food tree, the acacia. The upper lip extends well beyond the lower, and the extensible tongue, up to 18 inches long, is a marvelously adept tool for plucking leaves and twigs by drawing them along the lower front teeth, since there are no front teeth in the upper jaw.

The pair of horns on top of a giraffe's head are short, bony structures covered with hairy skin. In very early life these develop independent of the skull but eventually become attached to it. In some species there is a third horn in the center of the forehead, and still others have an additional pair of

Giraffes among the acacia trees — their favorite food — at the foot of Mount Kilimanjaro. Once they were called "camelopards" because they look somewhat like camels with leopard-like spots.

small horns immediately behind the major ones. The animal's cloven hoof may measure as much as 12 inches in length and width, but, despite the size of its feet, a giraffe can walk only on hard, firm earth. Long legs supporting such a heavy body would soon bog down if it tried to cross swampy ground.

The home range of the giraffe extends from the Sudan on the north to South Africa, then up the west coast to northern Angola, with an additional area in Nigeria. Each of the twelve species varies considerably in markings and coloring. In equatorial regions where the sunlight is direct and shadows are dark, the giraffe's spots and lines stand out strongly. In cooler regions with softer light and diffused shadows, its markings are paler and fade gradually into white.

During recent times the giraffe has lived exclusively in Africa, but its ancestral home was in Europe and Asia. The giraffe family dates back about 15 million years—a relative newcomer compared to other mammals. Fifteen to 20 years seems to be the average good life-span of the giraffe.

Early Boer settlers in South Africa were largely responsible for the rapid decline there in the population of these animated skyscrapers. Giraffe flesh is quite good to eat, and the animal has a tough and useful hide, in places as much as an inch thick—so tough that a soft-nosed bullet fired at close range will flatten out before it can penetrate any vital part. African tribes, too, took their toll; they relished the meat, prized the sinews for bowstrings and musical instruments and used the hide to cover shields.

It is difficult to imagine anyone today killing the inoffensive giraffe for sport, and there is little excuse for asserting that it is a menace to man. Indeed, there seems to have been only one occasion on which it tangled with human progress. When a 600-mile telegraph line newly erected in East Africa stopped working after only an hour, troubleshooters discovered that a giraffe had nearly decapitated himself by running at high speed against the wire, and three others were found entangled in it. The line was raised to a height of 30 feet and giraffe trouble ended.

For such tall animals, sleeping can be quite a problem. They often sleep standing, since the effort involved in lying down and getting up makes the reclining giraffe an easy target for lions. Nevertheless, giraffes do sometimes sleep lying down, with the neck turned backward and the head resting on the rump.

Giraffes are sociable animals, living in loosely knit communities made up of family groups of four to 20 individuals. Herds of over 150 animals have been recorded in the past, but in recent years 70 has been the largest number counted. Competition between bulls for cows is a familiar pattern, but the giraffes settle their quarrels in one of the strangest ways—by hammering each other with their heads.

The two opposing bulls will sidle up to each other, heads swaying up and down. When one finds an opening, he swings his neck sharply sideways and downward, bringing his rugged horns down with a powerful blow on his adversary's shoulder. All caution is abandoned and both animals pound each other mercilessly about the neck and body with their massive heads, sometimes rising on their hind feet. The fight continues until both bulls are tired out—and then, as if by agreement, they stop to rest before resuming! These battles usually end in complete exhaustion; and, except for bruises, neither animal seems much the worse for the pummeling.

Like elephants, giraffes roam over large areas. A mature bull may be the official leader, but it is the females that keep diligent watch, not only over their own young but over the herd in general. Mating may occur at almost any time. The young, all legs and neck, are born about 14½ months later. A single calf is the rule, and very occasionally there are twins—never more. A newborn calf weighs from 110 to 140 pounds and stands some six feet tall. Staggering uncertainly at first on its long, wobbly legs, it reaches its mother's side. For the first nine months it is dependent on her milk for food, but after this it is tall enough to reach the lower branches of acacia trees and feed itself.

Both parents will vigorously defend their young, and it is a foolhardy predator, man or lion, that incautiously comes within striking distance of the female giraffe's mighty hoofs, which can kick in all four directions. A hoof 12 inches wide, swung on a seven- or eight-foot shaft of heavy bone and muscle and backed by terrific driving power, inflicts a blow which has been known to decapitate a lioness.

The great height of the giraffe demands a very high blood pressure to drive the blood up to the lofty head. On the other hand, when the animal drinks, its head is lowered seven feet below the level of the heart; a few seconds later it may again be lifted nearly 20 feet in the air. The adaptations of the giraffe heart and blood system have been of particular interest to scientists. The blood supply is instantly controlled by a valve to prevent brain hemorrhage when the head is lowered or sudden drain of blood when the head is rapidly raised.

For years it has been said that the giraffe is mute, that it never makes a sound; but occasionally a cow giraffe has been heard calling her calf with a low moo, and other sounds have been reported. The postmortem examination of an adult bull which had been able to groan and moo revealed that it had undeveloped, ineffective vocal cords. The sounds are presumably made by strong exhalations of air.

Giraffes moving at full gallop across the African skyline seem to roll along with marvelous grace and rhythm. They may walk, trot, canter or gallop, attaining a top speed of about 32 miles an hour. The most usual gait, however, is a rolling pace, both legs on one side of the body moving forward together, producing an even, swaying motion.

During my stay in East Africa I never ceased to marvel at the towering height and quiet dignity of these graceful beasts. Imagine my reaction one day when, stalking a moving object I had caught sight of through an opening in the trees, I came face to face with my quarry—a snow-white giraffe! She seemed unnecessarily restless and nervous, as if fully aware of her conspicuousness. In a moment she galloped toward a dense orchard of acacia trees, where without slackening speed she swung her head low under branches and threaded her way between the trunks of the trees. I could see her white head and neck sway back and forth in rhythm with her rolling gait. She was the first and last white giraffe I saw, and I am glad to say that she was placed under government protection, safe from trophy hunters.

LOOK AT THE OSTRICH— BUT LOOK OUT!

Jan Juta

In Chapter 39 of the Book of Job we find an unflattering reference to the ostrich: "She is hardened against her young ones, as though they were not hers. . . . Because God hath deprived her of wisdom, neither hath he imparted to her understanding."

Job obviously had never studied the ostrich. Actually the birds are good parents. The cocks share the brooding period with the hens and sit in black majesty each night upon the eggs, out in the lonely scrub. There are 30 or more eggs in the dusty, scratched-out hollow that serves as a communal nest.

As I watched at a South African farm one morning, a man opened barn doors and out stepped a large number of birds, all in the gray plumage of youth. Suddenly, as if at a command, they started to rush across the paddock, darting this way and that, wings outstretched—some whirling round and round, circling in a frenzied dance. This is part of the ostrich nature, this desire to dance—to rush into the wide-open space, whirling in an ecstasy of freedom regained, or to perform the measured steps of the mating dance. Birds of all kinds dance during the courting period, but the ritualistic dance of the mating ostrich must be seen to be believed.

I saw it that same day. There were two handsome birds in a little clearing in the scrub. The hen, brown, dusty, nondescript compared to the superb black-and-white beauty of her mate, was walking round and round him as he sat majestic in the sand. She was shivering her drooping wings, emitting a sound like the faint clatter of small castanets. Suddenly the cock rose—wings outspread, the curling white plumes waving, and the bunch of feathers which formed his tail erect. Slowly he pranced up to the hen. Then, face to face, wing tip to wing tip, they began the dance, slowly circling—waltzing—their long necks curving and swaying rhythmically. Round and round they moved until the hen, breaking the rhythm, suddenly squatted down, wings outstretched, her long neck sweeping the ground, weaving from side to side over the dusty surface a pattern of motion further to fascinate her mate. The immense male, covered with the furlike mass of shining black feathers, wings stretched to display the curling white array of plumes, passionately stomped his dance of love.

The common saying about the foolish ostrich "with his head in the sand" arises from the bird's habit of extending his neck flat along the ground. It actually is a good means of concealment when the ostrich is sitting on the eggs. Once the long periscope of the neck and head is lowered, the humpbacked shape of the bird becomes merely a hummock or a boulder.

When I was ten years old and adventurous, I was anxious to see an ostrich on the nest. This was a dangerous business, for while one bird sits, the other circles the nest to keep off all intruders. I have seen an ostrich rip a dog almost in two with one kick of its huge, iron-clawed foot.

I had been told that if I was ever attacked there were two means of avoiding serious injury or death. One was to have a long forked stick at hand to thrust at the base of the bird's neck, thereby keeping it far enough away to avoid its murderous kicks. The other —a last resort—was to lie face downward with my head buried in my arms, for the ostrich can do little harm unless the powerful leg can be raised to rip at some vertical object. "The worst that is likely to happen," said my informant, "is that he will sit on you and peck at you if you move—so don't stir a muscle unless you want your eyes pecked out."

I was so intent upon my object that I missed the

Because of its long neck and awkward walk, the ostrich was once known as the "camel bird." When it feels in danger, it puts tail up and head down, to look like a bush.

silent, swift approach of the guardian cock from the far angle of the paddock. At a sudden angry "grunt" I turned to see the bird running toward me, wings outstretched. I fled, dropping my stick. Realizing I could not reach the fence, I flung myself into the dust, flattening myself to the hard earth. Momentarily I expected to feel the whole weight of the great bird crash down upon me. The blood was pounding in my ears, and my mind was a confusion of terror and prayer.

I felt a sharp stab at my ankle, where the metal tag of my bootlace caught the quick eye of the bird, and I tightened all my muscles to resist moving. As the minutes passed, I raised one arm a little to see where the bird was. Immediately I felt a sharp stab on the ground close to my side which shook my whole body, followed by another, and another. I was thankful that at least the back of my neck was protected by my felt hat, and that my folded arms hid my face and hands from view. As I prayed, a sudden stab at my sleeve made me wince. The bright metal buttons of my blazer had attracted the angry bird.

Long afterward my aching muscles obliged me to move my arm again. Little by little I raised it and,

opening one eye to peer beneath, I could see the feathery black curve of the bird's body on the ground only a few inches from my elbow. My mind was immediately filled with pictures of the ostrich sitting silently by my side, watching for any movement or sign of life, to rise in its fury and either trample me to a broken mass or peck me until, forced to move, I should be ripped by the tearing strength of those great claws. I lay, aching yet not daring to move, for what seemed hours before, carefully looking under my arm again, I suddenly realized the bird was no longer there. Gradually I lifted my painful body enough to enable me to see above the surrounding scrub. There was nothing in sight! I waited awhile, gathering my nerve and my remaining strength to make a dash for the barbed wire.

I had lain the best part of the day on the ground. I was later told that it was probably the changing of the egg-sitting period which had saved me. The secret call back to the nest to relieve the hatching hen had drawn the cock from my side. I returned to the homestead to tell the tale of my miraculous escape, with my buttonless sleeve to support my story.

ALMOST EVERYBODY LIKES HIPPOS

Colonel Robert Bruce White

In my heart there is a soft spot for hippos. For this reason I have sought them out in the lakes and rivers of Central Africa—not to shoot them but to observe the fascinating family life of these amusing, peace-loving, inoffensive animals.

Few animals are uglier than the hippopotamus. Father is somewhat larger than his mate, standing 48 to 65 inches at the shoulder; his length runs between 11 and 15 feet, and he weighs from 5000 to 8000 pounds. The record weight for hippos, according to the London Zoo, is 8900. Such bulk is most impressive, especially when you stop to think that his head alone may weigh nearly a ton. With eyes that seem to have been laid on his face (not set in, like the elephant's) and with funny little ears that often wigwag in excitement—one moving forward while the other goes backward—he is quick to detect an intruder. His nostrils are strategically placed so that when in the water he can breathe without exposing another square inch of his vast bulk to view.

But it's his slobbering mouth that intrigues me most. He seems to revel in yawns that expose a great expanse of pink gums and gleaming ivories. Like his distant relative the pig, he has incisors, molars and canines, the canines forming big tusks that curve inward and back but never extend beyond his bulging muzzle. His jaws are powerful enough to tear through a crocodile's armor plate as readily as you or I might crunch a celery stalk. A watermelon on his tongue is no more than a strawberry on ours. And what an appetite! He'll put more than 200 pounds of fodder into his 40- or 50-gallon stomach every day: grasses, water lilies and other greenery.

Hippos are admirably adapted to the amphibious life they lead. Their skin secretes a viscous, cinnamon-colored fluid that protects them in dry atmosphere when they come ashore to browse. Their tough, crinkled, leaden-brown hide, nearly two inches thick, may cover 200 pounds of fat. They appear almost hairless, but there is short, sparse hair over part of the hide. Tufts are also found on the upper lip, ear tips and on the end of the curious, undersized tail.

When he comes ashore, the hippo clambers up steep banks, even precipitous ravines, with astonishing power and ease. He walks like no other animal on Earth, for beneath his barrel-bellied hull his short but solid legs are set so far apart that their hoofs beat out two separate, parallel tracks. This ludicrous performance makes him look like a great, ponderous clown. But when he runs he can outstrip a man.

The hippo, not a fast but actually quite an adept swimmer, is built for paddling at leisure or walking on river bottoms. He floats like a log but, when alarmed, crash-dives like a stone, his nostril valves closing as he goes under. When he surfaces again five or six minutes later, the nostrils open with a loud snort and a whalelike blast of water.

Hippos love to relax in the still reaches of sluggish rivers, and they stay in the water much of the day. Sometimes they bask drowsily on sandspits, taking little interest in their surroundings, even ignoring the cormorants, starlings and egrets that like to perch on them. Occasionally they emit weird grunts, burps, snorts and bellows. Their usual cry I can compare only with the excited neighing of a horse: it is repeated several times, in basso profundo rising to shrill falsetto. Their mating calls are more moolike; in combat they emit a deep lowing and growling.

Baby hippos are the ugliest infants ever born—absurdly bigheaded, fat and crank-tailed. Yet in the soft, helpless way of all babies, they are most appealing, and the mother hippo's proud devotion is both comical and touching. But life with Father can be disastrous; one of a mother's principal jobs is to protect the baby from his father's immense bulk.

The female gives birth to her single offspring after a gestation period of seven and one half to eight months, and five to ten weeks later she may mate again. Birth takes place either in a dry nest among the rushes or, more frequently, in shallow waters. Weighing from 50 to 75 pounds, the raw pink infant becomes nearly as dark as his parents after a month or so. He suckles underwater, taking nourishment for a minute, then coming up for breath and diving again for another nip. The little fellow can swim before he walks, but to escape crocodiles and a clumsy father he often rides atop his mother's broad back. If he misbehaves she scolds him, and if that doesn't work she fetches him a smart rap on the head which usually sends him sprawling.

Any number of tales have been told about hippos charging and upsetting canoes, then crunching them in their jaws. This usually happens because a baby hippo is nearby. The enraged mother attacks a boat thinking it is some sort of crocodile. Actually the hippo has a mild temperament and usually prefers retreat to fight. There is, to be sure, that occasional exception, the rogue—an elderly male who has been expelled from the community. He may attack anything.

During rutting, however, any male hippo is apt to be belligerent, for it is then that vicious fights are staged for leadership of the herd. Such a battle may last eight hours—with time out periodically for brief rests. The combatants rush forward, biting at each other furiously. Legs, shoulder bones and teeth are broken, hides are deeply scarred, and some fights end in the death of both rivals.

Hippos always follow the same track from the riverbank to their private pasturage, a well-defined trail maintained by a bull for himself and his harem. Along this passageway and around the borders of the grazing area the bull will charge all trespassers.

Hippos can be insatiably curious. Probably the most inquisitive and certainly the best publicized was Hubert. From November 1928 to April 1930 he wandered over Natal and Cape Province, his lonely trek extending some 400 miles. He even entered the big city of Durban, where he terrified early-morning cyclists and pedestrians on downtown West Street, then invariably disappeared into the river just before the police arrived. He visited village after village in the area, peeping into doors and windows of scores of homes, shops, schools and missions. Once he stopped a railway train by snoozing on the roadbed, refusing to budge despite whistle, bell and angry shouts until gently prodded by the cowcatcher. But Hubert harmed no one. In time he became royal game, protected by law, a national hero beloved by all but those unhappy farmers whose gardens he bulldozed flat.

What happened to Hubert? He was shot by an irate farmer ignorant of the law and of the fun his innocent adventures brought to millions of people. And then Hubert sprang his biggest surprise. An autopsy revealed he was a female.

Although its name means "river horse," the hippopotamus is related to the hog and has hoglike ears and eyes. Liking company in the water, hippos are usually found floating or navigating in groups.

NATURE'S FABULOUS FAN DANCER

Jack Denton Scott

Tropical sun slashing through the dense jungle of central India turned the bird's breast into a shimmer of blue fire. It stood tall as an eagle in a clump of young bamboo 300 yards ahead. This was my first view in the wild of the world's most exotic bird, the peacock. I moved slowly forward to capture the sight on color film. As I got closer I could see that the bird was staring, hypnotized, at something before it—a leopard creeping through the grass. I lowered the camera and unslung my rifle. As I put the gun to my shoulder the leopard sprang to its feet, its hide fell off and an alarmed voice shouted in Hindi: "Don't fire!" The bird fled, crouching, swift as a snake.

My "leopard" was a frightened Indian professional fowler who had draped himself in the cat's hide. Ordinarily clever and shy, the peacock is fascinated by the spotted cat and will often stand and stare at it until killed. Aware of this, hunters in some areas don leopard skins to get close enough to net the peacock alive for sale or spear it for supper.

The Far East is native ground for two species of peacock, both related to the pheasant family—the blue-breasted of India and Ceylon and the green of Java and Burma. The Indian bird, called the "common" peacock, is the one known by us all. Domesticated in Judea during the time of Solomon and introduced into Greece by Alexander the Great, it gradually spread westward. In 1936, to the amazement of the scientific world, a third species, the Congo peacock, was discovered in Africa.

We call both the male and female birds peacocks, but only the male is the cock. The female is the peahen, and the true name of the birds is peafowls. Young male peacocks start their lives covered with drab brown down, but when they are only a few hours out of the egg they raise their tiny tails in a strut. It takes two years for train plumage to develop; by then the train or "nautch" projects beyond the tail from 40 to 54 inches, giving the peacock his magnificent tail-train 55 to 72 inches long. Train feathers, which he carries during a possible 15-year lifespan, are shed in late summer and grow back by December. They are bronze-green with a copper sheen near the tips, each feather having a distinct eye formed by a blue heart-shaped spot ringed with blue-green,

golden bronze, gold and rich brown. Unfurled, this fantastic fan in its spectacular sunburst of color takes the shape of a shield from which a thousand eyes seem to peer.

I first saw those eyes when a peacock did a fan dance at New York's Bronx Zoo, where I went with a couple of school chums. Our bird opened his great train by shaking himself until it rose in a multicolored halo. Before we really had a chance to see it properly he swung around, presenting his backside—a stiff grayish-brown tail and a puff of black feathers, giving the impression that he was wearing winter underwear. But finally he decided to let us see him. The great fan with its green, gold and bronze eyes rose and trembled, shaking us up so that no one said a word for ten minutes—a rare thing for boys our age.

I have heard peacocks calling at intervals all night. One cry is exactly like a child's plea for "help!" But the one most often heard resembles the cry of a tomcat on a backyard fence, a cross between a meow and the clear sound of a trumpet, coming out a surprisingly loud *phi-ao-phi-ao*. They also utter a shrill *ka-oan-ka-oan* alarm call. Naturalists call them the most alert of jungle creatures. One, Stuart Baker, said that they are "as sinuous as a snake, as stealthy as a cat and as wary as an old bull bison in watching for foes."

In India I spent nearly two weeks in a camera "hide," perfectly camouflaged, trying to film the impressive love dance that precedes mating. Moving a few yards every day, I managed to get within 200 yards of a peacock family. Then the suspicious guardian hens took off, rocketing like pheasants, rapidly overtaken by their frightened lord, his train streaming like a tail of flame. I never got the picture.

But, while sitting in a tree, waiting for a tiger, I did have a box seat at a show even more unusual than the mating dance. The tiger didn't come that day, but I never noticed. I sat enthralled with a dozen young peacocks performing under my tree. There wasn't a female in sight, thus exploding the theory that they strut only when hens are around. They were dancing with each other, strutting and bowing, paired off. First there was a forward dance, then an equally graceful backward movement, almost a rhumba—the jeweled fans quivering, the sun striking fantastic lights, not a noise coming from them. Then, suddenly, as if by some agreed-upon silent signal, the stately dance stopped, the nautches were folded and the peacocks quietly disappeared from my view, making their way single file through the jungle.

Like the turkey, the peacock struts and quivers his fan before his harem of three to six hens. But the hens don't pay much attention. Of the 50 times I have seen

According to Roman mythology, the pattern of the peacock's tail was created when Juno put the hundred eyes of Argus, the giant slain by Mercury, on the tail of her favorite bird.

wild peacocks displaying their glory before females, only twice did the hens stop pecking or lift their heads to see their master burst his color.

Jungle legend has it that peacocks and snakes are mortal enemies. In the jungles of Ceylon, naturalist William Beebe got close enough to see a peacock playing with a deadly Russell's viper. The bird circled and pursued, keeping at a distance but tempting the viper to strike again and again. "The bird didn't attempt to kill the snake, just teased it," said Beebe. "Then, tiring of the game, he ran down a slope and flew away, in the full light his train a wonderful colored tapestry."

Wild and shy as he is, the peacock takes captivity calmly, is found throughout the world on private estates and in zoos and aviaries. There is a community of contented peacocks in Arcadia, a heavily populated section of southern California. Brought there by Elias Baldwin in the 1870's, three pairs became 2000. The great Baldwin estate was finally broken up, but the

birds stayed. They spend their time on the residents' lawns and fences. Few people object to their presence. After all, how many of us can have peacocks in our gardens?

There are odd characters among domesticated peacocks. Lucifer, once the peacock pride of the Bronx Zoo, fell for a black turtle, Geraldine. Zoo keepers said that as soon as he saw the turtle he fanned his tail and walked out of the peacock section. For three years he lived with her in the turtle yard. He had to fight it out on several occasions with another peacock, Oswald, who came over to discover what he saw in Geraldine. Generally, though, peacocks in captivity are more ornament than pet, keeping their distance and remaining tame so long as they are fed at regular times and not molested. People who keep peacocks claim that once you've owned them you are hooked forever. Their beauty and flaming color are such that you feel something vital has gone from your life if the rainbow bird isn't around.

Chapter three

UNIQUE ABILITIES

Some animals have carved for themselves such spectacular reputations in the natural world that we cannot separate them from their abilities. When we think of the beaver we think of his dam; of the owl, his vision in the night; of the hummingbird, his breathtaking flight.

No one knows exactly why these stars of the natural world have such extraordinary talents, except perhaps because nature sometimes carries an idea to the extreme once she gets started. If stiff fur is uncomfortable to touch, then the porcupine's "fur," as stiff as spears, will turn back even the most insistent enemy. If there are bugs in trees, a living tool will get them out—the drill of the woodpecker.

The simplest everyday conditions may often demand some great task of a beast. Night requires more startling gifts than the day—and so there are bats with sonar which can avoid any obstruction by bouncing high-frequency sound from it. And when small animals die, there is that specialist of all specialists, the beetle that buries them.

The discovery of such details of animal existence have occupied the whole lives of some of the world's most gifted naturalists.

Beavers are sociable, peaceful, industrious and faithful to their mates and family—altogether they are the paragons of the animal world.

HOW DOTH THE BUSY BEAVER—

Bill Cunningham

Nature forgot to teach the beaver how to fight. Although he is big enough and armed with strong teeth and sharp claws, his disposition is so angelic that it never dawns upon him to battle it out with predators as they stalk him ashore or power-dive at him from the air when he swims about in the water. So he has to work; that's why he builds dams.

An average beaver is two and a half feet long, a foot high and weighs 50 pounds. His back feet are webbed like a duck's; his forefeet are little hands like a monkey's. His broad, scaly tail, ten inches in length and half as wide, is used as a rudder when swimming, a brace when sitting or standing, and as a means of transmitting bad news. When a beaver scents danger, he spanks the water with that tail; on still days the ringing spat can be heard a quarter of a mile and every beaver within earshot disappears. Surprise a beaver on shore and he'll run for his pond. He can dive and swim like a loon. By closing his nostrils, relaxing his muscles and dropping his heartbeat from 100 to 50, he can sink like a flatiron and stay down 15 minutes. If you keep him under much longer, however, he'll drown.

It's the icebound northern winter that makes a beaver build a dam. Winter means no open water to plunge into for refuge; the snow is hard to track through in the search for bark to eat. So the beaver creates a personal pond, in whose mud bottom he can anchor a whole winter's supply of eating timber, and on which he can build an impregnable mansion for himself and his family.

First he spots a forest plentifully populated with soft-barked trees—poplar, alder, willow and swamp ash—the bark of which forms his major diet. There must be a stream running through the place; he doesn't care how large or how small. If the stream has a current, the canny little engineer cuts a tree and floats it down until it jams near the point at which he plans to build. If it's a sluggish stream, he may start his logging operations downstream and tow his foundation up.

Once set, the tree catches silt and driftwood, and the beaver furiously lugs in material from the sidelines—mud, sticks, stones, grass—which he works into the mass. Mud, the major ingredient, is carried in his hands, and during minute-long dives to the bottom he works it into place with his hands and the sides of his face. He starts in the middle and builds toward either shore. A dam may be ten feet long or more than 2000. There's a 900-footer in Alaska, another almost as long in Yellowstone Park. The record is a 2100-footer in Montana.

Colonies are small. While several beavers may work at one time, they seem to pay no attention to one another. They do their work preferably on clear moonlit nights, almost never laboring in the daytime except in an emergency such as a break in the dam. As the dam goes up, each beaver couple begins to construct a house. This lodge may be affixed to the dam, to the shore or to an island in the pond. Its foundation is sticks, stones and twigs, so woven that it can't dissolve or collapse.

Once the dam is completed and the water level established, the residence is topped with a domelike room provided with a dry wooden floor that the water doesn't quite reach. This room is usually four to eight feet in diameter and three or four feet high. There are two entrances, through the floor and under the water. One of these is primarily for pulling in timber, the other is for family use. The two-door system is also convenient if submersible enemies enter to pay an unexpected call.

The top of the lodge, of heavily woven thatch, is not completed until freezing weather sets in. Then the beavers plaster it thickly with mud, which freezes into an armor plate often ten inches thick. Nothing that prowls has the strength in its claws to tear through that roof. It takes a pair of beavers about six months to build a lodge at leisure, but if rushed by threat of freezing weather they can do the job in 30 days.

In the meantime a winter's supply of edible timber has been felled upstream, ferried to the dam and anchored butt-first in the mud. Come ice and sleet and cold and snow, when anybody gets hungry the old gentleman merely dives down to the larder and returns with a sapling. They eat the bark only. The naked sticks are tossed out for use later in repairing the dam or the home.

The lodge is allowed to go more or less to rack

and ruin in the summer. The mud melts and the rains wash it loose. But when the nights grow chill and the leaves begin to turn to scarlet and shimmering gold, the family reassembles at the old homestead and gets busy repairing the leaks and sealing it tight again.

The beaver's logging operations are as amazing as his carpentry and engineering. Standing on hind feet, he eats around a tree until what are going to be the stump and the falling tree look like smooth, tapering spikes balanced point upon point. The wind or the law of gravity finally brings the tree crashing. While beavers usually work on saplings, they frequently fell trees 18 inches thick.

Only one beaver works on a tree. He cuts with long, curved teeth covered in front with almost unbreakable enamel; these teeth grow constantly, and he has to keep sawing in order to wear them down. When he drops a tree, his hope, of course, is that it will fall into the water. If it doesn't, he cuts it into smaller pieces and rolls or drags these into the drink. If his pond is old and the shores are pretty well cleaned, he'll dig canals back into the forest so he can float his timber out.

Surprisingly easy to trap because of his trusting disposition, and possessed of soft but durable brown fur once used exclusively in male millinery but now a favorite with the ladies, the beaver was almost slaughtered from the face of the Earth. Conservationists went to his rescue just in time, and he came bouncing back.

In 1920 three pairs were loosed in the woods of Palisades Interstate Park at Bear Mountain, New York, on the west bank of the Hudson River, some 40 miles from New York City. A survey 15 years later revealed that these six had become approximately 1000; that they had spread over 160 square miles and built more than 100 dams; that several had crossed the Hudson; and that one pair of rugged pioneers had migrated to the Catskill Mountains 75 miles northward. Today there are about 2½ or three million beavers in the United States and about five million in Canada.

Some years ago the U.S. Department of the Interior officially recognized the beaver as an agent of progress by capturing large numbers of his tribe and scattering them widely for the purpose of assisting human operatives in projects ranging from erosion control to the better housing of trout.

Nature taught the beaver to work hard, stay at home and keep the peace. There may not be much color in that type of living, but its aspirin content is bound to be low.

BUZZ BOMB FROM FAIRYLAND

Donald Culross Peattie

It comes like a bomb, a bomb in feathers. You hear an insect-like thrumming and see suspended in the air a metallic missile with propellers going at the rate of 75 beats a second—too fast for the human eye to perceive except as a blur. Rays of fire flash from its throat patch. Suddenly the tiny visitant may dart backward, drive off a roving bee, make a sideswipe at a kingbird, then roar off at 30 miles an hour, spraying the neighborhood with beauty and leaving wonder in its wake. All this in less time than it takes to say *Archilochus colubris*, the scientific name of the ruby-throated hummingbird.

These tiny creatures, weighing scarcely one tenth of an ounce, come to nest in your neighborhood from Florida or the West Indies, or even fly from Yucatan across the Gulf of Mexico nonstop—a little matter of 500 miles! Theirs is the most perfectly controlled flight; they can even fly backward. Their feats are possible because they have proportionately immense wing muscles and are proportionately the biggest-hearted birds in the world. Not only as a stunt pilot but also as a lover is the hummingbird a show-off. He will shoot back and forth in front of his lady, while her little head flashes from side to side following his gyrations. It doesn't take much of this sort of thing to convince her that he is a genius.

The nest of a hummer, often no larger around than a quarter, is accomplished, like everything else in its life, at high speed; a single day may suffice. Yet it is a work of consummate art. Perfectly camouflaged with lichens, it is almost invisible even though usually placed in plain sight on a branch or in such quaint spots as a loop of rope or atop an orange on its tree. The tiny cradle is lined with thistledown, milkweed silk or the "wool" from sycamores—the whole held firmly in place with spidery silk woven by the needlelike bill of the female. Here are laid two white eggs, the size of peas. When they hatch, the chicks are hardly bigger than a fingernail. All gullet and yelp, they have to be fed every minute or two at first. To see the mother thrust her bill in a lightning flash down the baby's throat, you would think she must surely pin the little thing to the nest.

Rubythroats are the only kind of hummingbird

Many flowers are too fragile to support the weight of a hummingbird, so it developed the power of hovering in flight, to sip nectar and capture insects that hide deep in the most delicate petals.

you will see east of the Rockies, but in my California garden there are five species. Throughout much of the West hummers are no more unusual than bees. The hummer's tongue, unique in the bird world, consists of two tubes, but how nectar ascends them is unknown. Besides nectar, they eat the minute insects they find in flowers and catch in flight.

Hummingbirds are skillful botanists in the selection of the flowers they visit. They go for flowers with trumpet-shaped corollas having deeply buried nectaries. Here they fear no competition from bees; only a butterfly with her long tongue could reach into such a blossom, and the hot-tempered hummer can easily send her flying.

It used to be thought that they preferred red flowers, but they go just as readily for blue, yellow or white, provided the shape of the flower is right and it produces abundant nectar. If you want to attract hummers, therefore, plant honeysuckle, scarlet runner beans, trumpet vines or morning glories beside your porch or window and you can watch the hummers as they dip, sip and dart, flashing their brilliant colors and tamer than any other wild bird I know. Indeed, sometimes they will come up and hover in front of your face, wondering perhaps what sort of creature you can be. In the open garden, salvias and fuchsias are favorites of the hummers and so are columbines. And as the little creatures make the rounds of your flowers, they carry pollen from blossom to blossom on their feathers; some flowers are pollinated by no other means.

You need not even plant their favorite flowers to attract hummers. Benjamin F. Tucker, a retired banker in California, hung out test tubes filled with sugar water and baited with collars of colored cloth in imitation of corollas. The hummers crowded to Tucker's Bird Bar, and he developed many refinements—gadgets to keep out bees and ants, as well as a sort of rail on which his thirsty guests could perch while quaffing.

You must go to the Andean region to see such hummingbirds as the sapphires, rainbows, fairies and sylphs. Altogether there are more than 300 kinds, and the namers have been put to it to find distinctive titles: ruby, amethyst, sunbeam, comet, coquette.

Where all is dazzling beauty, how can one choose the most beautiful? Some give the prize to the white-booted rackettail of Colombia, a glittering green elf with a forked tail almost three times as long as its body, and wings of ethereal violet. Others yield the honors to the topaz-throated. This orchid-haunting bird of the Andean forests has a body of metallic ruby; the head is velvety black, and the throat patch icy berylline green with a center of glowing topaz.

No wonder that birds of such a feather have been hunted since the days of the Aztecs, when cloaks of hummingbird skins were worn by the nobles of Montezuma's court. Even the Indians who greeted the Pilgrim Fathers of New England sometimes wore a hummingbird as an earring. With the Victorian era of overadornment, the slaughter of hummers increased. The glittering skins were made into millions of artificial flowers and useless dust-catchers until Uncle Sam outlawed this traffic by forbidding the importation of wild-bird plumage.

If you were to turn a hummingbird in your fingers as you would turn a gem, it would shoot forth an unearthly radiance of color. A tiny throat, at first sight merely black, would glow suddenly emerald. The pigmentation is not, however, in the feathers. The hummingbird's magic is done with mirrors. The tiny barbs on each plumule of each feather are so channeled as to break and refract the light, like a cut diamond. A hummingbird is a feathered prism, a living rainbow. It captures the sunlight for you and turns it into a jewel on wings.

BRISTLING FORTRESS OF THE WOODS
Alan Devoe

The porcupine is smaller than a beaver, but he carries enough murderous weapons to kill a mountain lion. Of placid disposition and disliking battle, he "advances" into a fray backward. He is so durable that he will keep right on his course despite repeated charges of buckshot. Yet a blow with a stick on the tip of his sensitive nose will kill him.

The porcupine is also called quill pig, urson, hedgehog, quiller and, scientifically, *Erethizon dorsatum,* which means approximately "the irritable back." But by whatever name he goes—and he goes almost everywhere through our forests north of parallel 40— he is North America's prize woodland curiosity.

A chunky, blunt-faced rodent about 30 inches long, with a six-inch tail, Porky weighs from 15 to 25 pounds. A bristling armory of quills sprouts from his head, back and powerfully muscular tail, and he rattles like a quiver of arrows when he walks. The quills are hollow, tubular and so lightly fixed in the flesh that they can be dislodged at a touch. They are sharp as needles and covered with a multitude of barbs. Furthermore, as soon as they enter the warm, moist flesh of a victim they begin to swell up, the barbs sticking out more and more. Because of the slant of the barbs, the quills work deeper and deeper into the victim's body.

Porky needs no sharp wits, no speedy legs. He goes placidly through life at a perpetual saunter, dawdling in the same tree for a whole day if the taste of the bark pleases him, ambling calmly through the underbrush while he mutters to himself in a low, preoccupied monologue of sniffs, squeaks, chattering and grunts, and staring with a dim and vacant gaze at the perilous universe against which

he has been rendered foolproof. If he should fall into the water, his air-filled quills keep him afloat as buoyantly as a cork. If he tumbles out of a tree, as he occasionally does, his quills cushion his fall.

When an enemy disrupts Porky's placid routine, his behavior is always much the same. If he can, he tucks his head under a log to protect his tender nose. Then he brings his feet close together, hugging the ground, to guard his unquilled underside. Next he raises his quills until, a fantastic pincushion, he looks twice his size, and vigorously flips his tail from side to side. A wise attacker promptly goes away.

The tender tips of tree branches are a special delicacy for the porcupine. To get them he pulls several branches carefully together so they will collectively bear his weight. Then, going out on them as far as he dares, he bends their ends back toward him in an upward arc and feasts.

But if the dog or lynx or man tries to close in on Porky, then—*slap!*—the muscular tail lashes side-wise and drives as many as 20 jagged stilettos deep into the molester's flesh. One slap is generally enough to drive off even a bear; but should the enemy still stand his ground, Porky "advances." He pulls his nose out from its hiding place, tucks it as far under him as he can and comes slowly backing out into battle, his tail flailing furiously. He backs until he comes to the handiest tree, lumbers undisturbedly up it and almost at once resumes his customary phlegmatic twig-chewing as though nothing had happened. Though other animals usually give Porky a wide berth, mountain lions and bears have been killed by porcupine quills.

Porky cannot "throw" his quills, but they are so loosely attached that as he thrashes his tail he every now and then sends one of them whizzing unpre-dictably. The lost quills will be replaced within a few months. Meanwhile Porky need not worry. Ten quills will drive off a fox; 20 will send a wildcat screaming away in pain. Porky has 30,000 of them.

Porky does most of his feeding at night. He travels only as much as he absolutely has to and may even confine himself for the season to just three or four trees. He settles himself in the most comfortable fork and simply eats as much bark as he can reach with-out bothering to move.

Porky has an odd whim for suddenly emitting a long despairing wail. When the spell is on him, he may sit in a treetop, blandly expressionless, screaming and war-whooping to himself for an hour.

Probably Porky's most striking oddity is his mania for salt. This passion brings him lurching and grunt-ing, quills a-rattle, into the woodsman's camp in the middle of the night. If he can find the butter, he will eat all of it. If the best he can discover is the empty wooden butter bowl, he will chew that up for the faint lingering taste of salt in the wood. He munches axe handles and canoe paddles to bits be-cause of the salty trace of sweat on them; and more than one lumberjack, awakened in the night by strange sounds coming from the shanty where the explosives are kept, has discovered Porky methodi-cally eating sticks of dynamite.

Enos Mills, the naturalist, once saw an encounter between a porcupine and a skunk. Each seemed to know instinctively what a fearful weapon the other possessed. Porky's restraint outlasted the skunk's. There was a blast of malodorous fluid, a loud *slap!* as Porky's tail retaliated and the battle was over. Porky would be smelly for a few days. But the skunk, his striped body riddled with any number of little barbed daggers, would have but a short time to live.

Porky wins most encounters with equal ease in the six to ten leisurely years of his peculiar life. Occa-sionally the fisher, a relative of weasels, manages to slip him over on his back and bite him fatally on his underside. In the past, hunters shot him until he be-came uncommon even in the Adirondacks, his favor-ite haunt; now he is protected by law in most areas.

Although not gregarious, the fact that Porkies con-tinue to survive and multiply in our woods is testi-mony that they are not completely solitary. Their mating takes place in October and the young are born in April, usually in a hollow-log nest. A female Porky is only some 30 inches long, yet her offspring are often 11 inches long, larger than the newborn cubs of a black bear. In fact, proportionately, porcu-pines produce the largest offspring in the mammal world. If human babies were as big, comparatively, as newborn porcupines, they would weigh some 80 pounds. Even before birth porcupines possess quills half an inch long, and woodsmen have for years shaken their heads over the problem of the delivery of such uncomfortable infants.

They also like to speculate on how two such spiny beings manage to mate at all. North-woods Indians say that the female porcupine hangs upside down on the underside of a small branch, the male ingeniously approaching her from above. There are many other theories. The sober fact is probably that Porkies mate in the same way as other quadrupeds.

CREATURE OF AIR AND DARKNESS
James Poling

Recently a zoologist friend of mine reached into a refrigerator and handed me a small brown bat. It was an unlovely thing, with its tiny foxlike face, big ears and wings like sheet rubber shrouding its fur-covered body. Yet as it began to thaw from the warmth of my hand, stretching its wings and yawning mightily, I found it strangely fascinating, even ap-pealing. I could understand why the zoologist, as he returned the quarter-ounce creature to its refrigerator roost, stroked it gently and said, "Go back to sleep, little friend."

Signs reading *Contents, Sleeping Bats, Do Not Dis-turb* can be seen hanging over refrigerators in many leading research laboratories. For bats harbor a num-ber of nature's unsolved secrets whose solution has

As bats soar through the darkness, the movements of their wings are those of swimming rather than flying. Shown here, the 3½-inch-long brown bat, common to North America.

become the goal of specialists in many fields from heart and circulatory diseases to gynecology.

The bat is warm-blooded while active but cold-blooded while slumbering. It is able to go into hibernation more quickly and easily than other mammals—which is why it can so readily be put in the refrigerator. It just drops its body temperature and falls asleep; the heart slows from 180 beats a minute to three, respiration drops from eight breaths a second to eight per minute. When the bat has some accumulated fat—as it ordinarily has in early fall before winter hibernation—it can live for months in cold storage, unfed and unattended, the "motor idling," while waiting its turn to come under laboratory scrutiny.

People associate bats with things dark, evil and unclean. Yet most scientists working with the little creatures develop a real fondness for them. According to Ernest P. Walker, former assistant director of the U.S. National Zoological Park, Washington, D.C.: "Bats are by no means unclean. They're clean as cats—they groom themselves every morning and after each meal. They are truly unique creatures."

"Unique" is the word that inevitably crops up in any discussion of bats. For example, bats are extraordinarily long-lived, which explains why they hold such interest for geriatricians and heart specialists. Ordinarily a mammal's life-span is related to its size. A field mouse seldom lives longer than a year, a dog is old at 12, a horse at 17. Yet our common brown bats—smaller than mice—can live to be 15 or more.

Stranger still, they live their entire lives on a diet of fatty insects apparently without suffering any ill effects. Preliminary studies suggest that there is no marked difference between the arterial walls of a 20-year-old bat and those of a one-year-old. How bats manage to age without arterial deterioration is something science would like to learn.

Even in breeding, the brown bat is a nonconformist. For the female bat is the only mammal that can apparently hold male sperm in storage to be used when it suits her convenience. Many bats mate in the fall, before hibernating, but not until the following spring does the female finally ovulate and allow fertilization to occur. Endocrinologists and gynecologists are now trying to discover her storage secret, which may advance techniques in the artificial insemination of livestock. We might also get new clues to the treatment of human infertility problems.

Infant bats (usually a single infant per mother) are born in "maternity wards" in June or July. The males seek solitary roosts while the females are pregnant, so the colonies of bats which infest attics, steeples and the raftered recesses of farm buildings are often made up of females awaiting the arrival of their young.

The only mammals with the true power of flight, bats fly with their fingers—their wings are the anatomical equivalent of a human hand with a membrane stretched between the fingers. While they cannot match the speed of the fastest birds, in maneuverability they are superior to any, even to swifts and hummingbirds. At full speed they can make a right-angle turn in little more than their own length. While flying, they can carry twice their own weight.

The armed forces have studied closely the bat's sonar system—the "echo location" system used both for navigation and for locating elusive insect prey. The bat emits beams of ultrasonic pulses which, when they strike an object, send back an echo. Scientists estimate that, ounce for ounce and watt for watt, the bat's sonar is a billion times more sensitive and efficient than any radar or sonar device contrived by man.

In one experiment 70 loudspeakers were installed in a dark room in which 28 hair-thin wires had been strung at random. The speakers were set to produce a volume of noise 2000 times as intense as the echo of the bat's beep and on the same frequency. But the bats were still able to fly through the maze of wires; with an auditory system weighing a fraction of a gram, they not only picked up their own sonar echoes as these bounced back from the wires, but also discriminated between these "real" echoes and the far louder "background" noise!

How does the bat avoid the jamming? How does it distinguish echoes bouncing off insects from those bouncing off branches to be avoided? How can a single bat recognize its own echo and fly, collision-free, through a cave teeming with thousands of other bats and their calls? The answer could revolutionize man's electronic guidance and detection devices.

Hunting insects in flight, bats send out up to 200 beeps per second. It had always been assumed that they caught the prey in their mouths, but recent high-speed photographs reveal that some bats scoop up flying insects in the membrane that stretches between their hind legs, cupping it like a pouch. Then they reach in and eat their catch in full flight.

There are some 1300 known bat species (39 in North America), and they populate all areas of the world except the polar regions. Contrary to public belief, none are blind, and not all of them hibernate. But those that do hibernate present another mystery. In winter many can be found in caves, old mines and abandoned houses—but never in large enough numbers to account for our summer bat population. Scientists estimate that 100 million North American bats vanish in the winter. Where they go no one knows.

OLD CHISEL-HEAD

Peter Farb

In the woods where I live, I was awakened one morning by the sound of sledgehammer-like blows on our favorite oak tree. I looked out the window and spotted a large woodpecker at work. Its head was a blur as it drilled, and clouds of sawdust and splinters were raining down. Resolved that this tree should not be pecked to pieces, I shouted the bird away, then climbed up and encircled the riddled part of the trunk with heavy wire mesh. Next morning I was startled to hear again the rat-a-tat-tat. I found the wire mesh in tatters and the woodpecker drilling deep into the trunk! Despite our attempts to scare the bird away, it persistently returned during the next few days. Finally it gave up, and we heard it drilling into more distant trees in the forest. We congratulated ourselves for so well defending our gnarled old oak.

Several years later, during a severe storm, the oak's trunk snapped at the point where the woodpecker had been drilling. Deep under the apparently sound bark I found a large colony of carpenter ants and a maze of galleries they had gnawed away inside the tree. Had we not interfered with the woodpecker, it no doubt would have cleaned out the ant nest—and we would have our oak today.

Woodpeckers are the only creatures who spend most of their waking hours banging their heads against wood. They do this because of the role they seem to have been assigned in the living community: to glean insects from under the bark of trees. They are the only living things able to locate and eradicate these insect hordes.

There are 179 species of woodpecker in the world, 22 of them in North America, ranging in size from that of a crow down to the sparrow-sized downy. Each has specialized equipment for searching out the insect pests that inhabit parts of trees. The little downy, for example, cleans twigs and bark crevices of destructive caterpillars; the flicker spends most of its time on or near the ground, lapping up ants with its sticky tongue.

The flashy pileated woodpecker is so enormous—19 inches from beak tip to tail tip—that it looks like a mistake of nature. The first time I saw one I understood why some people call it the "Good-God": it was whacking off chips three or four inches long, one after another. It is tremendously important to the wood-

The woodpecker's beak can probe for insects under bark, even in winter. The bird also uses its beak for drumming messages as well as for hollowing out the family nest.

land economy. It strips dead trees of their bark and prevents the spread of carpenter-ant colonies to sound trees nearby. It is unbelievably efficient: the ornithologist Alexander Wilson once saw a pileated remove 30 feet of bark in less than 15 minutes. And its appetite matches its efficiency: examination of the stomach contents of one bird revealed 2600 carpenter ants.

Almost every part of the woodpecker's body is directed toward the sole object of hewing wood. Its legs are short and powerful, and they grasp the bark by a unique arrangement of sharply pointed toes— two toes point forward, two backward, forming a gripping pair of tongs on each foot. The tail acts as a brace, propping and steadying the bird as it delivers jackhammer blows. The middle pair of tail feathers is unusually strong, and, by a remarkable adaptation, these feathers—the main props—do not fall out during molt until all the other tail feathers have been replaced and can support the weight of the bird.

The woodpecker's ability to locate insects is uncanny. Most ornithologists agree that its acute power of hearing is responsible. After the bird taps on the trunk, it pauses a moment, probably waiting to hear whether the tapping has disturbed any insects hidden inside. Also, the tapping probably produces subtle differences in sound on the wood. Once a bird has found a place where the sound indicates that further investigation is necessary, its taps become sharper. Then, as it zeroes in on the nest, the bark begins to fly.

Woodpeckers are remarkably equipped for slamming their heads against wood—sometimes more than 100 times a minute—without becoming punch-drunk. The beak is straight, very hard and pointed. The skull that drives it is unusually thick and is moved by powerful neck muscles. The bones between the beak and skull are not rigidly joined, as they are in most other birds. Instead the connective tissue is spongy and elastic, serving as a shock absorber.

But the woodpecker's tongue is its most extraordinary tool. Very long—in some cases four times as long as the beak—the tongue can be flicked in and out like a snake's. I once saw a woodpecker hunched over a hole it had drilled in a stump, looking like a cat lapping milk as it probed the hole with its tongue. When I split the stump with an axe at the place where the woodpecker had inserted its beak, I found the inside scoured clean of ants, even though the galleries contained intricate curves and bends. The tongue of many kinds of woodpecker is pointed and has barbs on the tip like little fishhooks. It is used to impale grubs and pull them out of their galleries. In addition, the tip of the tongue of many species is coated with a sticky substance. The flicker uses its sticky tongue as bait to catch ants: the ants rush forward to attack what appears to be a worm climbing into their nest, and they adhere to the tongue.

The sapsucker is unique among woodpeckers in the way it obtains its food. It drills a series of small holes close together into the bark of trees and licks the fountains of sap. The fountains also attract insects, which are thus added to the diet without the necessity of drilling for them. Occasionally the sap ferments, and after drinking this intoxicating beverage the birds can be seen carousing through the woods, dashing themselves into trees.

Unlike most forest birds, woodpeckers don't sing. But they have a call—a rattling or cackling sound in most species. They also drum—by striking their bills rapidly against a dry resonant branch or a tin roof—and often appear enraptured with the sounds they make. One woodpecker's drumming was analyzed by special recording equipment: it was found to consist of 500 to 600 bursts a day, with up to 40 rapid blows of the beak in each two-second burst. Drumming is a warning to trespassers on the bird's "territory" and also a means of attracting a mate. Once a mate has been won, the pair communicate with each other by tapping gently on a tree trunk at a much slower rate than when drumming. In some species the tapping is so varied that it seems to indicate a complicated language. When a male has investigated a likely place for excavating a nest, he calls to his mate by drumming, then begins gently tapping at the location. The female inspects it, may make a few taps herself. If she does not join the male in tapping, he tries another location—and extols *its* advantages by tapping. If she is interested, she begins tapping with him. The taps of the male grow sharper now, and soon the chips are flying.

Woodpeckers have an uncanny skill in gauging the strength of the wood in which they will nest. More than half the weight of the tree trunk may be above their excavation, yet they dig the hole in such a way that it does not put a strain on the tree. Rain and wind are kept out of the nest by drilling the entry passage upward before turning downward to hollow out the long, vertical nesting cavity.

Because of their intelligence and wondrous equipment, woodpeckers lead more comfortable and easier lives than most other birds. Since they can dig out insects winter and summer, their migrations are of limited range. Many species survive the winter by living off acorns and nuts which they have stored.

Most thrifty of all is the California acorn-storing woodpecker. It methodically studs the bark of trees with close rows of holes, into each of which it tightly tamps an acorn. One large sycamore near Santa Barbara had inlaid along its trunk, 40 feet high and three feet across, a mosaic of tightly packed acorns for wintertime meals. Embedded in one giant pine tree were acorns estimated to total at least 50,000.

It *is* possible, by the way, to make a pet of a woodpecker. A trapper friend of mine who kept a pileated claimed that the bird was affectionate and chatty but, when he didn't get his way, somewhat temperamental. "He would have been an almost perfect pet," he told me, "if he hadn't spent so much of his time cutting down the furniture."

NATURE'S UNDERTAKER
Alan Devoe

Everyone who has spent much time in the fields and woods must have asked himself: Why do we find so few dead animals and birds? Our Earth teems with animals—there are a hundred rabbits in the nearest small woods, probably a thousand meadow mice in the nearest field—and they all must die sometime. Yet we scarcely ever find a furred or feathered body. Why?

A major answer lies in the secretive, chiefly nocturnal activities of an extraordinary beetle called *Necrophorus*, or, more popularly, the sexton. Its role is plain enough from its name, Bearer of the Dead.

Suppose that you kill a mole in your garden. After turning up the soil to have a look, you don't bury him. You'll do it tomorrow. Then tomorrow comes, and there is no mole. The sextons have been at work.

In the darkness there is a whirry little clatter of wings, and beside the mole's corpse alights a black-and-orange beetle, smaller than a finger joint, with powerful black legs. The odor of death, carried great distances on the heavy night air, has brought it here. For some minutes the sexton examines the corpse, touching it lightly here, there, with its feelers. What it is determining we don't know. Clearly, however, it is making tests of one sort and another. When the sexton knows what it must know, it wedges its slightly convex body under one side of the corpse, scrabbles away at the earth to roughen it and clear away a little patch, then flips over on its back.

Everyone knows what tremendous weights can be supported by leg muscles when a man is lying on his back. As the sexton lies on its back, pushing upward with *six* stout black legs, it has almost unbelievable

power. The body of the mole begins to jiggle and rock as the little beetle works its way farther under the corpse. Finally, in a mighty pedaling motion, the sexton sends the mole's body lurching perhaps half an inch toward the edge of the garden bed.

The creature is moving the corpse toward a softer spot of sandy soil for burial. It may move the body a foot—or ten feet. It is quite capable of doing so. And it is pretty certain to obtain, any moment now, a helper. Another whirry clatter of beetle wings sounds in the darkness. A female sexton has arrived.

There is no courtship between these insects, unless it is their immediate joining together in the work of burial. In perfect team play, as if the thing had been rehearsed, the male pushes and the female pulls. When the male supports the cadaver on his legs and pedals it forward, the female scrabbles frantically to clear away impeding twigs and pebbles. When a rootlet gets in the way, one of the sextons hurries to chew it through. Inch by inch the dead body is juggled forward. In an hour, two hours, five hours—sextons are tireless—it is brought to the burial site.

The sextons whisk underneath and dig. Down,

Sexton beetles, shown here burying a mole, are led to dead animals at night by their superior sense of smell.

down the mole sinks, in a slow, jiggly descent into its grave. Loose earth settles on top of the corpse, and finally there is no mole at all, but only a heaving and rippling of the earth to let a watcher know that the sextons are still at their dark work, down underneath the interred body. When the corpse has been well covered, the sextons pluck away some of its fur and work it into a ball. They dig a side tunnel from the burial chamber, and there the female lays eggs. The fantastic preparations for the next generation are now completed. Many insects do not tend their young, but sexton beetles do. While they wait for the hatching of the eggs, they feed on the mole's body. Then, when their yellow grubs hatch out, the parents provide them with mouthfuls of the flesh, partly predigested. They keep up this feeding until the grubs are ready to change into adult beetles. Then the adults come tunneling up to the air and go their ways.

LORD OF THE NIGHT
Peter Farb

My car broke down in the gloom of a Virginia swamp one night a few years ago. I took out my red warning flashlight and waited for help to arrive. Then, remembering that most night creatures are practically insensitive to red light, I played the flashlight through the deep forest. In the red-hued mist I saw a wonderworld of hopping, crawling, running life. Suddenly, an instant after my light had flicked past a rabbit, I felt an eerie draft of air—and a great horned owl had seized the unsuspecting animal! I had not heard a sound as the owl captured prey I could not have seen without my light.

Owls are rightly known as "lords of the night." Their whole structure is designed around the fact that they must live successfully in the dark. With eyesight a hundred times as acute as ours, they can detect an image in the faintest glimmer of light, avoid tree branches and other obstacles, capture the most rapid of darting prey. (At least one kind of owl can capture prey when the light is the equivalent of that thrown by an ordinary candle burning 2582 feet away!) Their hearing is so acute that they can pinpoint a sound in total darkness. Their powerful claws are set in such a way as to clinch automatically on prey they may not be able to see.

A wealth of legend has gathered around the owl, and the bird is every bit as amazing as the folklore

The hoot owl's real name is "barred owl" because of the striped pattern of the feathers on wing, breast and tail.

it has inspired. It *is* true that owls often inhabit abandoned houses and dark church belfries, for, outrageously hunted by man, they have found refuge there. They *have* been known to glow with a phosphorescence as they swoop through the gloom; that is because the rotting wood of their nest holes may be coated with luminescent fungi which rub off on their feathers. And the wise old owl *is* heavy with age; one lived in captivity for 68 years, a record for birds.

Owls are, actually, among the most successful creatures in feathers. Roughly 135 species (17 of them in North America) have colonized all parts of the globe except the frozen antarctic. Related only distantly to hawks and eagles (their real relatives are the whippoorwills), owls sometimes have wingspreads nearly as great as a man's height; sometimes they are as small as sparrows. But we humans, prisoners of the daylight, rarely see owls. And since they do not undertake seasonal migrations, we never see huge congregations of them.

The screech owl, divided by scientists into 18 races which vary slightly in coloration and size, is probably the most widespread American owl. Second is probably the barn owl, which has thrived by taking up quarters in human habitations. The largest American owls, the great gray, the great horned and the barred, generally hunt in woods and are rarely seen.

During the day, when their specialized gifts are of little value, most owls doze in their roosts or sun themselves on tree branches. Lethargic, they sometimes become open sport for crows and jays, which mob them unmercifully. But so expert is the owl's concealment that he is rarely found.

For its silent hunting the owl's body is completely covered with feathers so fine and so soft that they act as mufflers of sound. The flight feathers have fuzzy edges, unlike those in other birds, so that almost all whir from striking the air is eliminated.

Owls frequently tangle with prey much larger than themselves—cats, porcupines, turkeys. Even the tiny pygmy owl of the Pacific states, a broth of a bird little larger than a bluebird, takes on gophers. How can they do it? Each leg has a thick tendon which runs down it and around a sort of pulley (what in our foot would be the heel), then branches to four needle-sharp talons. When the owl hits its prey, the legs draw up and the tendon clenches the toes, driving in the talons. The grip is so tenacious that sometimes the only way a person grasped by a stubborn owl can be freed is by cutting the bird's tendons.

Whereas human eyes have both cone cells (which help us to discriminate colors) and rod cells (for light-gathering), the owl's eye is packed tight primarily with rod cells. These contain a remarkable chemical known as "visual purple," which converts even a glimmer of light into a chemical signal, giving the bird an actual sight impression when a man would see only the presence of light. The owl's eye does not rotate in its socket. Each eyeball is fixed, like a car headlight. So, to see in different directions, the owl is endowed with an extraordinary ability to rotate its whole head.

For a long time ornithologists could not explain how owls capture prey when there is no light at all. Finally a graduate student at Cornell University, Roger Payne, proved how they do it. Payne sealed all the openings in a long shed so that it was completely light-tight, spread dried leaves on the floor and then gave a barn owl freedom of the shed. When he turned off the lights and released a live mouse, he heard the mouse move in the dried leaves, then felt a draft of air as the owl left its perch. Immediately he snapped on the lights. The owl had the mouse in its talons. Payne ran experiments to see if the owl was relying on its acute sense of smell, or if it was being helped by invisible heat waves, as rattlesnakes are. All results were negative. Final confirmation that the owl found its prey solely by acute hearing came when Payne plugged one of the bird's ears. Result: the owl went way wide of its mark.

Much of the owl's amazing hearing power comes from the design of its ears. The owl's face is ringed by stiff, curved feathers which collect and bounce sound waves into the eardrums, largest in the avian world. (The ear openings in some species, too, are so large that they entirely cover the sides of the head.) Beyond this, an owl's head is wide, setting the ears far apart, so that a sound wave arrives later at one ear than another—an infinitesimal time lapse, but sufficient to give a clue to the direction of a sound.

Studies of owl food habits reveal that owls feed almost exclusively on rodents and other harmful small animals which could overwhelm our crops and forests. Owls are, in fact, among the most beneficial of all birds, rivaling even hawks as controllers of the rodent population. One authority states that in a single night a barn owl may capture as much small prey as a dozen cats. A British study revealed that in one area owls take 23,980 rodents each year per square mile. Nevertheless, only 19 of the 50 United States and two of Canada's ten provinces protect all species.

Once common, owls are today being allowed to disappear from the landscape. They are being shot, their habitats are being destroyed by bulldozers, and the removal of dead timber from our woods decreases their nesting sites. Wouldn't we be wise to give more respectful protection to these lords of the night?

PART 4

THE NATURE OF ANIMALS

*The character and behavior of animals
are often as varied and surprising as their
appearances. Their roles in life, governed
by greatly differing demands of living, have
made them the fearless, the meek, the inquisitive
—all the diverse creatures that they are.*

Chapter one

THE FRIENDLY WILD

Everyone loves a friendly animal—the cricket that warms himself by our fire, the squirrel that helps himself to the nuts from our trees, the robin that makes our lawn his own. These beasts delight us because we tend to frighten away most creatures—they hide or run at the sight of us. Consequently the few that cling to the edges of civilization, poking their noses into our world, are a pleasure to see and know.

These beasts are friendly for a reason. Some are so naïve as not to know what vicious predators we are. They approach us out of curiosity and ignorance, like the penguin of the Antarctic wastes, who is wonderfully amiable because he rarely sees people. On the other hand, the swallow is so certain of his gift of flight that he does not need to fear us. He swings into the suburbs and over our heads as if we were no more than maple trees. Still others, like the seagulls, are friendly because they travel in a society. The group gives them a great sense of security, even among men, and they are unafraid as long as the voices of their gull friends ring in their ears.

Friendliness in some animals is self-interest. It is just plain appetite in the otter or pelican which tells him what side of his bread the butter is on, in our zoos and sanctuaries. Food and kindness quickly tame beasts that are flying fur and feathers in the wild.

Most of these intelligent animals are efficient at catching food in the wild and have leisure time on their hands. Like ourselves, they use it for play — they slide down banks, tumble, romp, play tag or, like the porpoise, just rock around in the water.

BEST-LOVED OF BIRDS

Donald Culross Peattie

Swallows must be the best-loved birds in the Western world. There are no statistics to prove it, but when was love ever measured by statistics? You can judge best from the folklore of birds. While owls and ravens are birds of ill omen, foretelling doom, the swallow is a bird of glad tidings, of comfort and joy. It was a swallow that tried to console Christ on the Cross. No Biblical authority for this, of course, only Christian legend. But it shows how people hold in their hearts the gentlest, most man-loving of birds.

Almost every kind of swallow in Europe and temperate North America has changed its aboriginal abode to come and live with man. For example, some of the cliff swallows which used to nest on sheer precipices such as Hell's Canyon, Idaho, are now the eave swallows of California. The purple martins (martins are swallows, too) which once dwelt in hollow trees were adopted by the red man at some prehistoric date because they kept mosquitoes away. The Indians put up hollow gourds for the martins to nest in; white men erect martin houses—sometimes elaborate, many-doored apartment houses on long poles. Some swallows of Europe live in chimneys, as the swift does with us. In our Far West that aerial acrobat in iridescent dress, the violet-green swallow, has taken to nesting under bridges and so has the brown, rough-winged swallow. Our barn swallow has left its primitive caves for the wooden beams of the hayloft.

Of all, this barn swallow takes the beauty prize, with its back as metallic blue as the finest of blade steel. Rose of breast, cinnamon of underparts, these swallows when courting dash in a "cross-tag" much like the game children play. Then, as their mating instincts become insistent, this becomes a game like kiss-tag, till at last the male and female put their cheeks together as they settle on the nest.

Quite commonly both sexes work on the cup-shaped clay nest, repairing an old one or starting a new one, often after much argument (the wife usually has the last twitter). She rushes to the nearest lake or stream, scoops herself a drink, zigzags in pursuit of a morsel of insect—then, never pausing in her flight or alighting, ladles up a gobbet of mud. She carries it in her mouth, mixing it with her gluey saliva, rolling it into a pellet, and disappears under the barn lintel. And now the male swallow shoots forth, to repeat the act.

With the coming of autumn, the restless pair will leave for subtropical wintering grounds, or for the tropics, or the temperate zone of the Southern Hemisphere, where they enjoy summer while we are snowbound. Some swallows are the greatest migrants in the world of land birds: one species travels from Europe to India and even Malaysia. They migrate by day only; they are slow about it, too, in spite of their ability to get up a dash of speed. But the remarkable thing is that in so many instances they return to the same nest—at least, one of the pair does. For swallows do not usually mate for life.

Swallows devour quantities of crop-destroying insects, and one appreciative Wisconsin farmer yearly makes quantities of spring mud by watering the earth around his barn to encourage the eave swallows to build their nests on his barn walls and keep his crops free of noxious insects. Thus he maintains a large colony of winged helpers.

No other migratory bird is more prompt in keeping arrival and departure dates, and because of this the swallows of the San Juan de Capistrano mission, between Los Angeles and San Diego, regularly break into the news. San Juan, of course, means St. John, and the Capistrano birds' departure date is generally, though not always, October 23, which happens to be the day on which St. John Capistran died. How do the scientists explain this remarkable coincidence? ask the mystics. Well, in the first place, it *is* a coincidence —the swallows have been leaving that area of the California coast on or about that date, you may be sure, since long before St. John died.

The swallow's wings in proportion to its body are long, accounting for the life-on-the-wing of these birds and their powers of sustained flight. The wing tips are slotted, with the result that swallows can brake, roll, descend or mount with the most accurate oscillations as they dart into their nests, under a bridge or into holes. Also, the structure of the wings permits the astounding "towering" of the birds, the sudden shooting up after a few starter flaps. Swallows can turn with a swiftness to outwit any flying insect, or drop straight down from the sky and then, just before touching the surface of pond or stream, shift vertical

The swallow's deeply forked tail feathers gave the name to the "swallowtail" coat. The young remain in the nest for three weeks, much longer than most other members of the bird world.

into horizontal flight. The weak point in swallow anatomy is the small size of their feet, which makes perching difficult. Telephone wires seem to be their easiest perches, and the young after leaving the nest are often fed as they cling to the wires.

Long have country people regarded the swallow as a weather prophet. When the swallow flies low, cool weather and rain are coming; when it flies high, warm sunny weather will continue. And this is, roughly, cor-

rect. For insects follow weather conditions, and where insects go, the swallow flies.

Swallows cling timelessly to certain sites and, while the individual birds of a colony pass, the colony's continuing existence gives a kind of immortality to their presence. To our human scene they provide a graceful footnote to the long tale of our lives. Swift-winged, they lift the heart. As no other bird, the swallow is a link between nature's wild and the ways of man.

A squirrel can jump from tree to tree and move gracefully along slender branches thanks to its magnificent tail, which acts as a balance factor, much as a parasol helps a tightrope walker.

TROUPER OF THE TREETOPS

Jack Denton Scott

One winter afternoon, from my house in the Connecticut woods, I watched a gray squirrel gyrate atop a wind-shaken oak. Sleet had glazed the tree, sheathing it in slippery silver, and I wondered how the little animal, even with his amazing agility, had managed to climb that high. As I sat fascinated, he suddenly slipped and fell, tail unfurling like a parachute as he plummeted 80 feet. Although he hit the frozen ground with a thump, he scampered off apparently unharmed. When I told a naturalist friend of the incident, he replied, "Welcome to the squirrel-watching society. But that fall was nothing." He said that he had seen a squirrel fall hundreds of feet, fluttering earthward with tail spread to slow its descent, and landing as easily as a bird.

That magnificent 8½-inch tail seems to be the gray squirrel's most valuable asset. The ancient Greeks, who had a word for everything, named the squirrel "Shadow Tail," or, literally, "he who sits in the shadow of his own tail." Squirrels sit by the hour grooming

that bushy appendage; not only does it ease their falls, but they use it as a shield when fighting. In cold weather they wrap it about them like a blanket. On rainy days I have even seen them sitting with tails arched over their heads as perfect umbrellas. The flying squirrel, cousin of the gray, uses his tail as a rudder when he glides from branch to branch, sometimes a distance of 200 feet or more. Gliding, not flying, is what he does, and a thin membrane on each side, connecting his front and back legs, is what makes it possible.

The 20-ounce gray squirrel is probably North America's best-known wild mammal, one of a family of 1300 varieties. Squirrels are found in most parts of the world. The five subspecies of the eastern gray squirrel have fascinated Americans ever since the Pilgrims landed. (The Revolutionary War was won against superior forces, in part because of the deadly accuracy of colonial riflemen—hunters who had become skilled by shooting squirrels for supper.)

In 1935 I watched a historic mass movement of gray squirrels in western New York State. It was an astounding sight: thousands moved down highways, across fields, through towns and villages, crossing lakes and rivers, many drowning or being killed on the busy roads. But they continued their determined, lemming-like trek. Similar migrations have occurred in many places. Robert Kennicott read into the Congressional Record his observations in Wisconsin of hordes of squirrels making a journey that lasted over a month and was repeated at five-year intervals. Naturalist W. J. Hamilton, Jr., concluded that these mysterious movements are caused by lack of food or overpopulation of the species.

With perhaps the widest range and greatest adaptability of any animal, gray squirrels can survive and increase on mountain or plain, in forest or park. They adjust their diet to the season, eating fruits and berries, wild honey, larch and pine seeds, even pine cones, fungi, tree buds and bark. They'll try anything. I once surprised a gray squirrel rolling goose eggs almost as big around as himself away from an unguarded nest.

This boundless appetite has caused no end of trouble for Bell Telephone engineers in Wisconsin, where the squirrels chew up about half a million dollars' worth of telephone cable every year, causing chaos in communications. The animals like the lead sheath in which telephone wires are encased. Bell engineers have tried everything from rabbit repellent to electric shock to discourage this activity, but the squirrels are still gnawing.

Contrary to general belief, gray squirrels do not store nuts for the long winter in one central spot, but bury them haphazardly a few inches under the ground. Naturalist Ernest Thompson Seton estimated that a hard-working gray squirrel will bury five nuts every 3½ minutes and will keep on doing this every morning during the three-month season until he has stored perhaps 10,000.

How the squirrel finds the nuts again during the winter has always been an intriguing question. But most naturalists agree that his superior scent is the main factor. Seton observed a gray squirrel dig straight down, without error or a trial shaft, to nuts buried in two feet of snow. Squirrels shell the nuts in an instant, with two pairs of long, curving incisors which grow continuously and must be honed by daily use to remain at a normal length. The buried nuts that the squirrels don't find again eventually grow into trees. Since hickories, butternuts and walnuts will not sprout unless planted underground, many naturalists claim that most of our wild nut groves have been planted by nature's own gardener, the gray squirrel.

The gray squirrel's vision is acute, especially his perception of movement. His hearing is also thought to be exceptional, enabling him, hunters report, to pick up the snapping of a twig at abnormal distances. In the woods, gray squirrels are adept at camouflage, freezing to a tree trunk or lying along a branch, almost becoming a part of it. One of their cleverest

tricks is "sidling"—rotating to the opposite side of a tree from where you are. I once walked slowly around an oak, pacing that nimble maneuver. The squirrel twirled to the opposite side 20 times before he tired of the game and scampered to the treetop.

Squirrels are protective parents. I saw one mother with a nest of half-grown offspring hiss, quack, chatter, rise up on her hind legs and actually box at a red-tailed hawk who thought he had found a meal. Apparently discouraged by all this aggressiveness, the hawk sailed off for easier prey.

The half-ounce young are born in spring or summer, two to six to a litter. Blind and naked at birth, they are suckled in the nest for seven weeks before they leave, timidly at first, testing footing in the treetops. At about ten weeks they are completely weaned, and by the age of five or six months they are on their own for their decade of playful life. The considerate mother makes them a gift of the nest home, building another for herself. These little spherical treetop homes of interwoven leaf and twig are marvels of construction, insulated with leaves and grass, chinked with moss and shredded bark. Their cleverly thatched roofs are rainproof, and entrances are camouflaged with twigs.

Some class this alert little creature among the most intelligent of animals. Frank E. Fite of Croton-on-Hudson, New York, has told of feeding gray squirrels until they became quite tame. The tamest would sometimes stop feeding and bounce up a tree, meowing like a cat. In each instance, Fite said, a cat soon appeared. Apparently the squirrel imitated the cat to warn the others. Naturalist A. D. Middleton recounted that in Yorkshire, England, several gray squirrels discovered how to extract corn from mechanical pheasant feeders by depressing a small wooden platform with their forepaws.

Today the gray squirrel is everywhere providing a growing spectator sport—squirrel-watching. Most public parks have resident treetop troupers whose agile performances delight everyone. The gray squirrel is the playboy of the animal world, spending most of his time, when he isn't hunting for food, dancing along a limb, scooting up a tree, somersaulting from branch to branch, barking and chattering with the sheer joy of life. Miss E. A. Robinson, of Northport, New York, watched four young gray squirrels regularly meet a cottontail rabbit at sundown for a romp and a game of tag.

People sit by the hour feeding squirrels nuts in response to saucy begging, tempting them to climb on their arms and perch on shoulders. Squirrel-watching will always be part of our North American scene.

CLOWN OF
THE ANTARCTIC
Richard Dempewolff

While we humans think that penguins look and act like people, there is sobering evidence that they think of us as just big penguins. During U.S. base-building activities at McMurdo Sound and Little America for the International Geophysical Year, our tents and camps were visited by scores of penguin welcoming committees. Ambling in from the rookeries by the hundreds, single file, these pint-size sidewalk superintendents would break off into groups to investigate a building project or a work party of busy Seabees. Having satisfied their curiosity and said a few words (their voices sound like a hoarse sheep bleating), they would stand around, slowly waving their flippers. If no reaction was forthcoming, the penguins grew bored. They were apt as not to tuck beak in soft shoulder feathers and go to sleep standing there. Finally, waking with a yawn and a shake, they would waddle off to mind somebody else's business.

Nearly everything about penguins caricatures something human. Their black backs and immaculate (sometimes) white shirt-fronts give them the appearance of absurd little men in formal dress. Their legs are set far back on their bodies so that they stand with exaggerated erectness. Their sleek flippers, covered with rudimentary feathers, give an illusion of arms in well-pressed, overlong sleeves, hanging properly at their sides or being swung in wide, leisurely gestures. And they have a truly human sense of possessiveness. Many times in the pack ice we would see a cocky little Adélie holding his ground on an ice floe we had nudged, waving his flippers angrily and squawking indignation at our 8300-ton icebreaker.

Of the 17 known varieties of penguin inhabiting the Southern Hemisphere, only two are true antarctic residents. The dignified "emperor" is the king-size edition, growing as tall as four feet. One big fellow captured by Captain Robert Falcon Scott's men in 1911 weighed more than 90 pounds. The smaller and more numerous Adélie grows slightly over two feet and tips the scale at about 12 pounds. His whimsical, quizzical appearance is heightened by the white ring around each black button eye.

To watch an Adélie walk, you'd never think he could get anywhere. Stumping along on three-inch legs at a rate of 120 steps per minute, he wheezes all

the way. Insatiably nosy, he keeps his eyes on anything but the road. The consequences of this outrageous jaywalking are often pretty silly. I have watched more than one waddling penguin, his head turned nearly backward for fear he would miss something, trip over a footprint in the snow and fall flat on his stomach. Invariably he popped up and marched off haughtily as though nothing had happened. Penguins generally walk upright, handling their flippers like balancing poles and swaying from side to side like short-legged fat men. But when they have a long way to go, and perhaps when tired or frightened, they bellywhop and propel themselves along on their stomachs, paddle-wheeling their toes against the snow and using their flippers like oars. Emperors have been observed making as much as ten miles an hour this way.

Of all penguins, Adélies are probably the greatest travelers. Having wintered at the northern rim of the ice pack, in spring they journey 500 or more miles back to their antarctic rookeries. Some have been observed 900 miles from home.

Home for an Adélie is a madhouse. One that we visited on Cape Bird during a bird-banding foray sounded, from half a mile away, like a World Series mob berating a bad decision. There, high on a volcanic ridge, we counted roughly 50,000 Adélies crowded on pebble nests only a foot or two apart. All were busily engaged in wooing, or in hatching out a summer crop of gray angora chicks. The confusion of crowded, bustling little bodies made a 40-acre sea of undulating movement. Weary fellows trying to catch 40 winks standing up were often sent sprawling by some culprit being chased through the melee by a furious cock whose mate he had tried to steal.

Penguin love life starts with a pebble, which the male carries in his beak to place gallantly at the feet of his light o' love. Scientists can rarely distinguish boy penguins from girl penguins without dissecting them—and there is a profound suspicion that penguins can't tell either. Often a suitor will drop his pebble before another male, discovering his error only when violently attacked by the insulted gentleman.

When Mr. Penguin does find a lady, she may accept his pebble graciously or he may get buffeted for his pains. In the latter case he hunches his head into his shoulders, shuts his eyes and submits to the abuse with resignation. Soon the lady's nervousness subsides and he sidles up to her. They spread their flippers, rub necks and go into a swaying love dance, honking raucously with beaks pointed skyward.

Ceremonies out of the way, the cock patters through the rookery collecting more pebbles to build a nest beneath his lady. There are plenty of pebbles lying around, but he prefers to sneak up behind a brooding hen and steal one from under her tail. A thief on the prowl looks ludicrously suspicious. Feathers drawn close to make himself appear small, he tries to lose himself in the crowd. If caught before he gets the pebble, he fluffs up and peers nonchalantly around as though he can't imagine what the fuss is about.

Once the usual pair of eggs is laid, both mother and father Adélie take turns insulating them against polar frigidity during the 40-day incubation period. Both male and female have "brood patches" on the abdomen—little radiators of flesh made extra warm by myriad blood vessels. While one Adélie sits, the other generally joins a party of pals who are also off duty. In fine spirits they head for a swim, hopping and waddling down the long slopes. Groups going

Although penguins long ago lost the ability to fly, they can leap to considerable heights when coming out of the water. The frolicsome group here are Adélies, about 30 inches tall.

down, with shirts soiled from days of egg-sitting, meet shiny-suited fellows dawdling back to work. Both parties invariably stop to chat before proceeding. With painfully human frailty several of the homeward bound succumb to temptation and return for another frolic in the sea.

At the edge of the ice nobody wants to be first in. The birds line up, batting each other off balance with their flippers, ducking blows and leaning backward to keep from tumbling into the water. There may be a grim reason for this comical performance. The leopard seal, a deadly enemy of penguins, lurks beneath the ice, waiting to dart out and snatch them with sharp-toothed jaws. The stomach of one such 14-foot monster was found to contain the bodies of 18 penguins. Killer whales also dote on penguin meat.

Sooner or later, however, one penguin will be shoved overboard. Chattering and splashing, very much alive, he is a signal for the rest to follow. Tumbling, shoving, calling to one another, they perform just like a crowd of kids in the old swimming hole. Adélies rarely stay underwater for more than half a minute when sounding for the prawnlike krills with which they stuff themselves. They prefer to whoop it up on the surface with their friends. Occasionally they hop a ride on a passing ice floe. A man on our expedition told me that two frolicking Adélies hooked a ride with *him* one day. They popped out of the water and landed squarely in the middle of his whaleboat.

Watching a party of penguins come ashore is hilarious. Swimming single file toward the ice edge, each will leap from the water about 30 feet from shore—to gauge distance—and then submerge. A moment later the leader pops up on the ice, landing squarely on his feet. One by one the others pop up beside him, exactly like wooden ducks bobbing up in a shooting gallery. Now, stuffed with food which they will regurgitate for the chicks, the penguins file homeward.

The life of a penguin chick is no picnic. Around the rim of the rookery, skua gulls swoop. These huge, hawklike birds, with four-foot wingspread, prey on penguin eggs and young. Let an egg go untended for an instant, and a skua dives in to snatch it. Besides this hazard, excessive enthusiasm on the part of penguin parents at the changing of the guard can smash a lot of eggs and hurt chicks. Also, frustrated old males, unable to line up mates, sometimes prowl around the rookery doing away with eggs and chicks.

The chicks that survive have learned to fend for themselves by the end of summer. Now the ice from the bays and inlets of the white continent begins flowing northward. On these floes the Adélies ride to warmer climes.

THE PRIVATE LIFE OF THE CRICKET
Donald and Louise Peattie

One of the world's humblest voices has for centuries been prized in many lands. It is the cricket's—a chirp of contentment in the rusty summer grasses. Fiddler, ventriloquist, acrobat, fighter and optimist (even when chill autumn nights warn of his end), the cricket long ago jumped into the affections of mankind. "I love it for the many times I have heard it, and the many thoughts its harmless music has given me," said Charles Dickens for us all in *The Cricket on the Hearth*.

Familiar in Europe, North America and the Orient, crickets hold a place in human life no other insect can claim. In his Swedish home the great naturalist Linnaeus kept crickets to send him to sleep. In Japan, where children delight in collecting crickets as American children trap fireflies, shops carry on a busy trade in caged crickets. In the United States a common species of pale-green cricket sings in unison at night, about 100 short chirps to the minute, so that to anyone walking in a wood the tiny unseen orchestra becomes its very voice.

Not that the cricket is calling to you or me. Only the adult male chirps, and he creates the sound partly for pure pleasure, partly to attract a lady. His instrument is delicate: each wing cover is set with a ridge of 100 or more fine triangular teeth, across which he scrapes the other wing, rather like a fiddler. This stridulation with lifted wings can be heard sometimes nearly a mile away.

Some entomologists have doubted that the female cricket hears the male at all. But to this unsentimental cynicism, experiment found answer. Male and female crickets were put in separate cages, out of sight of each other but connected by telephone. When the male crickets struck up, the females eagerly crowded close to the receiver in their cage. The monotonous chirping was music to their ears. (The ears are not like ours, but rather drumlike surfaces located near the front knees, which receive vibration like the tympanum within the human ear.)

Scientists have studied cricket chirps with tape recorders, stroboscopic illuminators, heterodyne oscillators and other gadgets, and have come up with accurate charts of the pitch, frequency and form of the music in the grass or trees. But, long ago, cricket lovers in China and Japan discerned with the unaided ear the exquisite differences between the crying of various species and gave each a lovely name—Golden Bell, Grass Lark, Little Bell of the Bamboo Grove.

A cricket can throw his voice as a ventriloquist does. A slight pressure of his wings against his sides makes the chirp seem to come from now here, now there, so that if you are hunting a cricket in the house you will be more on the jump than the insect is. Furthermore, weather changes affect the song: as it grows colder the pitch drops, the tempo slows. You can thus even tell the temperature by counting the chirps. The physicist Amos E. Dolbear, working this out in 1897 with the snowy tree cricket, came up with Dolbear's law: count the number of chirps in 15 seconds and add 39; the sum is the temperature in degrees Fahrenheit.

The house cricket was considered a luck-bringer in old England, but today we know that it will eat almost anything and is likely to leave holes in the clothes in your closet bigger than those made by a moth. A champion chomper, it can even chew through leather. Outdoors its appetite turns as easily to decaying food as to fresh, either animal or vegetable.

A mole-cricket father is likely to turn cannibal if he gets a chance at his own tender young. Understandably, the male and female of this species live apart, in burrows dug some six to eight inches under the grass roots. This kind of cricket has astonishing front legs which serve not only as digging tools but also as oars when he is lost at sea in a puddle. In front of Mr. Mole Cricket's tunnel there is often a bit of neatly swept earth shaded by grasses, rather like a veranda, where he likes to sit and pluck a guttural note from his fiddle. This has charms for the lady of the species, but she never trusts him to baby-sit. She digs a hole for a nursery at the end of her own burrow, carefully polishing its walls, and lays a great quantity of eggs. She is a devoted mother, even brooding her young on chilly nights under her six-legged body.

The gentle old French genius of entomology, Henri Fabre, once observed the hatching of cricket eggs. Each egg had a cap rather like the lid of a cracker box with a line of perforations running around it. Pushed open by the head of the infant cricket, the cap fell back to let the infant pop out, still in swaddling clothes. These were soon cast off, and within 24 hours the pallid mite, little bigger than a flea, had turned a handsome black and was already jumping like a jack.

In mating time male crickets may fight it out for a lady like the boldest of knights. Indeed, a cricket may be said to wear a light, elastic armor—the hard, protective chitin which covers his soft body. Perhaps it is this thorough equipment of high-jump legs, light

1. *Two domestic crickets.* **2.** *A head-on view of the nomad cricket.* **3.** *Two nomad crickets, whose color varies according to whether they live alone or in groups: the black cricket, a denizen of the desert, lives in a group; the green, a forest dweller, is solitary.* **4.** *The tree cricket.*

armor and strong jaws that gives a cricket the nerve to proclaim incessantly his presence, whether he lives in a house, a burrow, under a log or up a tree.

We may be grateful that he has such valor. Poet David McCord lamented, "The cricket's gone, we only hear machines"; but the cricket's chirp is still here for all who care to listen—a sound of peace, of longing, a chant of praise for the life we humans share with this humble companion.

WHAT A PECULIAR BIRD!

George S. Fichter

One of Florida's most successful advertisements is an ungainly, comical bird—the pelican. Its picture appears on thousands of postcards, with a legend extolling the capacity of its beak. And along thousands of miles of mangrove coast and sandy beaches pelicans make picturesque personal appearances, sometimes standing in stately rows on the sandbars, sometimes perched on pilings, sometimes winging single file in a slanted line across the sea. So skillfully do they ride the air currents that it is only occasionally necessary for them to flap their wings.

Wherever you see a pelican you are likely to see a good show. Near Miami I once saw a woman fisherman land a fine snapper on a causeway. But a pelican had had his eye on the catch, too. He followed the fish right onto the pavement, grabbed it, hook, line and sinker, and began flying off with his prize.

The astonished woman held the rod while the big bird stripped off yard after yard of line. Then, with a sharp yank, she started reeling in and pulled the loose-held fish from the pelican's bill. As it fell to the water below, the pelican, not to be robbed of what he thought his rightful catch, folded his wings and plummeted after it. He missed his target, however, for the woman was hauling in as hastily as she could—and this time she plopped the fish into a bucket and put a lid on it. She was still bent over when the pelican arrived on the scene. Finding the fish no longer in sight, the bird took a vengeful peck at his tormentor's posterior. The woman shrieked and kicked over the bucket, setting the fish free once more—this time unencumbered by hook and line. Whereupon the pelican grabbed it, sought safety on an offshore piling and gobbled it down.

One fish is no more than a tidbit for a hungry pelican, however; it can burn up the food fuel from one feeding in just finding another fish. One day while some friends of mine were seining for bait fish, they were joined by a pesky pelican who seemed to think they were there just to find food for him. So they decided to feed him all he could eat—literally. They tackled what almost proved a bigger task than they could handle. The pelican downed fish after fish, until finally the tail of one protruded from his bill. He was so stuffed that he fell over when he tried to walk. My friends set him up and watched to see what happened to that "last bite." Every few minutes the overloaded pelican gulped and the fish slipped a little farther down his throat. Then he jumped up and down to jostle the contents of his gullet into a more comfortable position. After half an hour of this he took a 15-minute nap—and as soon as he awoke he began pestering for food again.

A pelican cannot dive deep—its body is too buoyant. When this bird spies a fish, it folds its wings and plummets downward, often from as high as 50 feet. Its aim is so sure that it seldom misses its prey. But even with a full stretch of its neck and beak, plus the impact of its forceful dive, the pelican can take fish no deeper than two feet beneath the surface.

Net fishermen usually consider the pelican a helper. As they haul in their net, pelicans perch on the cork line or fly across the enclosure looking for fish; their constant dives keep the fish driven deep in the mesh so that they cannot jump out. Later, as the fish are sorted, the birds are tossed their pay in trash fish.

The wingspan of the diving brown pelican, commonest of the species, seldom exceeds six feet. This variety's head is straw yellow, its neck grayish white (except in mating season, when a brown strip runs from the crest of the head down the back of the neck). The upper parts of its body are gray, the underparts brown. The brown pelican shows up occasionally in such out-of-the-way inland spots as Minnesota and Wyoming, but it usually sticks to salt water and a warm climate.

Larger and far more beautiful is the white pelican, found mainly in Texas and the western states. The trailing edge of its wings, which may span as much as nine feet, is black, and its beak and legs are a bright yellowish orange. It makes a dramatic picture bobbing on blue water or soaring in wide circles in the bright sunlight. White pelicans never dive for their food. Instead they fly out to sea to find a school of fish heading for the shallows. Then they settle down on the water in a line behind the school and begin driving the fish shoreward. If the fish turn toward the sea, the pelicans churn the water into a froth with their wings and scare them back. When the fish are

Everything the pelican does is comic. The young, when eating partially digested fish from a parent's pouched bill, look as if they are about to be swallowed in the process.

herded into foot-deep water, the pelicans scoop them up with their outsize beaks.

Visit a pelican nesting colony where hundreds of birds are concentrated and you become aware of one of the pelican's greatest virtues: it is nearly speechless. Young pelicans cry for food with a rasping, whispery voice, but the only noise an adult makes is the whir of its wings in flight and the sharp snap of its bill when it is angry or begging for food.

At the rookery you will see male pelicans strut pompously, pump their wings and make feathered balloons of their bodies to win the affection of their females—but this, too, is done in silence. And when the wooing is over, both male and female settle down to the serious matter of making a nest. The result is

no more than a bulky pile of twigs and sticks which may be constructed directly on a sandy beach, on a high spot on an island or 20 feet up in a mangrove. The wonder is that so many pelicans hatch and survive.

You will learn that a mother pelican gets nervous when she has uninvited guests. She doesn't lose her temper, but she may lose worse—a pouchful of half-digested fish unloaded in your direction as she flies overhead. This was intended to be dinner for a young pelican, which involves a feeding procedure worth seeing. Following the custom of many birds, the mother pelican feeds first—at sea, where she makes her catch. Back at the nest she regurgitates the half-digested fish into the pendulous pouch beneath her bill, and the young dip in. As the supply diminishes, the children upend so that only their kicking feet protrude from the cavernous feeding trough.

Just as the pelican watches for a chance to get a free meal from a fisherman, laughing gulls keep a watchful eye on the pelican. When a pelican dives for fish, it comes up with not only fish in its pouch but three or more gallons of water. To separate fish from water it simply opens its big bill and lets the water pour out, at the same time keeping the catch inside. Gulls seize this opportunity to have dinner on another's bill—literally. They perch on the pelican's giant beak and as the big bird opens up to dump the water, they reach in and grab the fish. Looking somewhat abashed, the pelican sets forth to make another catch. But time and again it gets tricked.

At many municipal docks in Florida you will find pelicans tame enough to be fed by hand. In fact, they insist on it. Generally they go by the respectful monicker of Old Bill, but around West Palm Beach they are called Joe, and those at St. Petersburg should be greeted as Pelican Pete. A pelican becomes a pet almost as soon as a hand is held out to feed it, and as long as food is offered it will remain a *fast* friend.

PRANKSTER OF THE SEA
Jack Denton Scott

One summer day in 1955, on a beach near the village of Opononi, New Zealand, 13-year-old Jill Baker waded into the water to join a friend, one of the strangest playmates the world has ever known. A torpedo-like body streaked toward her and swam between her legs, spilling her into the surf. She put her arms around the huge creature, got on its back and took a ride. Later Jill tossed a beach ball to her playmate. Rising from the water, huge mouth spread in a grin, the creature batted it back with its nose. As the game progressed, people gathered on the beach, staring in amazement. Jill Baker's playmate was a porpoise.

The ancients, who called the porpoise a dolphin, knew him as friendly. "He is the only creature who loves man for his own sake," wrote Plutarch. "Some land animals avoid man altogether, and the tame ones such as dogs and horses are tame because he feeds them. To the dolphin alone, nature has given what the best philosophers seek: friendship for no advantage." Pliny the Elder wrote of a wild porpoise that took a boy for a ride at Hippo, a Roman settlement in

Africa; Roman coins of 74 B.C. show such a scene.

Everything about the porpoise could be written in superlatives. Not a fish but an air-breathing mammal, he swims incredibly fast, kills sharks, communicates with his own kind, herds fish. He may have the world's best sonar equipment. One scientist believes that his brain is so similar to a human being's that he might even be taught to talk.

Of the more than 20 species of small whale, our 300-pound playboy is identified by his gunmetal hide, his 8- to 12-foot length and his laughing face. The porpoise has no teeth at birth; they begin to appear (from 44 to 50 in each jaw) a few weeks later. Though he suckles for about a year and a half, he begins to munch small squid at four months. He breathes through a single nostril, a crescent-shaped blowhole atop his head that closes upon contact with water. This is also the source of his "voice," and he can vibrate it like a human lip. His eyes, set just back from the mouth, are like a human being's, capable of "ranging." He hears through a cushioned inner ear and periotic bone, and has the keenest auditory sense of any animal. The porpoise can stay underwater for six minutes without coming up for air. In motion most of his 30-year life-span, he dozes only in snatches, partially submerged, eyes usually closed for 30 seconds, but sometimes for as long as five minutes.

One of the most impressive sights I have ever witnessed was the birth of a porpoise in a tank at an oceanarium. A biologist friend had invited me for the big moment, and as we watched the blue-gray, nine-foot mother near the bottom of the pool, the baby appeared, tail first—a position in which it cannot drown. The birth took just over a half-hour; then the mother made a sudden, strong twist, breaking the umbilical cord and releasing the three-foot youngster, who, without hesitation, swam to the top, stuck its head out of water, took a breath of air, then went back to its mother. The biologist told me, "The baby porpoise can see as soon as he is born; he hears clearly, recognizes his mother's call, and 'talks' in whistles and grunts." We saw the baby feed from two nipples set in grooves near the mother's tail; contracting her abdominal muscles, the mother actually squirted milk into her offspring's mouth.

"Now watch!" the biologist said. The newborn porpoise was swimming near his mother when suddenly another adult porpoise appeared at his side and the three began swimming around the tank. "That's the assistant mother," my friend said. "Another female always joins an expectant mother during her pregnancy and for several weeks after the birth. She helps bring up the baby and fight off sharks." If attacked,

Although the porpoise is indeed a friendly creature, his smile is actually fixed by the curvature of his mouth—similar to the smile that is painted on the face of the circus clown.

the mother and her assistant whistle quickly to summon help, then circle around the shark. Suddenly they drive in, striking the shark with powerful thrusts of their heads. Once while fishing I saw a big mako shark hurl itself from the water, then plop back. Moving closer, I saw that six porpoises had him surrounded. One by one they went in for a torpedo-like attack, punching just behind the gills and in the stomach. The shark finally collapsed, sinking to the bottom.

Porpoises are fast—they have been clocked at 30 miles per hour, overtaking and keeping ahead of some of the fastest liners. Scientists have found that this speed is partially due to their skin, which is supported by a spongy mass of tubes and columns. This resilient material permits the entire body surface to undulate according to water turbulence. Unlike the rigid hull of a ship, the porpoise's shape assumes the contour of the water rushing past and matches the form of the waves. By thus adjusting to the pressure variations of the water, it can reduce friction drag by as much as 90 percent.

There have been many stories of porpoises saving human lives. One woman was wading waist-deep off the Florida coast when an undertow pulled her down. "I felt something give me a terrific shove up onto the beach," she says. "When I got to my feet no one was near, but in the water about 18 feet out a porpoise was leaping about. A man standing nearby said that the porpoise had shoved me ashore." Marine scientists point out that the porpoise's spirit of play is responsible for such incidents. He doesn't really try to save lives; he just likes to push things. For proof they offer photographs of four porpoises working desperately to push a waterlogged mattress ashore.

Thousands of people have witnessed the apparent enjoyment porpoises take in performing tricks in marine exhibits—playing basketball, blowing horns, leaping through paper targets. Porpoises in a mischievous mood often grab a fish by its tail, swim backward several feet, then release it unharmed. At Marineland in Florida, I have watched a young female place a turtle on her nose and give it a ride around the pool. Because of their skill at herding fish, porpoises are often called "seagoing cowboys." A Florida fisherman told me of seeing ten porpoises surround a school of mullet and herd it along to the shallows, where, acting in perfect coördination, they flashed in one at a time to take their mullet meal; each then returned to close the line while another darted in to dine.

Porpoises are on record as having guided ships through treacherous channels. "Pelorus Jack," a famous wild porpoise, first appeared in Pelorus Sound,

New Zealand, in 1888, swimming ahead of a ship and leading it through the rocky channels of Cook Strait and French Pass, where many ships had piled up. The seamen began looking for him, and the skippers followed his fin as he swam past the bad spots. Pelorus Jack soon became a harbor celebrity, meeting every ship. Some thought that he simply liked the sound of motors, since he never guided a sailing craft.

Whatever his reasons, we know that Pelorus Jack swam safely through the tricky channels guided by his own porpoise sonar, which, according to Dr. Winthrop N. Kellogg, of Florida State University, is far superior to man's invention. In man-made sonar a train of repeated signals is emitted by an underwater transducer, and echoes are reflected from large submerged objects. But sensitivity and selectivity are limited. Mechanical sonar cannot distinguish between steel ships and wooden ones, submarines and whales. Porpoise sound-perception, on the other hand, may even surpass that of the bat and is highly selective. "Porpoise echo-location doesn't merely sense an echo," Dr. Kellogg says. "This animal has the ability to interpret, evaluate and identify that echo." Using hydrophones, special tape recorders and a pair of porpoises, Dr. Kellogg found that his subjects emitted strange clicking sounds, and could detect a single BB shot dropped at the far end of a 70-foot pool.

If probing the porpoise's brain will unlock secrets of the sea, perhaps psychophysiologist John C. Lilly will one day have some answers. At his Communications Research Institute, at St. Thomas in the Virgin Islands, he is trying to understand the porpoise's language and teach it ours. Dr. Lilly has found that a 300-pound porpoise's brain weighs 3.7 pounds. A 150-pound man's brain weighs 3.1 pounds. Furthermore, the cell count per cubic centimeter is the same as man's, and the brain is highly developed. By wiring porpoises' tanks and taping their sounds, Dr. Lilly eavesdropped scientifically. Sometimes he heard words that were falsetto imitations of his own voice. Once he snapped back at a porpoise that was making irritated noises at him. "He mimicked my voice so well," he says, "that my wife began to laugh. Then he gave a fine imitation of her laugh!"

Some marine biologists believe that porpoises may have a higher potential IQ than man; they have never had to develop it because they are so perfectly adapted to their environment. What could happen if they ever did develop their brain power is limited only by the imagination. If the porpoise's big brain proves as complex and competent as some believe, it is possible that man one day will talk to and understand another species for the first time.

Gulls have their own "language" in which sounds and caresses make their courting seem almost an idyl of love. Shown here is the best known of the North American species, the herring gull.

THE SOCIABLE SEA GULL

Jean George

Every year I go to the shore and watch the sea gulls —wheeling and soaring against the bright blue sky, crying their sad-sounding "Meeew," sometimes speeding seaward without moving a wing and dropping straight down upon a fish. Beautiful to behold, they are also fascinating to know. The gull is the world's most ubiquitous bird, with at least 43 different species. Of them all, the herring gull, with white belly and black-tipped gray wings, is the most familiar—the one commonly called the sea gull. No bird on earth has a more intricately patterned social life. Each gull, whether you see it alone on a ship's mast or flying among hundreds of others, is a member of a small, exclusive club. Club life begins anew each spring when the birds migrate back from their roamings to their own ancestral breeding ground, or gullery: a remote, hidden area of rocks and dunes. Day after day a flock of 200 or more gulls will join in circling over the sand dunes and grasses where they were raised.

Finally all members alight at once in a spectacular descent. The loose aggregation of birds has turned into a tight social order.

One March morning on Block Island, off the Rhode Island coast, I watched a flock of herring gulls come down. It was a kind of Grand Parade as, fanning their gray wings, they dropped onto the sand. When the sky had cleared, I saw that the birds were neatly arranged in clubs, each group of 40 to 50 birds in a distinct area of its own. A club comes complete with president, old birds with status, newcomers (youngsters) working their way up—and a few members every gull picks on. Gulls keep to the same mate year after year; but for the young bird not yet mated, the club into which it was born serves as a meeting and courting place. And, as in all gull social activities, courting follows rigid rules.

I recall a young pair on a Virginia gullery. A male was standing quietly on a sand dune staring out to sea. Suddenly a female walked up to him—it is usually the female gull who makes the choice—circled him, head forward, then called softly, "Klioo." The male puffed his feathers and lifted his head. That pleased the young lady and she circled him again. He preened. She tossed her head coquettishly. He choked up some delicacies from the sea and fed her while she closed her eyes in pleasure. The sea gull had his mate for life.

Each couple has an area of land about seven feet square on which to live, build a nest and raise young. (For comparison: a hawk has acres.) It is primarily for protection from enemies that gulls live so close together, and in order to do so they have developed intricate laws. The first one is simple and serious: invasion of property means a fight.

Fights are highly ceremonial. On the Block Island gullery I watched an old bird put his toes on a young couple's land, hoping to get a few more inches for himself. The young male turned on the intruder, lifting his wings a little—the equivalent of the growl of a dog or the clenching of a man's fist. The neighbor was not scared. The young bird stretched his neck (a snarl, in gull ceremony); still the old male did not move. Finally the young bird was so angry he leaned over and pulled grass. This is a terrifying thing to do—like pointing a gun—and most fights end here. But even this did not scare the old male. He pulled grass, too! Then with a sudden loud *whack* the young bird struck the old one with his wing and was about to bite, when the offender retired into his own yard.

The first rule the newly hatched gull must learn is, "Play in your own backyard." Parents know their own chicks from all others, and if a strange youngster steps into their yard they are apt to strike it dead. Because of this rule, I became the owner of a sea gull. Going onto the Block Island gullery, I borrowed a chick off a nest for study. After sketching and measuring him, I took him back and placed him in the basket of grass I thought was the right one. When a bird above called, "Hahahaha haha," the gull alarm cry, and dived at us, I knew my guess was wrong. To save the little sea gull, I took him home.

The early life of a sea gull is not easy. After 26 days in the shell and a 24-hour struggle breaking out of it, there comes a crucial moment. To get food, a gull chick taps a red spot on the underside of his parent's beak. This usually causes the adult to choke up food and put it on the ground. Then the sight of food-*and*-chick inspires parental instinct and stimulates the adult to feed the youngster. So ceremonial are these birds that if a baby gull fails to press the red button, it may die for lack of nourishment.

My gull, named Sol, nearly died because I did not know about this Rube Goldberg ceremony. The first day, I could not get him to open his beak and eat. I forced food down his throat, but he only choked it up again. By evening he was weak. In Niko Tinbergen's outstanding book on gull behavior, *The Herring Gull's World,* I learned about the red spot and wondered if this might not work both ways: maybe my sea gull needed to tap in order to open his beak. I put a daub of lipstick on my thumb and held it above him. He struck it with ferocity, opened his mouth and let me stuff his enormous gullet.

Once a chick has learned to knock for food, he must next learn to keep his neck in. A high head and stretched neck constitute a status symbol, and it infuriates an adult to see a presumptuous juvenile sticking his neck out.

On the other hand, another rule is firm: a gull cannot strike a bird who has his head in. A friend of mine tells of watching a male that managed to walk across another bird's land by keeping his neck in. He sneaked along, head pulled low; then, when the landowner walked over to him to do something about it, he crouched like a juvenile, a pose which provides immunity from attack. The sneaky fellow came on, over the beach grass, across the sand, right up to the sleek gray-and-white female—who ruined his plot by softly saying, "Klioo." This made the sneaky one stand up and puff out his feathers. When he did, he was hit so hard he spun for ten feet.

Much of a gull's time is spent in preening its feathers. This always seemed like idle vanity to me until I put my own sea gull on a pond. As I transported him in my hands, he struggled violently, messing his feathers. I put him on the water's surface and, to my astonishment, he sank. I pulled him out. On land he preened, running his beak down the shafts of each feather to lock the barbs which I had unlocked in the tussle. Several hours later Sol stepped onto the water and sailed as high and proud as a Chinese junk.

Preening not only keeps a gull afloat, it also keeps him aloft. With a light skeleton of hollow bones—about one seventh of the bird's weight—and a wing-spread of more than four feet, the sea gull is airborne almost the moment it lifts its wings. To perfect its takeoffs, it preens the top wing covers into a smooth, frictionless airfoil. All this accounts in part for its success on wings. A gull can fly 35 to 50 miles an hour, and travel over 700 miles in 24 hours.

Gulls as they soar are not always searching for food; they may be merely having fun on the wing. A gull flying along the shore is taking advantage of a wind current formed when the sea air strikes the warm land and rises. Gulls also love the lower, weaker air currents that form about three feet above the waves; they ride them for hours, tipping from one current to the next. Most people think that gulls ride behind boats for the food; actually, garbage is only a part of their diet, clams and fish making up much of it. The sea gulls follow boats for the ride—on the thermal currents the ships create at sea.

Vacationers like to watch gulls open clams by dropping them on rocks. It seems ingenious, and indeed it is, but it is an instinctive habit that proved a nuisance in England several years ago. A manufacturer of nuts and bolts put glass skylights on the roof of his factory. These made the building pleasant until the day he decided to dump some faulty nuts and bolts on the nearby dunes. The sea gulls found

them. Because they were hard and shell-like the gulls instinctively picked them up, carried them aloft and dropped them on the factory below. While glass shattered and bolts rained, the employes were rushed out into the dunes to bury every bolt in sight.

Rigid and complicated their ways may seem to us, but they have served the sea gulls well. Their kind of social life has ensured their success over aeons of time, and without it they cannot really live. This was emphasized to me by my gull, Sol. Tethered alone in our backyard, far from the ocean, Sol lost his vigor. He spent most of the day contemplating his feet—an activity peculiar to the breed, but not usually carried on for hours on end.

One morning a naturalist friend suggested that Sol needed other sea gulls. "By himself he is not a gull, but a specimen," he said. "It takes a whole society to make a gull."

The next day I drove the bird to the shore and put him on the lonely, windswept sand. The waves boomed, crabs scurried to the sea. Sol drooped his neck and contemplated his feet. But suddenly he cocked his head, listening. Slowly he lifted high his head and stretched his neck and gently raised his feathers until he appeared enormous. Then with deep and powerful strokes he soared into the air.

As he disappeared he called "Meeew"—the wild, sad-sounding cry that is in truth a cry of contentment. Turning to go, I climbed a dune and stopped to take one last look at Sol. I spotted him, out beyond the breakers, where 50 gulls rocked, heads tilted, listening to his cry: "Here I am, I feel wonderful. I am here." Then he circled three times, wheeled down and landed in their midst—to become a gull at last.

PLAYFUL FRIEND
Leland Stowe

Picknickers along U.S. Route 14 near Homer, Minnesota, often find it hard to believe their eyes when they see, scampering across the fields behind a broad-shouldered, spectacled man, a bouncing pack of stump-legged creatures curiously like a mixture of dachshund and weasel. Emil E. Liers, the Pied Piper of Otterdom, is giving his gay companions their daily outing. The otters are trained better than most dogs. They rally at a toot from his police whistle, they dive into and out of a boat at his commands and retrieve ducks, pheasant or quail, delivering them undamaged.

Liers has been a friend of the otter for more than 30 years. One day in April 1928 he was removing a drowned female from his trap when he heard piteous whimperings downstream and found two snub-nosed, sleek babies. Liers never trapped another otter. The motherless twins, which he and his wife fed by bottle and named Toquesh and Nashtash—Labrador Indian for Good Girl and Bad Girl—justified Ernest Thompson Seton's description of otters as "the most beautiful and engaging of all pets." Extraordinarily affectionate, graceful and frolicsome, they completely altered Liers' life, transforming him into North America's foremost authority on these animals and the first successful breeder of otters. He has given thousands of lectures on them before naturalists' organizations, schools and clubs. His pets have traveled all over the country with him by car.

When their first otters were fully grown, the Liers obtained two wild males as pen mates for them, but they could find no information on breeding otters in captivity; no one had ever done it. Twelve years went by before the Liers at last welcomed the first baby otter—appropriately named Eureka. Soon their otter dynasty was assured with the arrival of Tara, a smart-as-a-whip female who became a perfect mother. By the most recent count, Liers has raised and trained more than 300 otter pets. Some have gone to individuals, some to zoos in Detroit, New York, Chicago and other cities.

Otters have whiskered faces, bright black eyes and a superlative grace which they inherit from the weasel family. Their long arch-backed bodies are perpetually in motion. Thanks to their webbed feet, powerful stubby legs and broad tails, they are champions at aquatic sports. They inhabit all continents except Australia; there are 18 subspecies in North America. Largest is the regal sea otter which roves the Pacific. Liers' pets measure some 45 inches in length and weigh 20 to 25 pounds. Land otters dwell along rivers or lakes in abandoned beaver houses, in muskrat or woodchuck burrows, in hollow logs or in dens with cunningly concealed underwater entrances. Always scrupulously clean, Mother Otter teaches her six-week-old pups to use a far corner of the home as a toilet, to dry themselves after swims and keep their rich coats groomed. Inveterate vagabonds, each family roams its own range, covering its circuit of up to 50 miles with fortnightly regularity.

The language of otters varies from low chattering or soft chuckles to chirping dinner calls; they snarl only if menaced. When frightened, however, their hair-raising scream—matched in shrillness only by that of eagles and loons—can be heard a mile and a half across water.

Liers' first important discovery was that otters do not feed primarily on game fish, as sportsmen claim. "The otter's favorite natural food is crayfish," Liers reports. "Then come eels, frogs, turtles, snails, mudminnows, burbot and snakes. During almost daily outings with my otters since 1928 I have seen them catch only a few trout." Scientists' autopsies on trapped otters confirm these observations. The nonfish diet Liers created, which is 74 percent ground horsemeat, keeps his pets in glowing health. By adhering to it, the Detroit zoo became America's first to raise and breed otters successfully. Liers was once brought into court by irate fishermen who accused him of depleting Minnesota's trout streams with his pets. He showed the court a movie in which otters ignored nearby trout while avidly capturing crayfish. Case dismissed! Liers has also made underwater close-ups of his charges killing and eating the fish-destroying lamprey eel, whose depredations have threatened the Great Lakes' whitefish and lake trout with extinction.

In early breeding experiments Liers discovered that female otters are choosy about selecting mates. "I've had 58 males which never made a conquest," he reports, "and only nine that were never refused." During their December-into-April mating season both males and females are seized with a mania to wander, which Liers regards as nature's way of preventing inbreeding. Captives often smash holes in their pens and for days roam the countryside far and wide.

Somewhere between the ages of two and three years the female produces her first litter—one to four black, silky-coated pups whose eyes open after 30

The magnificent-coated otter is rapidly becoming a rarity. For all its intelligence, it cannot escape that mighty hunter, man, because it is by nature friendly.

days. She cares for her young alone during their first few months, rigidly barring contact with the father or any other living creature. "Even when their puppies are nearly half-grown," Liers says, "the tamest mothers will not permit me to play with them. When I disregard her growling hint, the mother grabs my hand gently and forces it away. If I persist, she bites me hard. If I coax her cubs, she warns them plainly. If they approach me, she punishes them."

Swimming lessons start when the rollicking offspring are about three months old. Gulping and sputtering, the cubs have to be wheedled and pushed. The mother uses crayfish to lure them into deeper water. She sometimes takes a pup piggyback and dumps him where it's sink-or-swim. But the young quickly master the dives and twists which make otters supreme water-ballet artists among land animals. Since they often trail in a row behind their parents, each breaking the surface in a series of undulations, a swimming otter family may easily be taken for a serpent 30 feet long.

Otters gambol tirelessly, playing tag, staging mock combats and frolicking riotously with any like-minded creatures. Unlike most carnivores, they rarely fight among themselves, and they are extraordinarily sociable and gregarious. "It's fun to watch them make friends with dogs," says Liers. "Soon they romp together like one family. When I tamed a white raccoon and a red fox, my otters immediately enlisted them in endless games."

Wildlife observers watch enthralled when they are lucky enough to come upon an otter family indulging in its favorite pastime—water-sliding. Tucking his legs back for maximum speed, papa takes a headlong belly-flop down a steep mud bank, followed in swift succession by ma and the kids. Often they keep this up for hours. Their exuberance involves them in endless drolleries. One day Liers' Jocho, a 12-year-old matron, took her three puppies calling at a neighbor's home, pried open the screen door, took a bath in the upstairs toilet, then crawled into bed to dry off.

Despite its size, the little otter is unbelievably courageous and invariably foils or defeats all its natural enemies. "It is the one animal that all woodsmen agree is pure grit," wrote Ernest Thompson Seton. A swimming otter attacked by an eagle has been seen to tread water, gnashing so violently that the mighty king of birds turned and flew away. Otters have been known to kill wildcats, and because of their incredible swiftness they are sure death to snakes, regardless of size. Forcing an attacking reptile to coil and strike, the fearless little animal weaves barely an inch beyond the fanged thrusts; then in a lightning pounce it seizes the snake behind the head, dispatching it in seconds.

The only mortal enemy that the otter cannot cope with is man. The rare beauty and durability of its fur have seriously reduced the otter population in America. Otters are trapped in fur-yielding climates during the winter–early-spring cycle when the females are either pregnant or are nursing mothers. Thus, countless young are killed unborn or doomed to starvation.

To all who cherish this affectionate and frolicsome creature, trapping them is an unforgivable crime. "What otters need most," says Emil Liers, "are friends who will fight for their preservation."

THE GENTLE GARTER SNAKE
Alan Devoe

Inside his membranous envelope the infant snake wriggled. Some of the sacs near him had already burst, and the dark cranny in the old stone wall was full of a rustling sibilance. There was a smell of roots and rain, and a pervasive fetidness, like musk. It was an average litter—there were 20 of them. Because they were garter snakes they had not matured slowly in leathery eggs—as king snakes and milk snakes do—but had sprung from the cold body of their mother full-formed and wriggling, encased in thin shrouds.

The snake flexed his body and the birth casing collapsed. Slowly as a slug, he glided forward. Ahead was a glimmering of daylight. He reached it; his narrow head emerged from the stone wall an inch, two inches, then was motionless. He extended his pink forked tongue, delicate as a moth's antenna. That was how the snake came into the world in the spring.

In succeeding weeks he grew in size and in awareness of his universe. As he moved through the grass the world presented itself as a soundless jungle, its periphery never more than a foot or two beyond his cold, questioning jaws, for his small, dark eyeballs—fixed forever in a lidless stare—were capable of only the tiniest movements, and where other creatures have ears, the snake had only unbroken skin. Thus, to him the world was only a region of odors, of pressures and temperatures felt against his flesh, of subtle vibrances detected by his extended tongue.

In the mornings, when the sun had taken the chill from the earth, the snake emerged from his crevice to lie on a warm stone and heat his sluggish blood. Warmed, he would explore the grass soundlessly, now and again raising his head above the forest of blades, his thin tongue flickering testingly. Not even the gentlest tread on the earth was too delicate and fleet-

The best-known, most common and most widely distributed of all North American snakes, the gentle garter snake, can be readily recognized by its long stripes and brilliant colors.

ing for his nervous flesh to detect. If he met no adventure after an hour or two, the snake would crawl into a patch of shade and dispose his length in a loose loop, lying as motionless as though dead. The object of his vigil might not appear for several days. If it was a slow and blundering toad or earthworm, the snake raised his head slowly and stared at the victim. Sometimes, in this moment of contemplation, his head swayed gently from side to side, not to hypnotize, but only as a kind of involuntary preparation for the strike. Then the head would flash forward and the keen teeth would fasten on the meat. Because the bones of his two jaws were separated and the flesh of his head was so rubbery soft, he could easily eat a fat toad.

There was little ecstasy and little torment in the snake's life, but now and again came brief interruptions in the torpor of his days. Summer heat was an agony, for his blood had no independent temperature of its own, but was warmed and cooled at the dictate of the earth. His sole refuge from heat was in the damp crevices of the stone wall, from which he would venture forth only in the early dawn.

Sometimes, too, the snake grew uncomprehendingly aware of a dull hungering inside him which frog blood did not fulfill—and he would glide in search of a female to lie in a cold embrace. Another interregnum

was heralded in the snake's dim consciousness by an itching and tightening which he felt all over his body. He found it hard to breathe or move, and his eyesight was curiously dimmed. The snake crawled to the rough stones of the wall to rub his scaly nose. His skin split, frayed and loosened. Finally, as he glided gently forward with his body pressed against the stone, his whole skin peeled off inside out. His sight was clear now, and his striated body was again smooth and glistening.

Then came a morning when the snake reached his sunny stones and felt them cool against his belly. The air against his extended tongue was cold. Heavy with sluggishness and feeling a numbness creep through his coiled length, he set forth through the grass. It was full of smells of mice and slugs, but the snake sought a curious pungence, heavy and fetid, like musk.

Finding this scent, he followed its trail to a part of the stone wall where some winter's frost had left a fissure. The snake entered; the musky smell inside was heavy, and the crevice was full of rustling. Discerning a seething and undulating mass, the snake crawled to it and inserted his own body among the other loops and coils. The dim urgencies in his body and brain waned and grew dim, and an opaque unawareness descended upon his being. Winter had come.

Chapter two

MALIGNED AND MISJUDGED

In the secret corridors of the wilderness creep reptiles and birds and beasts about which most of us know little. Their frightening size or lethal weapons prevent familiarity. Tales of horror spread and grow. A shy gorilla becomes a raving monster. The wary rattlesnake is a charging dagger of poison.

Eventually these tales are righted. The scientist in the wilderness observes, takes notes, collects and studies. Finally the truth is out. Most of the beasts with terrifying weapons have gentle dispositions. They do not need to charge and attack man. They inspire fear without baring a tooth.

As the human collects data, the world of the beasts becomes more tolerable, less frightening. The animal that "swallows people," the octopus, does not even like to touch a person, much less strangle him. The ferocious-looking gorilla would rather sit and eat celery than fight. The fearless skunk is affectionate and kind, for he can afford to be.

Any beast, when up against man, fights to save his life. Those we misjudge and fear most strike only, if at all, in self-defense.

A DAY WITH GORILLAS

Martin Johnson

"You know," Carl Akeley, the naturalist and photographer, once said to me, "there is one animal in Africa that has been libeled more than all the others put together. I mean the gorilla. For instance, you will see old woodcuts picturing this ape, club in hand, beating the brains out of some shivering savage. Again, he is pictured carrying a screaming woman away into the mountain tangle. Some would have you believe that he mates with these captive women, to bring into the world beings half human, half beast."

Later, in my discussions with native guides, I repeatedly asked them about such tales. The question about a gorilla kidnaping a woman for a mate always drew a laugh—it seemed so silly to those who know these animals. And I never met a person who had seen a gorilla using a club as a weapon.

Fully grown, the gorilla attains a height of more than six feet and weighs well over 475 pounds. A heavy coat of black fur covers him from head to foot. He has no claws. Nails of the toes and fingers, although black, are like yours and mine. Like all the ape family, the gorilla has no tail. The forehead slants to protruding brows that shelter close-set eyes, quiet, studious and solemn. The nose is flattened above sneering lips which hide daggerlike fangs and powerful teeth. The complexion is black, like patent leather treated with oil. When walking in the shadows on all fours, the gorilla resembles more than anything a huge, shaggy dog with the shoulders of a bull and the head of a man.

One trip to Africa took us to the slopes of Mount Mikeno in the Congo, where we found these beasts by the hundred. Cold, damp weather usually prevails in the gorilla haunts, which is the reason, I presume, these animals are often heard coughing as though suffering from pulmonary ailments.

Gorillas live on bamboo shoots, wild celery and the buds of mountain trees. Heavy dew and frequent rain keep these plants juicy with sap, making it unnecessary for the apes to seek water at streams or pools. The mountain bamboo grows in thick patches, laced together by creeping vines into a formidable barrier against man. In their constant travels, gorillas fashion tunnels through this tangled jungle and often lurk in these dark trails. From all appearances, they live in family groups. Mother gorillas take good care of the young, and it is generally believed that a male and a female, on mating, remain together until they are separated by death.

The gorilla is really retiring, almost shy, and wishes to avoid contact with man. These animals have charged at me dozens of times to within eight and twenty feet, always stopping after such bluffs and retiring to cover. In all my experience with gorillas, I never found it necessary to shoot one for protection.

A day of unusual excitement for a pack of 30, which is fairly large as gorilla tribes go, would run something like this: An hour before sunset the family selects a favorable site in a bamboo shelter. Each animal sits down, pulls grass all about it in a circle, then gathers twigs to fashion the walls of its nest. Maybe two mates join together and build a double bed. A mother, preparing a nest for herself and baby, builds a sort of bed-and-a-half.

Sleep comes with darkness, and unless something

extraordinary happens, the gorillas will remain quiet in slumber until the morning sun pries into their retreat. Then they are up—very dirty and smelly. Every nest we examined was filled with dung, crushed by the sleeping animals. They start eating their breakfast of bamboo sprouts, traveling slowly as they do so, and leaving a pungent aroma in their wake.

This journey continues aimlessly. Gorillas usually travel no more than three or four miles a day. Tiring now and then during their endless meal, the members of the family sit down and just do nothing but stare into space, or quite possibly pick their teeth. (I have seen gorillas clean their teeth in this manner often.) A playful youngster offends a mother, who springs toward him. Quick as a flash he is into the branches, crawling out on a weak limb where his heavy parent cannot follow. There he remains until he thinks the incident is forgotten.

Peace of the day is broken by our arrival, our porters carrying cameras. Immediately the pack moves to cover. An old silverback gorilla takes up his position in the center of a trail or tunnel. He paces restlessly back and forth, fangs bared and ready for battle. He stands on his legs, screaming defiance at us and beating his heavy chest. The scream is ear-splitting, blood-curdling and fearsome. All the other gorillas begin to scream, their voices swelling into a terrific chorus as though hellish demons are about to attack the Earth with weapons of fire and brimstone. Added to the raucous din is a minor background medley as flat hands thump against hairy chests. It sounds for all the world like a drunken drum corps pounding away in the dark. We try to creep along the trail. The old silverback will not stand for this. Rushing forward with fangs bared, he snarls and screams. We stop. Silverback whirls in his tracks, returning to the jungle tangle.

The rest of the pack runs noisily deeper into the bush. Silverback remains on guard, sometimes for nearly half an hour, charging, angry and defiant. Slowly he retires along the tangled path, but we are persistent. Other males join forces with the silverback. Together they strut back and forth on flat feet and the knuckles of clenched fists. In turn they charge, growling and yelling like a pack of wild ogres; but always they stop short of us. The slow, noisy retreat continues until the remainder of the pack is safely in hiding. Then the rear guard, tired of the game of bluff and bluster, fades away into the darkness of the jungle.

This brush with us upsets the gorillas. Their nerves are brittle, and they are restless as they break the young bamboo. A bold spirit among them offends the old silverback. Immediately the leader is upon him, shrieking and screaming, stabbing with murderous fangs. Others join in. The brawl becomes a free-for-all. Gorillas are ripping and tearing at one another, screaming, cursing, insane with bloodthirsty rage. Five or ten minutes the battle lasts, and then ends as suddenly as it started. I heard one of these family fights at Mount Mikeno, and later picked up handfuls of gorilla fur along a battleground splotched with blood.

The scrap over, quiet reigns; slowly the gorillas begin to wander away together as though nothing had happened. The evening sun begins to climb the mountainside and the dank chill of jungle night steals upward. It is time to sleep. The gorilla pack wends its way into the bamboo, there once more to make nests—double beds for mates and mothers, twin beds for anthropoid buddies, single nests for those that sleep alone.

LO, THE POOR OCTOPUS!
Myron Stearns

No other beast of the sea has ever been so misrepresented, feared and vilified as the octopus. Its very name, *devilfish*, damns it. It has come to stand for horror and evil. The truth is that the octopus, for centuries the prey of eels (especially the ferocious moray) and of humans, is deathly afraid of anything larger than he is.

My interest in octopuses started a few years ago in Palm Beach. I watched a pair of them in two six-foot tanks at the Marine Biological Laboratory. With their tentacles extended they were a couple of feet across. I was fascinated by the way they moved about, their miraculous way of changing color, the way they caught little crabs with a sudden flip of their tentacles, and by their almost human eyes, which seemed amazingly intelligent. These octopuses certainly did not appear dangerous.

Of the hundred-odd varieties of octopus, most grow no larger than three feet across. Some are so tiny that, full-grown, they could sit on your fingernail. In the Mediterranean, where octopuses are common, a very few grow tentacles seven feet in length. Only in the depths of the Pacific are there believed to be really tremendous specimens; tentacles found in the stomach of a whale are said to have been as much as 50 feet in length—which would

The terrifying-looking Congo gorilla, a shy animal, attacks only in self-defense, shuns meat and likes to gorge himself on bamboo shoots and mountain celery.

make the entire animal more than 110 feet across.

But the tales! Pliny tells of a 700-pound octopus with a head as big as a barrel. French sailors told of one that attacked their schooner, slinging its arms around the mast and nearly capsizing the boat. At least part of the terrifying reputation of the octopus stems from the vivid imagination of Victor Hugo. In *Toilers of the Sea* he wrote, as if it were solemn fact, that an octopus will swallow a human being much as we might swallow an oyster. "The tiger can only devour you," his account runs; "the devilfish inhales you. He draws you to him, into him, bound and helpless. To be eaten alive is more than terrible; to be drunk alive is inexpressible."

Actually few scientists believe that octopuses ever intentionally attack human beings. Frédéric Dumas and J. Y. Cousteau, who wrote of their underwater adventures in *The Silent World*, tell that they shuddered at the thought of meeting an octopus. Then one day Dumas pulled in a small one. "It writhed desperately to escape and broke loose. It made off by slow jet propulsion, exuding spurts of its famous ink." He tried wrapping the tentacles around his arm. They would stick for a few moments, then drop off, leaving only a temporary red mark.

Another tall tale about the octopus deals with the incredible speed at which it shoots through the water. In reality, though they can move fairly rapidly under stress, they are usually anything but fast. Watching the little fellows at Palm Beach, I found they had two principal methods of getting about. In jet-propulsion swimming they opened their gills and drew in water, then squirted it out through a sort of exhaust pipe. Each squirt would jet them ahead for two or three yards. Their progress was slow and jerky. The other method is by walking on their tentacles, but it doesn't look like walking. Traveling along the sandy floor of the tanks, they seemed to flow like blobs of jelly. The tentacles, however, can be as swift as a whiplash in snaring prey and are surprisingly strong. In captivity, octopuses have been known to pull out bungs that were flush with the bottom of their tank, letting the water out.

The longer I watched them, the more I realized that they were enthralling creatures. For instance, they have an incredible ability to ooze through a crack. I saw this happen time after time. To get from the main tank into a smaller compartment an octopus would in some way ooze—that's the only word for it —between the right-angled glass frames through a space no more than half an inch wide. Christopher W. Coates, director of the New York Aquarium, tells of shipping octopuses about three feet across com-

pressed into cigar boxes which contained a ⅛-inch slit between the top and the box. Repeatedly the octopuses escaped through this narrow opening.

Equally amazing were the color changes I saw them go through. On the sand at the bottom of the tank an octopus would be a pale yellow. On rocks he would turn red or dark brown, and he would become bright green on seaweed. On a mottled surface he would make himself mottled. His skin would be either smooth or corrugated, to match surroundings. In his skin are microscopic sacs of different-colored pigments. He can expand the sacs—in some cases to 60 times their original diameter. If the red sacs are expanded and the others are contracted he turns red, and so on. If an enemy frightens him he may turn pale, much as we pale with fright. If terrified he may flash from one color to another.

I watched a photographer at the Marine Biological Laboratory try to get color pictures of the pigment changes. He netted one of the octopuses in the tank and transferred it to a small glass aquarium. A dozen of us stood around for an hour while he prodded it with a stick to make it change color. It refused. Finally he gave up and started to transfer the octopus back to its tank. Just as he lifted the creature above the rim of the aquarium it shot its brown ink all over his shirt. It didn't squirt at anyone else, although we were just as close; it squirted at the man who had been tormenting it. And not until it had a clear shot.

The ink which an octopus squirts is still something of a mystery to scientists. It has no effect on human skin, and seems to have none on fish passing through it. For centuries it was assumed to be only a sort of smoke screen. Recent researches suggest that the sepia may also paralyze the sense of smell of the sharp-toothed moray eel, age-old enemy of the octopus, so that it cannot recognize its prey. After being squirted, a moray in a tank appeared unable to tell that it was almost nuzzling an octopus.

Another safeguard that nature developed for the perpetuation of the octopus is its fertility. Some species lay about 45,000 pearly-white eggs, each about half as big as a grain of rice, festooned on rocks in long strings. The mothers care for the eggs, refusing food for the six to eight weeks of incubation, squirting water over them to keep them scrupulously clean and protecting them against enemies.

To avoid enemies, the octopus is a night prowler. During daylight hours he keeps to himself. He finds a niche in a rock and makes it his home. "A typical home," Cousteau and Dumas write, "was one roofed with a flat stone two feet long and weighing perhaps 20 pounds. One side of the stone had been raised

The octopus has eight arms (whose suckers are flush with the skin); its relatives, the cuttlefish and dangerous squid, have ten (with raised suckers). The humanlike eyes are lidless and staring.

eight inches and propped up with smaller stones. In front of the lean-to was accumulated debris: crab and oyster shells and stones. A tentacle extended from the dwelling and curled around the rubble; the owl-like eyes of the octopus peered over the wall. When we went closer the tentacle contracted, sweeping the debris up against the door, concealing the inhabitant."

Getting enough to eat is a daily preoccupation for the octopus. Fish, as a rule, are too fast for it to catch. Usually it eats crabs and other small shellfish, dissecting them with its parrotlike beak.

"The octopus," wrote Edward Ricketts and Jack Calvin in *Between Pacific Tides,* "has eyes as highly developed as ours, and a larger and better-functioning brain than any other invertebrate animal." It has the same five senses that we ourselves possess, and its muscular system, with great strength and perfect control of all its eight tentacles, is in many ways equal to ours.

Octopuses are easily tamed and can be trained to take food from the hand of an attendant or visitor. Some will even pull your fingers open to get at a tightly held bit of food. An octopus in Brighton, England, is said to have learned to leave its own tank at night, make its way along a wall to another tank where some small fish were kept, help itself to one and return.

Many experiments, during the past few years, have been made to see just how intelligent these big mollusks really are. The zoologist Dr. Paul Schiller, while studying animal intelligence at the Yerkes Laboratories in Orange Park, Florida, trained an octopus to push the lid off a jar to get at a crab inside. Another octopus was presented with a white card along with a crab to which an electric wire was attached. The instant the octopus touched the crab it got a shock. Then it was fed an ordinary crab and got no shock. After only three experiments it learned to leave the crab with the white card alone.

The value of these experiments, for science, lies in the fact that the brain is far more accessible in the octopus than in any creature protected by a skull. One part or another of the brain of an octopus can be delicately cut away and the subsequent effects on octopus behavior observed. Since there is much to be learned about how our own minds work, scientists hope to learn more about us by experiments on the humble octopus.

THE TRUTH ABOUT HAWKS
Peter Farb

Of all the birds that populate the Earth, none is more maligned or more senselessly slaughtered than the hawk. There are 32 species of North American hawk, but most people simply classify all of them as "big" chicken hawks and "little" chicken hawks, and are quite willing to believe they are bloodthirsty creatures that kill for sport.

The truth is that hawks kill only when hungry, never for sport. They can be trained to the affectionate obedience of a dog, and are as mischievous in the air as otters are around a pond. "It is hawks' near-human qualities of love, anger and playfulness that have made them the favorite birds of most ornithologists," says Dr. Frederick C. Lincoln, famous birdman of the U.S. Fish and Wildlife Service.

An exhaustive study by the U.S. Department of Agriculture, based on analysis of the stomach content of 2690 hawks and owls, revealed that few hawks preyed on chickens or game birds. Most hawks, it has been found, wage a ceaseless war on rodents and destructive birds, and on insects whose fertility, if unchecked, could overwhelm our food production. Professor Harrison B. Tordoff, of the University of Michigan, has estimated that a single hawk saves farmers $110 a year in rodent damage.

Ranging in size from miniatures no bigger than robins to majestic giants that will attack a gazelle, hawks have been endowed with skills and adaptations that make them the most widely ranging lords of the ether. To search out their quarry, for example, they are equipped with eyes that rival the eagles'. A naturalist reported having seen a falcon, flying high over a mountain ridge, suddenly close its wings and make a long, unwavering dive for a small bird, which it snatched in its knuckled talons. When the falcon first spotted its prey, the two birds were at least 1½ miles apart! If we human beings had comparable visual acuity, we could read newspaper headlines a quarter of a mile away.

Much of the hawk's amazing sight comes from the size of the eyeballs, which are often as large as ours and extend far into the skull. In addition, the retina (the tissues in the back of the eye on which the picture image is thrown) is nearly twice as thick as a human's, and is packed with millions of minute visual cells. To shut out the glare of the sky, the eyes are coated with droplets of yellow oil that act much like a camera filter. Last summer I saw a little sparrow hawk hurtle down from a height of 100 feet and neatly pluck a grasshopper off a leaf. Astounding as the feat was, more extraordinary still was the physical transformation that had taken place inside the bird's eye during the dive. While the hawk was circling for prey, its eye lens was working like a telescope; by the time it had plummeted to the grasshopper, the lens shape had altered to that of a microscope.

Sandwiched between the two giant eyeballs, the hawk's brain is necessarily small. Regardless, hawks perform prodigious feats. It is almost unbelievable, for example, that a bird could recall the ravages caused by storms from one year to the next. Yet the osprey, when about to migrate south, often buttresses its nest with fresh sticks to withstand the winter blizzards. Furthermore, when these "fish hawks" rise above the water with a catch, they always turn the fish's head forward, to lessen air resistance.

Hawks exhibit just about every technique to be seen in the world of flight. Watch the master flier of them all, the peregrine falcon, also called the duck hawk. Many times I have seen one, high above me, turn its nose downward, give a mighty flap for thrust, then close its wings and plummet toward the earth like a hurled stone—sometimes attaining the incredible speed of 250 miles an hour. Suddenly there is an exploding puff of feathers as the falcon strikes a bird with its large, clawed fist. The prey is usually killed outright. But then comes the most amazing maneuver of all: the falcon darts under the falling bird, *flips over on its back* and catches the prey in its talons.

A completely different method of flight is found in the big, soaring hawks we often see wheeling in lazy circles. These birds are living gliders, among the most buoyant aloft. Nearly every one of their skeletal bones is hollow and filled with air sacs that supplement the lungs and decrease weight. Too, the wings and tail are extremely broad, providing a large lifting area in relation to weight. As the soarers slowly patrol their territories, they coast on deflected air currents and on columns of rising warm air known as thermals, gliding from one to the next. That a hawk can pick up tremendous momentum riding the thermals was shown when an osprey was once clocked at 80 miles an hour in a mere four-mile-an-hour wind—and not a wing tip was twitching!

The ability to hover sometimes results in unique methods of hunting. The little sparrow hawk, for example, coaxes mice out of their burrows by hovering a few inches above the ground and squealing

Favored with extraordinary vision, a young red-tailed hawk sits on a high perch, scanning the earth below for likely victims. Having sighted one, it takes off, wings high overhead to catch all the air possible for the initial thrust forward. The wings surge forward in a rowing motion until, plummeting, it snatches its prey.

loudly. When the rodent pops its head out to see what the commotion is about, exit one mouse.

It is in their mating flights that some hawks put on their greatest exhibitions of aerial acrobatics. One spring in South Carolina I saw an ecstatic male marsh hawk plunge wildly downward from a height of 100 feet, flip a somersault at the bottom, bound up again and top his rise with another somersault. Then, his mate shrieking approval, he started all over again, tossing in a few barrel rolls for good measure.

Hawks are among the most devoted of feathered parents, and are believed to mate for life. Many return to the same nests year after year. (One osprey nest was in continual use by successive generations for 125 years, and one of Britain's falcon eyries is known to go back to Elizabethan times.) Although, unlike most other birds, the female is larger than the male, the male does most of the hunting. Occasionally, however, the female joins him, and one naturalist reports having seen a pair of peregrines team up against a nighthawk and fly off with the victim, tossing him back and forth like a football.

Many thousands of hawks have been senselessly shot—even near Hawk Mountain Sanctuary in Pennsylvania, which some 25 years ago was set up as the first sanctuary to protect migrating hawks during their autumn passages. Here is the major eastern flyway for hawks, a narrow 60-mile-long funnel in the mountains where the birds bunch together and boil over the peaks by the thousands. But within a 30-mile radius of the sanctuary, and despite years of education as to the practical value of hawks, there used to be more than 100 shooting stands. With Maurice Broun, curator of the sanctuary, I hiked those "bloody ridges" and saw the woods littered with dead birds. Broun estimates that, before protective legislation was enacted in 1957, upward of *1500 hawks a day* were shot there during migration.

Hawk protection is gaining. Today 21 states protect all species; all but four protect some. In Canada the birds are fully protected in three provinces, partially in five. But laws alone cannot save the hawks. First, an alerted citizenry must be ready to plead the facts. In Lambertville, New Jersey, some facts were dramatically demonstrated by Paul Fluck, a physician and nature enthusiast. In a pen harboring chickens he placed a wounded red-tailed hawk. Farmers, who had frequently shot at this species of hawk, wagged their heads knowingly. But for three months, while the hawk's wing was healing, it lived almost affectionately with the chickens, and not a chick was lost. Gone, however, were the rats and mice which formerly fattened on the chickens' feed.

THE KING OF SELF-DEFENSE
Alan Devoe

Cree Indians call him *Sikak;* mammalogists label him *Mephitis mephitis;* and his pelt is apt to be camouflaged as *Alaska sable.* Simplest and commonest name of all, certainly the most richly fraught with disparaging implication, is plain skunk. By that terse epithet he is known from coast to coast, and seldom do we speak it with affection. But seldom, either, do we make any effort to know Mephitis better, or to understand him and his skunkly way of life. It is too bad, for we miss acquaintance with one of the most amiable and entertaining creatures in our North American woodlands.

It is usually in late April or in May, when the veined green spathes of skunk cabbage are thrusting up in marshy places, that the baby skunk is ushered into life. He is one of a litter that may contain almost a dozen, and the place of his birth is most often a vault-chambered burrow in the frozen earth, patiently lined with dry leaves and matted grasses against the chill of spring nights.

Newborn Mephitis is a helpless mite no larger than a meadow mouse. His babyhood is long. When he has reached the age of a month—an age at which wild birds are fully fledged and the white-footed forest mice are nearly ready to beget progeny of their own—he still weighs no more than ten or eleven ounces and has not yet ventured to peep out upon the sunny wonderworld at his doorway. But already there are clear signs that he is a skunk. The downy black fur of his wedge-shaped little head bears a white stripe from between his eyes to his nose, and there are white stripes along his sides. He is beginning to develop a gait which will be characteristic of him all his life, very like a bear's.

By the seventh or eighth week young Mephitis, at last weaned, is ready for forays into the Great Outside. As he waddles solemnly in his mother's wake among the daisies, his small, furry head is filled with an immediate consciousness that this is a world which holds no terrors for him. He stares at it with a kind of complacent acceptance and blurry affability.

He begins at once to earn his way. It is his good fortune to have an appetite almost uniquely catholic and comprehensive. He eats his weight several times a week in grasshoppers, crickets, June bugs, field

In his second spring the skunk sets out to find a mate, often traveling great distances to do his courting. He may even use his odorous spray when fighting a rival for a female's attentions.

mice and potato bugs, all enemies of the farmer. He likes tobacco and tomato worms; he is the best destroyer of army worms. He is, in short, the most valuable of all animals as a pest destroyer.

Mephitis, full grown, is as large as a house cat and weighs eight to ten pounds. Of his 28 inches from nose tip to tail tip, fully ten inches is tail. A superb and lovely tail it is, nearly as broad as it is long, and tipped with pure white. It trails behind Mephitis as an undulant feathery plume—a suitable tail for a creature so amiable and imperturbable.

For such is the character that Mephitis has developed with maturity. His bright black eyes show neither hostility nor terror, but have a kind of philosophic calm. His contentment is not even marred by that urge toward personal independence which so often makes young animals and young human beings fretful. With his mother and the whole full-grown

brood he continues to inhabit the earth burrow where he was born, and the whole family still goes on periodic hunting trips together. On these occasions they all proceed, by some curious ancient understanding, in single file. Sometimes, too, they play.

Not many men have witnessed the playtime of the skunks. It is usually in the early dusk that the little company forgathers for the game. Five or six or even more range themselves in a circle, noses pointed toward its center, and there ensues a kind of ceremonial dance. In unison the plume-tailed players advance by stiff-legged hops until their noses touch, and after a moment they retreat with the same prancing gait to the periphery of the circle. As many as a dozen times they act out this grave and grotesque ritual, each move as unvarying and precise as clockwork. Then, suddenly, the group disperses on the nightly quest for insects and salamanders.

There comes a time, of course, when Mephitis must undergo the experience from which no creature of Earth is exempt: he must meet an enemy. The moment when Mephitis, lumbering placidly along a country lane, is confronted for the first time by a hostile farmhouse mongrel is the moment when he achieves the full expression of his skunkhood. It is now that he follows, at the bidding of an instinct suddenly awakened, the immemorial behavior pattern of all skunks.

Tranquilly, with neither fear nor malice, he eyes the mongrel in his path. So great is his reluctance to mar the peaceful tenor of his evening that he stands for a moment quite still, hopeful that the din of barking will presently subside and the barker take his leave. Instead the dog advances in a growling rush. It is a serious error. Very slowly Mephitis lowers his furry, striped head, delicately arches his back and with grave earnestness thumps his forefeet on the ground. It is not a terrifying sound, this little pattering staccato, but the wild wood folk understand it perfectly and respond to it as quickly as to a rattler's whir. But the foolish, unknowing dog sees Mephitis' gesture as only a silly antic, and he makes another charge.

Not yet does Mephitis respond to the challenge. There is a prescribed skunk ritual for such times as this, and Mephitis follows it scrupulously. Standing stock still, he stares straight before him with unwinking eyes, and very slowly he shakes his head from side to side. It is an odd gesture—a fanciful naturalist might almost read it as a rueful one. It is Part Two of the three-part warning.

Still the uncomprehending dog gives no heed, and the time has come for the third and final caution. Gracefully Mephitis lifts his broad, plumed tail. He raises it straight over his striped back, and the drooping white tip is gradually erected. Only for an instant longer does he hesitate; then abruptly he wheels and presents his rear to the dog. His strong little back arches in a sudden convulsive movement. A thin jet of liquid glimmers phosphorescently in the summer dusk. As far as a rod from where Mephitis stands, the trees and grass are spattered by a burning spray. An acrid, choking odor saturates earth and leaves, and drifts on the air for hundreds of yards around. Chipmunks scurry deeper in their crannies to escape the suffocating fumes.

From far away there reaches Mephitis' ears the agonized yelping of a running dog who never again is likely to trifle with a skunk. His hide has been drenched by the sulfide that scientists call mercaptan, and the fiery spray has entered his eyes and been inhaled into his lungs. For a day or two, at least, he will be totally blind.

Such is the way of Mephitis when reluctantly he is forced to warfare. But such encounters are rare, and mostly he waddles abroad in the evening coolness, learning how to pinion the little green grass snakes with his heavy, flat-soled paws, and becoming adept in catching bees and wasps. He routs them out, as a bear does, by prodigious scratchings, and then as they swarm angrily around his furry head he beats them to earth with his strong forefeet. They often sting him on the inside of his mouth and lips and gullet, but he does not feel the stings at all. It is his good fortune to be totally immune.

All through the autumn Mephitis continues his nocturnal prowling. Sometimes one of his tribe will raid a poultry yard, but such individuals are rare. As the first snows come sifting down, he hunts and eats with mounting ravenousness and his gait grows slower. Mephitis is very fat now.

At last, one blowy winter evening he does not come out from his burrow at all. Snow, which has been falling steadily, chokes it, sealing out the cold, and Mephitis remains unmoving in his grass-lined nest. His mother and his brothers are there with him, and usually a friendly visiting skunk or two, and all of them lie curled together without sound. Mephitis has entered his winter sleep.

He will stay there, dreamless and hardly breathing, until a subtle impulse warns him that mid-March of his second spring has come and that it is time to mate. He will beget his own striped progeny, and he will resume his leisured quest for grubs and beetles. Year after year this will continue to be the unvarying cycle of his life.

Efforts are increasing to take Mephitis out of his fields and to domesticate him on fur farms. Some prudent skunk-farmers make a practice of depriving him of his musk glands by surgery, but others have discovered that this is needless. Mephitis takes to domestication with perfect equability. So long as he is gently treated he makes no effort to employ his formidable battery. Given a wire pen and a nest box approximating the size of his natural home, he breeds and dozes as complacently as though he were no prisoner at all. Mephitis remains unchangeably the same—a grave and friendly little fellow who wants no more (but wants this much with inexorable insistence) than to be treated with civility.

It is good to know him not only because he is a valuable economic ally, but because one of the great cities of the United States, Chicago—Sikako—was named in his honor.

THE SNAKE WITHOUT A FRIEND

Virginia Duncan

If there is a critter in the world without a friend, it is the rattlesnake. Many animals and birds, even other snakes, kill and eat rattlers. Ranchers destroy them to protect livestock. People collect them for zoos and reptile gardens. They are used for laboratory experiments and for production of antivenins. It is amazing that the rattlesnake has survived at all.

When I was a child in Texas, I saw a rattlesnake disappear into a prairie-dog hole. As the last rattle passed out of sight, prairie dogs bobbed up everywhere and started scratching dirt into the hole, tamping the soft earth down with their heads. They buried that rattlesnake alive. Chaparral cocks (commonly known as roadrunners) will dart at a rattlesnake until it strikes, and then peck at its eyes and head. Eagles and hawks feint several times until the snake uncoils and then seize it, catching the snake behind the head with one talon and about the middle of the body with the other. If a bunch of turkeys finds a rattlesnake, the hens stand aside and let the gobblers kill it with their beaks and wings. Chickens often eat baby rattlers, just as they would worms. The Mexican hog is a snake eater. Many times I have seen a sow with a snake in her mouth running and squealing in her attempt to eat the snake without sharing it. Hogs, generally, are not affected by snakebite because their subcutaneous layer of fat retards absorption of venom. Other snakes—the coachwhip, indigo and king snake—include rattlesnakes in their diet. I once saw a king snake swallowing a rattlesnake so large that the feat seemed impossible. But after 30 minutes there was a thoroughly stuffed king snake and no rattlesnake.

A rattlesnake's venom-packed bite is poisonous, sometimes fatal, but the snake is not so dangerous and aggressive as most people think. For more than 20 years I lived on a ranch in the Southwest where there were lots of rattlers, but I was never bitten. When approached out in the open the rattlesnake almost invariably rattles, but if it is protected by a log or bush, it may lie perfectly quiet—depending on silence for protection.

The bizarre stories which are the basis of people's fear of rattlesnakes are almost all untrue. Rattlers can't strike over half their length. They do not chase people. Many times I have annoyed a rattlesnake with a long stick until it struck four or five times in succession, but I never saw one show any inclination to chase me.

There are 47 species and subspecies of rattlesnake in North America. The sidewinder, less than 30 inches in length, is one of the smallest species, and the leader in size and amount of venom expended at a bite is the eastern diamondback, found throughout Florida and northward into the Carolinas and as far west as Louisiana. It attains a length of over eight feet. The western diamondback, second in size, ranges from the southeastern part of California through most of the Southwest and northward to Oklahoma, Arkansas and Missouri. It is very much like the eastern variety in markings except that it has a more faded appearance.

Usually western diamondbacks den up during the cold months in mountain caves or under overhanging rocks in ravines and canyons. They are very sensitive to cold, and the temperature determines the length of their hibernation. In southern Texas and in Mexico they have been seen crawling every month in the year. On chilly days in late fall I have found them in fields, so stiff from the cold they couldn't move. You could pick them up just like crooked sticks.

Awakening from hibernation in the early spring, a snake first thinks of a mate. The gestation period requires about five months and the young have to be born long enough in advance—August or September—to feed and gain strength before facing their first winter. About a foot long at birth, they possess well-developed fangs and a birth rattle, and begin killing their food, principally field mice, a few weeks after birth. They shed for the first time when about ten days or two weeks old, and it is then they acquire their first permanent rattle.

Rattlesnakes shed on an average of three times a year, and with each exuviation a new rattle appears. However, the amount of food taken, the climate and the general health of the snake affect the annual growth of rattles and the shedding of skin. The age of rattlesnakes seldom can be determined by the number of rattles because these break off or are gnawed off by rats while the snakes are hibernating.

Rattlesnakes can live about a year without eating; and this is about the extent of life for rattlesnakes in captivity because after capture they usually refuse food. George Motl of San Angelo, Texas, who captured more than 5000 snakes in 20 years, never had one in his collection which would eat.

Out in the open, a rattlesnake is less dangerous after it has eaten, because in killing its prey it expends about two thirds of its venom and replenishing

If his sinister-sounding rattle does not halt the approach of an enemy, the rattlesnake raises the forepart of his body into an ominous S-shaped curve and holds his head high, ready to strike.

the supply takes about two weeks. Moreover, the snake is less active when it has a large undigested lump in its body. It is several days before a snake fully digests a large rat, a rabbit or a bird, but the gastric juices are so strong that even the teeth and bones swallowed are dissolved.

The senses of sight and smell are well developed in rattlesnakes, but they do not hear in the ordinary sense of the word. Tests made by one herpetologist proved that they paid no attention to loud noises made near their heads, but they did respond when a footstep caused vibrations through the floor. The forked tongue, which continually flicks in and out,

touches the ground lightly, helping the snake determine the kind of surface it is crawling over. The tongue is also an aid to smelling. It picks up odor particles in the air and transfers them to two tiny cavities lined with sensory cells in the front of the roof of the mouth.

Hounded incessantly by enemies, attacked by man while it is attacking other enemies of man, the rattlesnake leads a disagreeable, uncertain life and is always instinctively on the defensive. To cap it all, rattlesnakes don't seem to like even each other. In one case I know of, two rattlesnakes bit each other. The smaller one died three hours later.

Chapter three

PESTS AND MENACES

The Pandora's box of pests—mites, flies, cockroaches, mosquitoes, rats, starlings, sparrows and even sharks—costs the United States over three billion dollars annually in damage to property and health. Although all animals, including these very creatures, have their own personal pests, man has far greater number of tormentors than any of his animal friends. We are fair prey for thousands of beasts both large and microscopic. We are relentless in getting rid of them—and, at the same time, are intrigued with the cleverness of the evil characters that plague us.

These conniving beasts are not dull. Like characters on the stage, the diabolical ones are often much more interesting than the good ones. The appearance of almost all these bedevilers strikes a note of revulsion in us. The naked whiteness of the termite, the jagged teeth of the shark, the plungerlike mouth of the fly, annoy us as much as do their deeds.

Nevertheless, we have to give them grudging admiration. With all our brains plotting against them, they remain with us, achieving through biological change and adjustment new shapes and forms to beat our poisons, sprays, repellents and fumigants. Most of them have had millions of years of success fighting back. If a chrysanthemum kills a fly with its chemicals, the fly breeds a new generation immune to the flower. So it is with our man-made "miracle" chemicals. So it will probably always be.

WATCH OUT FOR SHARKS!

*Leicester Hemingway
and John C. Devlin*

One Sunday afternoon in August, John Brodeur, a 24-year-old accountant, waded into the combers at Sea Girt, New Jersey. The sea was roiled from a recent storm, and the waves were rolling in at a thunderous clip. He and his fiancée waited waist-deep in the water for a good wave that they could ride ashore. Suddenly Brodeur noticed a long, dark object not ten yards away. Seconds later something seized his right leg and held on, shaking furiously. In the shock of it Brodeur felt no pain, but the water was turning red with his blood, and bits of his flesh were floating to the surface. He fainted. When he came to, his fiancée and two other bathers were dragging him up onto the beach. As the result of that encounter with a shark, Brodeur lost his right leg at the knee. The doctors who performed the amputation told him later he was lucky to be alive.

What makes a shark attack a man? No one can say. The shark has been swimming the oceans of the world as predator and scavenger for 350 million years, a living throwback to the pre-dinosaur age. With a skeleton of cartilage, he predates the modern fishes which have skeletons of true bone. Hated, feared, shrouded in superstition and misinformation, he has been known at once as killer and coward, as fearless sea gladiator and dull-witted, self-propelled garbage can. The truth is that almost any shark can be each of these things, given the right conditions.

Today we are learning what these conditions are. From the world's first scientific shark-behavior studies and a list of shark "incidents" collected by the Shark Research Panel of the American Institute of Biological Science, biologists are finding out what the shark's habits are and when he is most likely to attack. Sharks are deep-water creatures, but, as the Brodeur attack indicates, they will strike in the shallows; in northerly waters they tend to be most vicious during the summer months when water temperatures are in the high 60's and the 70's.

An incredibly keen sense of smell permits a shark to pick up and follow a scent as dilute as one part of blood to 50 million parts of water. He uses his nose as a homing device: when a scent comes stronger in one nostril, he turns in that direction. He is also acutely sensitive to vibrations in the water, and, the Shark

Panel now believes, the *kind* of vibration is important. Sharks are more likely to be attracted by erratic, fluttery or irregular motions—like those of a hooked or wounded fish. According to Dr. Perry W. Gilbert, professor of zoology at Cornell University and chairman of the Shark Research Panel, "The behavior of a man in the water often determines the behavior of a shark. Panic can be dangerous, for irregular, frantic motion suggests something that is wounded or in trouble—just what a shark likes to investigate. If you see a shark, the best thing to do is to swim for shore, using your regular swimming stroke."

There is dramatic evidence that a person who keeps calm in the midst of attack, even by several sharks, may have a chance of escaping with both life and

The shark spends his entire life looking for food. Cruising at four miles an hour, he may travel 35,000 miles in a year—nearly one and one half times around the world.

limb. Richard P. Chung, a medical student from South Korea, was swimming off Ocean City, New Jersey, when he saw a shark's fin coming toward him. The shark seized his left leg. Almost immediately another shark hit him a glancing blow on the right leg. Chung struck out with his fists, hit the first shark on the nose. It released its hold. The water was bloodied, and Chung swam away from the area. Then he pulled the belt from his swimming trunks, fashioned a tourniquet around his left thigh and swam for shore. It took him nearly an hour. The bones of his left leg were bared from ankle to knee, but the leg was saved.

One of the most carefully documented shark attacks on a human being occurred one afternoon in May 1959, while Albert Kogler and Shirley O'Neill, fresh-men at San Francisco State College, were swimming off Baker's Beach near the Golden Gate. Suddenly Shirley heard Kogler call out. She turned to see "a big gray thing" in the water beside him. Kogler shouted to her to go ashore; instead she courageously swam out to him. Finding his left arm nearly bitten through at the shoulder, she put her arm around him and dragged him to the beach, but Kogler died of his injuries. Within three hours of the tragedy, Dr. Gilbert was on the phone to Panel correspondent W. I. Follett, curator of fishes at the California Academy of Sciences. Professor Follett had already interviewed observers at the scene. He had measured water and air temperatures; from tooth marks he identified the killer as *Carcharodon carcharias*, the great white shark, the

one to which the term "man-eater" is usually applied.

The tragedy revealed an important item of shark information. For some time scientists had been suspicious of the old theory that sharks dangerous to man seldom venture into water colder than 65 degrees. Follett had reported a water temperature of 55 degrees. Thus, if a shark is hungry enough, he will come into relatively cold water.

A big hunter shark's appetite is appalling: he is always on the lookout for something to ease his terrible hunger. Almost anything will do. The crew of a tramp steamer in the Red Sea reported feeding one shark a biscuit tin, a sack of coal, newspapers, a brick wrapped in a piece of cloth, a broken alarm clock and a wooden crate. Even puppy sharks are born hungry, fully outfitted with teeth and ready to carry on the scavenging traditions of their tribe.

The shark is almost perfectly adapted to cleaning up the oceans. His mouth is on the underside of his head so he can scavenge off the bottom if necessary. His maw is large in proportion to his body—the jaws of one giant tiger shark caught off Panama could comfortably encircle two men standing back to back—and it is equipped with four to six rows of razor-sharp teeth. His stomach walls are thick and leathery, and his digestive juices are so strong that a single drop will blister human flesh.

The Shark Panel has exploded several myths. Sharks have long been thought to have poor eyesight, for example. But microscopic scrutiny of the shark's eyeball reveals that it has a very sensitive retina and can distinguish objects in extremely dim light—an asset when feeding at night or in very deep water. When scent or vibrations bring a shark within range of a possible meal, he will use his eyes to help locate it. Similarly, the belief that all sharks have to keep moving through the water in order to aerate their primitive fixed gills has been disproved. Tiger sharks and others have been observed lying for hours with their bellies resting on the bottom, their mouths and gills slowly pumping water to keep their massive bodies in oxygen.

The first serious study of ways to discourage shark attacks on human beings was initiated by the U.S. Navy during World War II. The Navy sought to protect men swimming in shark-infested waters after a plane's forced landing or a ship's sinking. Scientists at Woods Hole Oceanographic Institution had observed that sharks tended to stay away from semidecayed shark flesh, also from a squid or octopus that had voided its ink into the water. So the scientists prepared a compound of copper acetate (which has some chemical properties similar to decayed shark meat) and nigrosine dye (to simulate squid ink). When tests

showed that sharks were almost always repelled by it, the compound was fixed in water-soluble wax cakes. Distributed all over the world to men aboard ships, it undoubtedly saved many lives. (Later experiments with the components of these cakes proved that the dye, rather than the acetate, is the repelling factor.)

The day when scientists were inclined to belittle the shark as a man-killer is gone. In Dr. Gilbert's office at Cornell are 30 carefully documented dossiers on shark attacks in one year. Twenty-five of the dossiers bear white labels, indicating that the victims recovered from their injuries. The five red labels mean fatalities. Seven of the dossiers fall into the special category of provoked attacks. "Skin-divers, mostly," Dr. Gilbert says. "They refused to believe that sharks can be dangerous. Had to find out the hard way by molesting them—poking them with spears or swimming up near their faces."

In years to come, more and more people will be invading the shark's domain, either by catastrophe or by choice. To reduce the danger of shark attack, the Shark Research Panel scientists offer the following advice: Always swim with a companion, and avoid swimming at night or in extremely turbid or dirty water where underwater visibility is poor. Don't panic if a shark is sighted; leave the water as calmly and quickly as possible. If an attack does occur, every effort should be made to control hemorrhage at once—even before the victim reaches shore. If the wound is serious, the victim should be hospitalized as promptly as possible.

THE "BUG" THAT EATS HOUSES
Jerome Beatty

The subterranean termite, the most destructive of all chewers of wood, is also one of the most elusive. Termites work under cover and usually are discovered only after they have been gnawing for five or ten years—perhaps when the man rolls in a new refrigerator and it crashes through the sill of the kitchen door. Once in your property, they are difficult to exterminate.

In 1951 termites were discovered in a huge Kansas City warehouse. Pest-control men were about to attack when Kansas City was hit by a great flood. For seven days the bugs were underwater. "Well, anyway," said a company official when they started to shovel out the mud after the flood, "all the termites are dead." The exterminators poked around to make sure and found the pests alive and rarin' to go.

Termites are fighting a winning battle against assaults by state and federal entomologists and thousands of professional exterminators. Thirty years ago Dr. Thomas E. Snyder, senior entomologist of the U.S. Department of Agriculture, now retired, estimated termite damage in the United States at about $40,000,000 a year, mostly on farms. Today the bugs are going great guns in cities and the National Pest Control Association guesses the total loss at about $250,000,000.

Termites live in underground nests, deep enough to reach damp earth and avoid cold. They live on cellulose, which composes the bulk of dead wood. Termites cannot digest cellulose, but have in their alimentary tracts microscopic protozoa that digest it for them. In the spring or fall, on a warm, sunny day, the termites come out in yard or basement, swarm, make short flights to start new colonies, then discard their wings. These swarms and wings are clues to watch for. In basements the wings usually are shed near windows and doors.

These termites have brown or black bodies and two pairs of long, gauzy wings of equal size; their overall length is about half an inch. They should not be confused with flying ants, which are comparatively harmless insects. Flying ants can best be distinguished by their thin wasp waists. Termites have thick waists. Nor should the work of termites be confused with that of powder-post beetles and carpenter ants, which bore holes in wood and leave telltale grains of sawdust. Termites don't betray their presence with sawdust, and if they accidentally bore into the outer air they immediately plug the hole.

Termites are most destructive in the South, and once it was thought that cold weather would keep them out of the northern states. But they bored under warm basements and now are causing increasing damage in every state and in Canada. In Indianapolis, in 1938, a survey of 100 houses showed termites in three. Ten years later they were in 40 of them. In Washington, D.C., experts say, there is hardly an acre that doesn't house at least one colony.

The first organized war on termites started in 1928 when California realized that big trouble was at hand. An extensive survey was made, the public was warned, buyers of real estate began to require inspection reports, pest-control laws were passed and exterminators licensed. But with over 400 established companies at work, damage still increases.

Subterranean termites must keep constantly damp. They must find food without exposing themselves to the open air, where they would dry out and die.

Like ants and bees, to whom they are completely unrelated, termites live in colonies which have a complex social structure. Only the workers do the boring. Thus they provide food for the soldiers and royal members of the colony.

By some instinct they go straight through the earth to dead wood in or touching the ground, or they build small earthen tubes up the side of a foundation to reach wooden beams. Under houses where the floor is only two or three feet from the ground, they may build a stalagmite-like structure from the ground up to the wood. Termites almost invariably stop eating inside a beam just before it is weakened enough to crash and betray them. One way of detecting them is to stab with an ice pick all sills, beams and other wood that is close to the ground or touching it.

The shelter tubes up the outside of foundations or up the inside of basement walls are the most noticeable evidence of termites, but usually colonies don't have to build them because careless construction gives them direct access through wood that touches the soil—cellar steps, outside steps and supports of porches. Termites can also get up into beams through cracks in cement or through hollow-block foundations. Slab-foundation construction, with cement floors touching the earth, is made to order for the pests. They seldom have trouble in getting up over the edges and reaching the wood.

Before a new colony is strong enough to start to damage a house, it multiplies by feasting for eight or ten years on dead wood outside the structure. A contractor who buries scrap lumber from a new house is setting up a Stork Club for termites.

When termites show up you should repair the damage, poison the bugs and have the building termite-proofed by an expert, who will cut off every possible entrance—remove wood that touches the ground, seal openings and place shields on top of foundations. The soil under and alongside the house must be poisoned to a depth of several feet. An annual inspection is cheap insurance.

Racketeers have thrived in recent years because few homeowners take the trouble to get expert termite information. After making a free termite inspection, these confidence men report that your house is in terrible condition and try to urge you into instant action. Once you sign, the racketeer gives the premises a superficial spraying, collects his money and vanishes, often advising that the transaction be kept a secret, claiming that the house cannot be sold if it becomes known that it has been treated for termites.

If you suspect the presence of termites, don't become panicky; the jaws of the bugs grind slowly and there is time for considered action. But even after an efficient job is done, there will still be a lot of live, hungry termites out in the yard, hoping you'll not have a checkup once a year.

THOSE GREGARIOUS STARLINGS

Richard C. Davids

When a giant jet airliner crashed into Boston Harbor in the fall of 1960, killing 62 persons, America was astounded at what investigators found to be a contributing cause: starlings, sucked into the air scoops, had choked one or more of the big engines. Six weeks later at the same airport, as another airliner raced down the runway for takeoff, a swarm of starlings suddenly loomed dead ahead and hit the plane. "Like machine-gun fire," the pilot reported. He slammed to a halt on the runway just in time to avert still another disaster.

U.S. airports swung into action, destroying nearby roosting and nesting sites, mowing bird-attractant weeds, cutting berry-producing shrubs. Boston posted patrols to report any flocks to the control tower. Washington's National Airport installed ten small gas cannons along the runways to boom away at three-minute intervals from dawn to dusk. The Fish and Wildlife Service, the Audubon Society and the Federal Aviation Agency set up new studies of bird control. And bird-embattled farmers and gardeners all over the country took hope that at last something would be done about those persistent troublemakers, the starlings.

A black-feathered, cocky bird slightly smaller than a robin, the starling is an immigrant to the United States, brought to New York City's Central Park from Europe in 1890. In the years since, starlings have spread like measles. They reached California some 20 years ago. The first starling was seen in Vancouver in 1946. By 1954 there was a roost of 500. Four years later it had grown to 25,000.

An industrious parent, the starling has two, sometimes three broods of four or five young a year. Unemployed bachelor starlings have been known to help feed the fledglings. But some of the starling's habits are less appealing. He battles other birds for their nests, tosses out their eggs. His winter roosts, often in evergreens, are enormous. An Oregon holly grower reported, "When the flock comes swooping in to roost in my grove, it sounds like a tremendous waterfall. The backdraft kicks up dust, even pulls off leaves. The litter makes holly leaves wither, ruins the crop."

Often flocks move into town for the warmth of big stone buildings. Washington, D.C., a starling heaven,

The first starlings—40 pairs—were brought to New York from England in 1890, when a lover of Shakespeare and birds decided to introduce into North America every bird mentioned in the bard's plays. Their population explosion in the New World caused a national headache.

illustrates the trouble cities are having. In three decades Washington has tried everything from revolving stuffed owls to rattling tin cans. But more than 10,000 birds still take up residence there in a single block, defacing buildings and embarrassing human residents. In 1960 Congress voted $29,500 for installing electric bird-shockers on the Supreme Court Building to rid it of the 35,000 birds that roosted there. That same year, to safeguard dignitaries and spectators at the Presidential inauguration, the inaugural committee spent $8600 to spray the trees along the parade route with a product alleged to smell highly unpleasant to starlings. To protect their city halls, New Orleans, San Francisco and Boston sprayed them with a substance irritating to birds' feet. Massachusetts even smeared it on Plymouth Rock.

Mount Vernon, New York, engaged a 71-year-old Kansan who claimed to have cleared public buildings of starlings in Louisville, Indianapolis, Wichita and Des Moines. He said he had taught himself starling-chasing after his home town, Great Bend, Kansas, had spent $1500 for aluminum owls to frighten starlings. The starlings had used them to perch on. The birdman came to Mount Vernon with secret equipment in a small black box sealed with two padlocks. He signed a five-page contract with the city—$4000 to be paid when he succeeded there. Next evening he strode through the streets slapping together two aluminum paddles and tinkling a chime that hung from his neck. Covey after covey of starlings rose from their roosts and swept off into the dark of the night. Next morning most of the birds were back. The birdman stayed around town for almost a month, repeating his performance. Then he himself departed in a huff, unpaid.

Farmers have made heroic efforts to protect crops from starlings and their cousins, the red-winged blackbirds. In New Jersey they use aerial flash bombs, plant "decoy crops" of Japanese millet, cut roadside brush and trees that birds perch in before dropping into a field. Sweet-corn growers harvest early, hoping to beat the birds, which like corn a little tougher than people do. One man hot-rods around his fields in a car without a muffler, a shotgun beside him from which he fires "cracker" shells that air-burst above the crop. But birds quickly learn gunshot range. He says, "Keeping a million birds off a field is like trying to stop it from raining. I've spent $2000 on guns and ammunition this year and all I've done is chase the birds to my neighbors' fields." His neighbors tried hiring a plane equipped with sirens, to fly at tassel height. It cost $10 an hour and had no effect on the stubborn birds.

Scientists at the U.S. Fish and Wildlife Research Center on the Patuxent River near Washington and at a Denver substation have been tracking down every promising lead on starling controls. So far results with most have been discouraging. Firecrackers linked by fuse to explode continuously in fields or at airports at first looked good, but they are dangerous— and tempting to children. In one New Jersey community, youngsters pilfered and exploded them in a school cafeteria, breaking windows and dishes. Cannons firing at three-minute intervals like those at the Washington airport were successful at first, but their effectiveness seemed to wear off. Tents made of chicken wire, tobacco cloth or treated paper do a good job of saving berries and fruits, but may cost $1000 an acre to install.

One promising method in use at present is electronic; it was pioneered in 1953 by Hubert Frings and Joseph Jumber, biologists at Penn State University, and by Frings' wife and co-worker, Mable. The idea is simple. If you hold a starling tightly in the hand, he will yell bloody murder. If you record that call and play it over a loudspeaker at dusk as birds come winging in to roost, they'll fly off. If they return, give them another blast. In August 1953 the Frings tried the idea on a roost at State College, Pennsylvania. After five nights the birds got discouraged and left. Two weeks later the Frings tried their experiment in the village of Millheim nearby. After four nights the birds left town and began roosting in a woodlot on the outskirts.

The next summer Rochester, New York, asked the Frings to help. The starlings there shared a roost with martins, cowbirds, robins and grackles. On hearing the record the starlings fled. The others didn't budge. Returning starlings, seeing other birds unmoved by the racket, appeared to settle down. Near Buffalo, however, where starlings roosted with other species, all the birds left. The reason for the difference be-

tween the two groups' reactions is still a mystery.

From Denmark the Frings got an urgent request from the Peter F. Heering company, producer of the famous cherry liqueur. Starlings were plundering the firm's 150,000 cherry trees. Frings airmailed instructions, pointing out that American recordings probably wouldn't work, since birds recognize their own local dialects. Danish recordings did the trick and have been in use ever since. Several owners of vineyards in France and Germany report fair to good success; so, too, do olive growers in Tunisia. When the Union Carbide Metal Company put up a building in West Virginia, they wired it for permanent starling control, using Dr. Frings' suggestions, with built-in speakers under the eaves.

Effective as the electronic control method is, it merely tends to drive the birds from one spot to another, where they may become equally objectionable. For this reason, current research is investigating chemicals as a means of limiting the starlings' ability to reproduce. But biologists are reluctant to agree to the total elimination of the starling population from our skies. They point out that, despite all the figures available on bird damage, little research has been done on the starlings' value in dollars in keeping down beetles and grubs.

OUR ENEMY, THE FLY
Alan Devoe

From two things, the adage has it, none of us is exempt: death and taxes. The naturalist might add a third: flies. Buzzing at the sunny windows, hovering hungrily over the dinner or outdoor table, flies are so inevitably a part of warm-weather existence that most people accept them casually.

In sections of the United States and in many parts of the world where there is poor pest control, this indifference costs more than we know. We pay for it with cholera and anthrax, with typhoid, trachoma, tuberculosis, and with much of the inexplicable summer dysentery of babies. *Musca domestica,* the housefly, close relative of the dreaded tsetse fly, can be as deadly an enemy as we entertain.

Our housefly starts life as a tiny egg, much smaller than a pinhead, deposited by a female fly in a manure pile or in any rotting refuse. Within 24 hours it hatches forth as a transparent, legless grub. Before a day has passed, its size has so tremendously increased that its inelastic skin can no longer contain the body. The skin therefore splits, and the grub crawls out to grow a new one. Three times within as many days this splitting and shedding of old skins occurs, and then on the fourth day, its transparent color changed to a dull white, it crawls away from its feeding place and burrows into the ground.

During this underground burial of about three days, there form inside the pupal jacket the striped body, the six legs, the two veined wings, the multi-faceted eyes—a tremendous metamorphosis for so short a time. Then the pupa bursts and the adult fly emerges. Tunneling upward, it comes out into the sunlight, ready—when its wings have dried and stiffened—for its eight or ten weeks of adult life.

From egg to adult has taken less than ten days. And this adult fly is ready immediately for breeding. If a female, in less than a week it will probably lay its first batch of 100 or more eggs, repeating at ten-day intervals. In view of this speed, and of the housefly's vast fecundity, it becomes apparent how huge the tribe would grow were it unchecked. From mid-April to August the offspring of a single pair of houseflies, if each one of them lived, would amount to 191,010,000,000,000,000,000 flies.

The adult housefly's life is no prettier spectacle for the squeamish than was its infancy. Its prime concern is food. It relishes with equal enthusiasm decaying garbage or other filth and the lumps of sugar on your dinner table. And it flies directly from one kind of food to the other, a disturbing fact in view of its highly specialized anatomy and physiology. First of all, its entire body is covered with a tangle of fine, close-growing hairs; and similar hairs grow on its legs and feet. The fly is thus equipped with the finest of catchalls. In the second place, there is the extraordinary structure of its feet. Each foot is equipped with an adhesive pad of sticky hairs. It is by means of these that the fly negotiates slippery surfaces so nimbly and can walk upside down on ceilings; but it is also by means of these sticky pads that it picks up and transmits myriad germs.

The greater part of a fly's head is taken up by its eyes, which are compound organs made up of thousands of six-sided facets. Each facet is a complete eye in itself, and the total picture seen by the fly is a composite of what is seen by the individual facets. Shown here, a horsefly.

Furthermore, the mouth parts of the housefly are a pair of soft, fleshy lobes at the end of its proboscis. There is no chewing mechanism. (The flies that bite you sometimes in muggy weather are not houseflies, but another variety called tabanids.) Accordingly, a fly can feed on a lump of sugar only by first softening it. To do this the fly regurgitates on the sugar a drop of fluid from its last-digested meal. It is this gruesome antic that the fly is performing at our dinner table when he seems to be exploring the sugar bowl; these regurgitated droplets, together with the insect's excreta, make up "flyspecks."

Such, then, is the life story of the fly—a creature born and matured in filth, and uniquely equipped for transmitting that filth wherever it may go. Its danger to man can hardly be overstated. Careful tests have shown that the bacteria on the hairy body of a single fly may number as many as five million.

What can we do about it? The answer is that, while as individuals we can accomplish a good deal, as whole communities acting together we can accomplish much more. Flies are migrants: tests have revealed that a flight of 20 miles is by no means beyond the fly's ability. It will do little good, therefore, for the citizens in a town's residential section to battle against houseflies if a few miles away there is an unsanitary dump or exposed manure pile where they breed by billions. No leakage above ground should be allowed from cesspools or town sewer systems. Every one of us must see that our garbage cans are of metal or plastic and tightly covered. We must make sure that our town or city disposes of its garbage by incineration and not by dumping. When adult flies get into our houses, we must fight continuously, wielding the old-fashioned swatter, spraying, using flypaper.

Musca domestica, like every other creature under heaven, has its natural enemies. A part of our fight should be to encourage these. We ought, for instance, to protect spiders, probably the housefly's most effective enemy, and also toads, lizards and salamanders. Above all, we ought to encourage birds. It would be impossible to reckon how many houseflies are devoured by such expert aerial hunters as the swallows and swifts, or how many eggs and larvae are consumed by vireos, orioles, nuthatches and chickadees.

The ancient Greeks sacrificed an ox to *Musca domestica* every year at Actium, and the Syrians of antiquity made similar propitiations. But, despite his long and deadly presence in our midst, there is every hope that, with effort, we may one day enter into that blissful era, prophesied in the Koran, "when all the flies shall have perished, except one."

DON'T UNDERRATE BROTHER RAT
Alfred H. Sinks

A scientist, Dr. Clarence M. Tarzwell, when he was at the U.S. Public Health Service laboratory near Savannah, put a cage full of freshly captured Norway rats in a pickup truck. Somehow one got out. He found her more than a month later, still in the truck. She had made a comfortable home in back of the seat and was raising a litter of nine thriving young. Meanwhile she must have got in and out of the truck dozens of times to search for food.

A caged female rat in the laboratory planned an escape as shrewd as any devised by a human convict. Each night she gnawed the wooden wall around the copper pipe that brought drinking water into the cage. Each morning, before the attendant came in, she skillfully covered the evidence with litter. The attendant had no suspicion of what she was doing—until too late.

There are two main species of rat: *Rattus norvegicus* (the Norway), a burrowing rat; and *Rattus rattus*, a climbing rat. The Norway is the more aggressive. Attack a climbing rat and he runs. Poke at a Norway with a broom or a rake, and quick as a flash he's leaped up and bitten you. Norways dig extensive burrows in the spring, usually near a source of food, and stay in them until the first frost. In the fall they move into buildings. They can jump three feet or so, or climb wherever there is good footing. But their nimbler cousins can climb a tree, a waterspout, a cable, or even a brick or concrete wall as fast as they travel along the ground. They nest in trees, under rock ledges or eaves, in lofts and attics. Both species eat anything edible, including their own kind.

How many rats are there around your place? Harold Gunderson, rat specialist at Iowa State College, has worked out the following rule of thumb for farmers: If you never see a rat but do occasionally notice droppings or signs of rat damage, there are from one to 100. If you see them occasionally at night but never in the daytime, there are from 100 to 500. If you see many rats at night and several during the day, there are probably from 1000 to 5000 of the bothersome creatures—not unusual on a farm.

One of the country's biggest poultrymen says rats cost him $10,000 worth of feed a year. Another says rats have killed 1500 baby chicks in a night, and have carried off 80 dozen eggs in a week. It has been calculated that rats annually eat or spoil as much food as 265,000 average farms can produce.

"Very few building materials can be considered absolutely ratproof," the scientists at Savannah reported. "Rats readily penetrate wood, have gnawed through most building-board materials and can in time penetrate heavy-gauge, hard-tempered aluminum. To test building materials in the Savannah laboratory, a cage was divided by a sliding panel made of plywood with a hole in one corner. Each night a solid panel of the material to be tested was substituted. The rats got used to going through the hole to get food, and at night they gnawed at the spot in the test panel which corresponded to the hole in the wooden one.

In one Savannah test it took rats just eight nights to tunnel through a two-inch panel of foamglass. A panel of ordinary aluminum, half an inch thick, was penetrated by rats in six nights. Of ten different grades of aluminum alloys tested, rats succeeded in drilling through all but one.

Wild rats and tame rats differ greatly in aggressiveness. Test panels which tame laboratory rats failed to damage in 52 nights were cut through by freshly captured wild rats in two to four nights. Laboratory rats come to know that each day the test panels will be removed and they can then get all the food they want. They get lazier and lazier at their work and have to be replaced.

Cleanup campaigns make only temporary dents in the rat population. In a large rat community there are generally a few wise guys who will neither nibble poison nor walk into a trap. Veteran exterminators tell of battle-scarred old rats that have been known to kick a spring trap around until it went off, eat the bait and

The rat is one of the most cunning and tenacious animals in the world. Each year some 110 million rats cost the United States and Canada well over a billion dollars in food alone.

then go in search of another free meal. Even experts, working under ideal conditions, expect no more than a 95-percent kill. The few remaining rats multiply so rapidly—theoretically a healthy pair can produce a third of a billion offspring and descendants in three years—that within nine months to a year they are as numerous as ever. The only effective campaign is the kind that never stops.

THE PESKY MOSQUITO
Allen Rankin

Few people on Earth are free from attacks by mosquitoes, those midget dive-bombers whose whining descent so often foretells a nerve-shattering bite. They plague man from the tropics to the Arctic Circle, from coastal marshes to far-inland deserts. Here are the questions most frequently asked about them, and the scientific answers:

Q. Why do mosquitoes bite us?

A. Only the female does. The male is not equipped to bite; his only vice is pursuing female mosquitoes. Entomologists now believe that the females of many mosquito species need an occasional sip of human or animal blood as a kind of essential vitamin, and that if they don't get their nip at least once every 25 generations their breed begins to weaken and die out. Luckily, the female's *principal* food is plant nectar.

Q. Why do we get bitten most often at night?

A. Probably because the species that is the biggest nuisance is the "house" or "rain-barrel" mosquito (dubbed *Culex pipiens* or "peeping fly" by the Swedish naturalist Linnaeus, a name which seems doubly suitable because it has a passion for peeping into human habitations and getting in through openings in screens), and this mosquito is a night feeder. Turning out your light is like ringing its dinner bell.

Q. How do these air-raiders find their targets?

A. Like some other insects, they are equipped with "chemoreceptors," a combination sense of smell and radarlike sense of "feel," with which they beam themselves in on the heat waves and odors given off by your body. The "nose" of most species is located in their whiskery antennae, but some have a sense of smell in the hairs of their legs.

Q. How far will mosquitoes fly to get us?

A. The house mosquito and its relatives seldom fly more than 1000 feet from their birthplace. They make up for this limited range by breeding within easy striking distance of people—in ditches, barrels, sewers. Some of the big saltwater-marsh breeders, however, can make mass raids on towns and cities from distances of 50 to 75 miles.

Q. How does a puny little mosquito get a grip on a human's tough skin and then penetrate it?

A. The female's feet are soled with friction pads and hooks which combine the hold-on virtues of the tennis shoe, the baseball cleat and the alpenstock. In her snout she carries a veritable toolbox of needles, probes and drilling machines. Her main instrument of torture is a marvelous high-frequency drill in the form of a hollow tube. In this tube are lancets to stimulate the flow of blood and a siphoning device to suck up the blood. This tube slips easily through the toughest flesh.

Q. Why don't we slap and kill a mosquito the moment we're jabbed?

A. Perhaps she may not hit a sensitive spot. If she does, we will feel it. But as soon as she punctures the skin, she gives us a hypodermic—a local anesthetic which, like novocain, deadens the victim's feeling. This fluid, administered via the hollow needle of the mosquito's tongue (which advances just ahead of the drill), also thins the blood. Thus, though ordinary blood tends to coagulate in narrow passages (the smallest tube that medical researchers have been able to draw blood through is many times the diameter of the mosquito's delicate sucking-tube), the mosquito can siphon off her pre-thinned drink quite readily—by means of a palpitating pump which is located in her head section. She sometimes draws out three or four times her own weight in blood.

Q. How does a mosquito generally manage to take off just before we slap?

A. The sudden tension of our skin "telegraphs" the blow. To the mosquito the slightest nervous rippling beneath her is like an earthquake, a warning of impending disaster.

Q. Why do mosquitoes bite some people and leave others alone?

A. Recent studies indicate that our breath, or rate of breathing, may be the attraction. Certain mosquitoes may be attracted by the large amounts of carbon dioxide exhaled by some people and animals, while other mosquitoes may be repelled by it. The experiments of Dr. W. A. Brown, conducted at the University of Western Ontario, provide dramatic evidence for this theory. He constructed two robot dummies, heated to body temperature and dressed to look like men, and placed them six feet apart. When the dummies were indiscriminately saturated with carbon dioxide, they failed to appeal to mosquitoes.

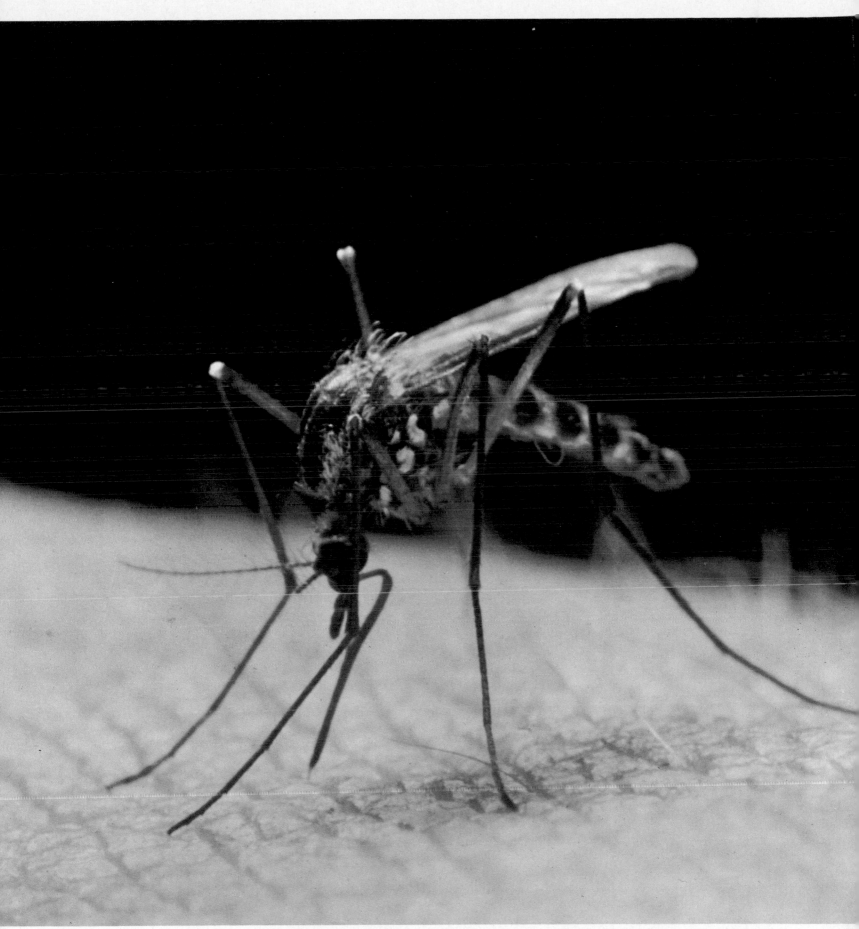

The mosquito has a head with compound eyes, antennae and a proboscis or beak. To its thorax or chest are attached two wings and six legs. Here, greatly magnified, is a female mosquito poised to pierce the skin of a human victim with her stiletto-like proboscis.

But when the carbon dioxide was exhaled from the heads of the dummies at a normal breathing rate, both their heads and bodies became attractive to mosquitoes. The moral seems to be: if you don't want to attract mosquitoes, stop breathing!

Q. Does the kind of clothes we wear affect our mosquito appeal?

A. Apparently. In his experiments Dr. Brown found that one tenth as many mosquitoes landed on white clothing as on dark. In general, the lighter the color, the fewer mosquitoes attracted. Texture most avoided —luminescent satin.

Q. Why do most mosquitoes sing when hovering around for a bite?

A. They don't. That five-notes-above-high-C aria comes from their vibrating wings. The insects may make other sounds, but of such low frequency that they cannot be heard by the human ear.

Q. How long does a mosquito live?

A. The average male's life is only eight or nine days. Shortly after his birth he chooses and woos a mate in mid-air, then flits pointlessly about, sipping an occasional vegetable juice. The luckier female generally lives for about 30 days. If winter catches her before she has a chance to deposit her eggs, she hibernates until conditions are favorable for her offspring—sometimes four or five months.

In warm weather it takes ten days for an egg to develop into an adult. In a temperate climate each spring-summer-fall period produces about 15 generations of mosquitoes. In only six generations the normal 100 eggs laid by a common mosquito could result in 31 billion descendants—if left unmolested. So mosquito control is not a luxury but an urgent necessity.

The mother's eggs are laid on the surface of water. In the larval and pupal stage they look like tiny snorkel submarines; periodically they thrust a "snorkel tube" above the surface for air. That's why oil spread on water kills mosquitoes in these two stages; their snorkels cannot break through the oil and as a result they die of asphyxiation.

The pupa finally splits open and launches a full-grown mosquito, which, the moment its wings are dry, leaps from its discarded shell. The males hatch a few minutes before the females and hang in the air above their launching sites, instinctively waiting for their mates-to-be to burst from their containers.

Q. Do most mosquitoes carry disease?

A. No. Of approximately 3000 species, very few are known to be disease carriers. In the development of human medicine, however, the mosquito was the first insect to be incriminated as a transmitter of disease. The great discovery was made in 1878, in China, by Britain's Sir Patrick Manson, who found that the *Culex quinquefasciatus* mosquito transmitted filariasis, a dread affliction which causes limbs and glands to swell and sometimes results in elephantiasis. By 1897 certain types of *Anopheles* mosquito had been proved to carry malaria. And in 1900 the *Aëdes ægypti* was indicated as a yellow-fever carrier. Other outlaws are now accused of transmitting various forms of encephalitis, or "sleeping sickness."

But the complete defeat of even these gangster mosquitoes may now be in sight. Vaccines have made it possible to check epidemics of yellow fever. The United States has demonstrated how modern medicine plus mosquito control have helped to hold down malaria. In 1962 only 119 cases were reported in the United States; military personnel stationed abroad and overseas civilian travelers accounted for 99 of these.

Q. Are mosquitoes good for *anything?*

A. Entomologists say that they are an important, easily caught source of food for other insects, birds, animals and fish. They say that without them many insect-eating birds and animals might be hard-pressed for food and might even perish, allowing even worse pests than mosquitoes to increase and plague us.

THE CASE OF THE BAD NEMATODE
Charles Morrow Wilson

They have no hands or arms, yet they take about a tenth of our harvests. They have no brains, yet for centuries they have outsmarted people. They lack noses, but they can trail better than bloodhounds. The name is nematode—Greek for a usually tiny, thread-like worm which has probably been on Earth longer than man. With an estimated 10,000 different species, nematodes are among the most varied and widespread of animals, but we rarely see them. One species or another is entrenched in every part of the Earth from polar tundra to the bed of deepest tropic ocean. They are parasites of birds, fish, insects and mammals. The largest species—27 feet from tip to tip—hitchhikes in whales. The smallest—about 1/75 of an inch—prefers people. At least 32 species, including pinworm and hookworm, cause diseases such as anemia and trichinosis in man.

There are good nematodes, too. To date, no more than one species in ten stands convicted as harmful. Thousands of species feed on decay organisms. Many feed on a great variety of pests, including insects and misbehaving nematodes. But the bad ones hog the limelight. Their biggest damage, only recently coming to be recognized in its full extent, is to agriculture. In the United States they are currently plundering some 30 of our important crops. The damage they cause is estimated at anything from 100 million to one billion dollars per year.

In 1941 the golden nematode, which has so fouled much of Europe's best potato land that a crop can be planted only once every four to eight years, turned up for the first time in the United States on two farms on Long Island. Great patches of green vines turned a sickly yellow and stopped growing; in five years the infestation had spread to 41 farms. New York State and the U.S. Department of Agriculture joined hands to check the invasion: soils were fumigated, seed potatoes sterilized, crops restricted, shipments embargoed. Nonetheless, by 1955 the infestation had spread to some 12,500 acres on 300 farms, and today, after the expenditure of almost ten million dollars of public money, the 25-million-dollar Long Island potato crop is gradually being rescued from these wormy villains.

About ten years ago another newcomer, the soybean cyst nematode, appeared in North Carolina. Two years later it turned up in Missouri and Tennessee, then in Arkansas, Kentucky and Mississippi. Scientists examining the bean plants found their roots infested with worms 1/25 of an inch long, behaving in a way characteristic, although not universal, among nematodes. Each nematode—most were female—had in her mouth a tiny needle like a hypodermic syringe, with which she slit open a root. Burying her head in the slit, she injected into the root tissue an enzymatic fluid to help her digest the plant juices, and began to feed. As she fed, her projecting rear swelled and exuded a jelly-like substance in which she laid eggs—which soon hatched and joined her in attacking the beans. She also produced eggs inside her own body until it was a distorted mass. Then she died, and her skin turned brown and hard to form a cyst attaching the eggs to the root.

It is these cysts that make some nematodes so hard to check. The eggs in them can lie dormant for years, until conditions are favorable for hatching. Development of chemical compounds strong enough to penetrate the cysts without killing the plants is a prime challenge to manufacturers of nematocides, but the challenge is being met.

Not all plants show the same symptoms of nematode attack. Often the damage is of the kind blamed on "worn-out" soil—the plants just don't flourish, however good the care. The designation "spreading

decline" is apt. Sometimes this gradual running-down is caused not so much by the nematode as by the fungi and bacteria which enter the roots through the nematode's puncture.

The "spreading decline" of Florida citrus orchards was first noticed in a few trees near Winter Haven in 1926. Dug up, the trees showed rotting roots. While researchers were studying the fungi and bacteria present in the rotting, the infection spread inexorably to some 1300 groves in 19 counties and cost growers millions of dollars.

In 1953 scientists finally identified the real culprit as the burrowing nematode, whose puncturing of the citrus roots opens the door for decay-causing organisms. In 1955 the Florida legislature appropriated $1,800,000 to launch the most drastic campaign ever

Within the roots of a cherry tree, mysterious, harmful nematodes and larvae feed on plant juices. Once a torment to farmers, they are now being conquered.

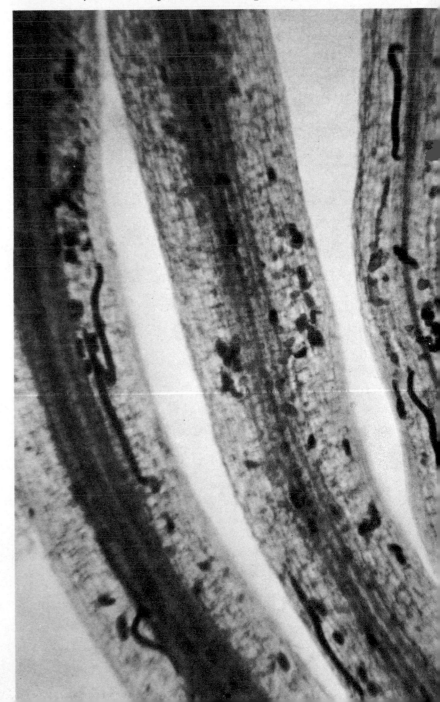

waged against a crop pest. With or without the land-owner's consent, State Plant Board men with bull-dozers have thus far ripped out 6378 acres of severely infested trees and burned the remains. The land is plowed, treated with a powerful fumigant and then given a two-year furlough before it is replanted to citrus. Some grove owners vow that the treatment is worse than the disease!

The burrowing nematode might have been un-masked sooner had it not been for the fact that nema-tology, a branch of zoology, is a comparatively young science. Even today there are only about 200 ac-credited nematologists in the world, most of them located in the United States and a few in Canada. These men have not yet found an altogether satis-factory control.

One natural defense is to build up the organic con-tent of the soil with decayed vegetation and manure. This increases the tolerance of the plants, and also encourages the beneficial nematodes and fungi that trap nematodes. Both are common in the soil. Another defense is crop rotation—moving a crop to a new field before the nematode population can build up. Spad-ing or turn-plowing the soil in hot, sunny weather also helps, because many of the plant-puncturing spe-cies cannot withstand drying. Breeding nematode-resistant crop varieties likewise offers some hope. (A commercially successful variety of resistant alfalfa has been developed, and a seed stock of a nematode-resistant potato is now being built up and will be made available to potato growers, it is hoped, in 1965 or 1966.)

The "scent" line of approach is especially intrigu-ing. Scientists have learned that the root of practi-cally every plant gives off a scented excretion or diffusate. Some attract nematodes; others do not. Many vegetable nematodes, for example, seem to abhor the root scents of asparagus or mustard; many nematodes which thrive on corn roots have no ap-parent liking for rutabaga. Some scientists hope that the strategic planting of herbaceous lures and repel-lents may perhaps be developed eventually into an effective defense.

Meanwhile chemical control—the use of soil fumi-gants that check populations of harmful nematodes without destroying the beneficial organisms in the soil—seems to be the most effective weapon. For a time chemicals had to be applied to the soil before the planting of a crop because they damaged the plants, but now chemicals are available which can be used in the soil without injuring the plants. Al-though not yet closed, the case against the bad nema-tode seems well on the way to being won.

THE FRIENDLY NUISANCE
Dorothy and Lewis Nordyke

The sociable little prairie dog who has burrowed deep into the heart and folklore of western America has had as rough a battle for survival as any sod-busting homesteader on the wild frontier. One of the best-liked of our wild animals, he has at the same time been thoroughly hated and persecuted.

The prairie dog is found only in lonely country, but there is nothing he likes so well as conveniently close neighbors of his kind. He enjoys a highly de-veloped community life, living gregariously in a craf-tily engineered colony of burrows and mounds that is so much like a city it is known as a town. Once uncounted thousands of these thriving towns spread over the rolling prairies and deep valleys of the plains and mountain states. In Texas alone, some 65 years ago, 90,000 square miles were occupied by prairie dogs. One single dog town—a vast metropolis—was 250 miles long and more than 100 miles wide; its population was estimated at 400 million. The total prairie-dog population of Texas was reckoned in the billions! These prolific creatures were usurping mil-lions of acres of rich range and farming land. As set-tlers moved in, the price of land shot upward—some of the land once perforated by holes about as close together as those of a miniature golf course is now worth more than $1000 an acre. Two hundred fifty-six dogs consumed as much grass as a cow, and on some of the big ranches there were tens of thousands of the unwelcome grazers.

Major ranchers initiated the slaughter of prairie dogs late in the last century. The animal was pecu-liarly vulnerable because he never wandered far from home. Acre by acre, in a country so vast that it took months to cover one range, men walked, scattering poisoned grain. As a follow-up they pumped poison fumes into the burrows.

It was not only the prairie dog's diet of grass that made him a pest. It was also one feature of the con-struction of his burrow: at the end of his hole he may tunnel upward to within inches of the surface of the earth, so that a few licks with his deft paws can quickly open up an air vent or escape hatch. These excavations cost the leg of many a fine horse. A good cow pony, if given his head, can gallop across a dog town without stepping in a hole, but he cannot see

Not dogs at all, but perky members of the squirrel family, prairie dogs were given their name because of their habit of wagging their tails and giving quick, sharp barks when they are excited.

an unfinished escape hatch beneath its thin surface.

To be crossing a summer-browned stretch of treeless range and come suddenly upon a prairie-dog town is an unforgettable experience. Not long ago we spent an afternoon on the outskirts of one that had escaped annihilation. Keeping our distance so we wouldn't frighten the alert animals, we saw grassless mounds, varying in height from six inches to two feet and fashioned craterlike around the entrance holes of the burrows. They were as neat as pins and sloped spaciously. Some of the prairie dogs seemed to be using their mounds as front porches, nonchalantly sitting there on their haunches and leaning back on their tails. Others were standing bolt upright.

A sleek animal loped to an outlying burrow and barked. Another emerged from the hole and the two wandered away together. We saw seven dogs gather at one mound, sit on their haunches and bark as if they were talking. Within ten minutes there were at least 20 as other dogs came to the powwow.

Elsewhere in the town there was vivacious activity: bright-eyed animals strolling and bowing, the young rolling and tumbling. When two females met away from their own burrows they bowed and then, standing straight up with their forepaws touching, they put their mouths together as if kissing. A male and female did the same thing, but when two old males came together they whirled and tried to cover each other with kicked-up dirt.

By some unfathomable system there are always sentries standing at rigid attention with their eyes alternately roving the sky and the ground. At the sight or sound of anything unusual, the sentries yap out warnings: two sharp barks and every prairie dog races to its own mound and stands upright.

Breeding occurs in the early spring, and the pups —only one litter of from two to nine a year—are born 28 days later. The chipmunk-sized young emerge into the sunshine when three weeks to a month old. The young ones linger at home for a little over a year, then pair off and dig their own homes, but they may not breed until the next spring. Just before autumn, prairie dogs gorge on all available food and fatten for winter. In the northern regions they hibernate; however, from Nebraska southward they pop up to the surface on sunny days.

The prairie dog is highly adaptable. He does well on desolate land that looks as if it couldn't support a spark of life other than a few clumps of dry grass, scattered weeds, dwarfed brush. Circumstances alone make him a vegetarian. In captivity he eats almost anything, and a jellybean is his favorite morsel. Like the squirrel, he lifts his food in his forepaws and sits comfortably on his haunches as he nibbles rapidly. He belongs to the same rodent group as the squirrel, the beaver and the pouch-cheeked "pocket gopher."

The animal is a superb engineer. His burrow, about four inches in diameter, goes straight down for eight to 22 feet, making it a "plunge hole"; other animals are content to race into a sloping burrow, but the prairie dog wants to dive deep into the earth when danger is near. A few feet below the surface is a niche, or "barking place"; if the danger alarm is not of an emergency nature, the animal stops here and barks irritably. At the bottom the hole makes a sharp turn, runs horizontally for eight to 30 feet, then slants gradually upward to the escape hatch.

With his engineering skill, the prairie dog provides air circulation and protection against flooding. Some years ago a Texas rancher ditched the water of a lake into a prairie-dog town. Three feet of water covered the surface for 30 minutes. Shortly after the water disappeared into the holes, prairie dogs started popping out; they had opened their escape hatches.

There is growing speculation that the prairie dog may have contributed tremendously to the land he so voraciously denuded of grass. Once in a period of 48 hours F. W. Ansley of Amarillo, Texas, poured 15,000 gallons of water into a prairie-dog burrow and didn't fill it. K. N. Clapp, an amateur naturalist of Lubbock, Texas, and E. G. Pope of the Fish and Wildlife Service agree with Ansley's conclusion that much of the water under the plains of Texas—a virtual ocean which is pumped out of wells and used for irrigation—penetrated the hardpan by pouring down prairie-dog holes.

After years of studying prairie dogs and killing out many of their towns, Fish and Wildlife Service Agent Pope believes the animal's troubles began with its name. "If it had been called anything else," Pope says, "it would have been a fine game animal. It would have been an eating animal and would have been controlled instead of exterminated. The Indians feasted on prairie dog. But, unless starving, a majority of the pioneers wouldn't touch the flesh of an animal called a dog. Actually the prairie dog, being a vegetarian in his native home, is as clean as many of our edible animals. I've tried the meat and found it tasty." Clapp, another who has eaten the meat, says it is superior to wild rabbit or squirrel.

Clapp has contributed in a major way to saving the prairie dog from extinction. Back in the 1930's he was a member of the Texas Parks Board and chairman of the Lubbock City Park Commission. When Mackenzie State Park was being developed in the Yellow House Canyon at the edge of Lubbock, workmen found two prairie-dog burrows in the park area, each containing a lonely pair. Killing the animals was the normal procedure, and Clapp was asked for money to buy poison. "Leave them," he ordered. "Someday we may have the only prairie-dog town in the West. People still like to watch prairie dogs."

Clapp's foresight has proved correct. Today the descendants of the two pairs number in the hundreds and dwell sumptuously on six well-grassed acres. More than a million persons flock to the park every year to watch the fat little animals caper.

Lubbock's example has led many other cities, some of them far from the small animal's native plains, to establish prairie-dog towns. And in much of New Mexico, Colorado, Wyoming and Arizona the dogs are coming back on national park land. They are kept under control—that is, prevented from spreading and becoming damaging pests—by trapping and shooting. In recent years some Texas ranchers have started small colonies for sentimental reasons and also for shooting. These colonies are likewise kept under strict control.

The strangest and most poignant prairie-dog town we have seen is on the playground of a home for children in a residential section of Amarillo. It is all that remains of a once vast dog city. The few animals that escaped extermination retreated to a vacant area and dug in. When the children's home was located on the ten-acre plot several years ago, the planners didn't have the heart to destroy the personable animals.

Attendants at the home told us that the prairie dogs have been of tremendous therapeutic service. Like the dogs, many of the youngsters coming to the home have had their little worlds suddenly blotted out, and they are sorely troubled. Often these lonely children wander out and watch the prairie dogs in their friendly and fascinating community life. Finding interest in the animals, the children gradually lose their heartache and, as the chin-up wild animals have done, adjust themselves to a new way of life.

Chapter four

CLEVER AND CRAFTY

We listen with pleasure to the tale of the fox that outwits the hunter by circling back and walking behind him, or the crow that sits on top of the scarecrow, or the big bass that won't bite the fisherman's lure.

Not long ago biologists said a beast could not have enough brains to be called clever. Such attributes as wit and intelligence were human traits. However, when scientists began to observe animals rather than dissect them, a new concept dawned. Animals *did* learn, they *were* crafty. Two British scientists discovered that the lowly octopus would pursue and devour crabs in his tank until an electric plate attached to the crab gave the octopus a shock. After that he studied his food before he ate.

In the United States, raccoons were given IQ tests and the startling results showed that some of them were smarter than some people. Studies of puppies revealed that the first time their food was covered they would experiment—sniff, paw, stand on the lid, tip it—until they got at the food. After that they did not bother with the preliminaries, they simply tipped the lid. The testers proved that the puppies had "learned."

No such tests were ever needed by those who have spent their lives with animals in the wild. Woodchucks and leopards, coyotes and baboons— indeed, both the hunters and the hunted—live by their wits from day to day, hour to hour.

That distinctive feature of the raccoon, his black mask, is really an ingenious protective device —nature's way of making it difficult for his enemies to locate the vulnerable pupils of his eyes.

BURGLAR FROM THE WOODS

George Heinold

The nocturnal raccoon, one of the fat men of the animal kingdom, is also one of its mental wizards. In laboratory intelligence tests the raccoon was found to be only a shade behind the astute monkey. Cooney was rated also as "temperamental, nervous, bilious."

Cooney's temperament may in some way tie in with his high IQ, but his nervousness may have a simpler explanation. He has been forced to spend a great deal of his time dodging hunters, trappers and clamorous hounds. His fur, a pleasing mixture of gray, black and brown, arrives on the market at the rate of a million pelts a year. Cooney has good reason for nervousness.

His biliousness can be blamed on greed. Few animals indulge in more food and less exercise. Cooney will sample nearly anything that is edible. When victuals are plentiful he stuffs his belly, belches, naps about 30 minutes and then gluts himself again. Such excesses neither improve his figure nor qualify him for long foot races. A 'coon that measures 32 inches from nose to tail tip often weighs more than 30 pounds. One Vermont bruiser weighed in at 49 pounds.

Slow and ponderous, the 'coon moves over the ground like his hulking relative, the bear. But this drawback is offset by marvelously dexterous paws. With these he can open the latched doors of poultry houses, climb metal posts, even snatch insects in flight. One raccoon, after breaking into our camp, unscrewed the metal tops of honey jars and ate their contents.

Unlike the rest of his pudgy body, Cooney's head resembles the fox's. It is finely chiseled and sensitive, alert and arrogant. Mother Nature has accentuated the brigand look with a black patch under each of his eyes. Prowling about at night, he looks exactly like the burglar he is.

Cooney's family is distributed throughout North America, from Mexico to southern Canada, wherever there are woodlands, marshes and streams to his taste. Pine and spruce forest, however, do not please him, for they do not provide ready-made homes in hollow trees and he does not build shelters. He finds hard labor distasteful. Sometimes he will establish residence in rocky crannies or in burrows vacated by groundhogs or skunks. On warm, sunny days, being an agile tree climber, he will borrow the nest of a hawk or crow as his solarium.

Cooney likes flesh, eggs and the produce of orchards, grainfields, nut groves, beehives, vegetable gardens and berry patches. But the bulk of his diet comes from the shallow waters of brooks, ponds, rivers and swamps. Frogs, trying to escape, seek sanctuary in the mud, where Cooney's tactile fingers unerringly seek them out. Clams, opened with the skill of an oyster shucker, and crayfish are also included in his bill of fare.

Late one night I heard a commotion in one of our plum trees and went out to investigate. In the light of the half-moon I saw a family of raccoons. The parents had climbed into the limbs and were shaking the fruit down to their young, who devoured it with gusto. When the ground had become blanketed with plums, the parents joined in the feast.

The extra poundage that Cooney's gluttony has accumulated hasn't taken the steam out of his wallops in rough-and-tumble scraps. A courageous battler, he never flinches. He can shake off a dog twice his weight, and his own sharp teeth and claws have made mincemeat out of many a hound.

Cooney's habit of rinsing most of his food before eating has won him a wide reputation for cleanliness. True, he washes his frogs and shellfish to rinse away unpalatable mud and grit. But there is still another reason for Cooney's apparent cleanliness—his lack of saliva. A dog, having plenty of saliva, can gulp down a hard biscuit without much trouble. But captive raccoons, who also enjoy dog biscuits, must soften them with water before swallowing them. They will eat foods of high moisture content without washing them.

By the time cold weather arrives, a northern raccoon, his sides bulging with fat, is ready for a winter sleep. Raccoons cannot, however, be considered true hibernators. In the Deep South they do not go into a winter sleep at all. In the north their fat nourishes them for months, but they do not lose touch with the world.

One sub-zero January day, logging on the edge of a swamp, we sawed through a tall whitewood tree. As it fell, one of its branches slapped against a hollow den tree. Almost instantly a blur of gray fur shot from its opening. It was a raccoon. My partner's dog gave chase. On the swamp's edges the ice was frozen solid, but in the center it was thin and treacherous. Cooney ran out onto the solid ice, stopped and paused to size up the onrushing dog. Then he employed an amazing bit of strategy. Turning on his side, he rolled across the perilous passage. The ice bowed and quivered, but Cooney's weight was well distributed. He reached the opposite bank and took off into the woods. The dog, not so astute, plunged recklessly onto the thin ice. A freezing bath ended the chase.

Young raccoons are born in early spring, in litters of from three to six. When about one-third grown, the cubs leave the den tree to hunt food and care for themselves under the tutorship of the mother. Cooney *père* hovers around to draw the chase upon himself in case an enemy happens by.

Cooney more than squares himself with man for his manifold burglaries. He saves thousands of trout, bass and other game fish by consuming turtle eggs. In the woodlands, when frogs and other delicacies are scarce, he goes after mice which destroy seeds before they can develop into young trees. Cooney may have a multitude of sins chalked up against him on Mother Nature's judgment day; but so long as his belly is full he will probably accept his fate with equanimity.

THE PRINCE OF CATS

Jack Denton Scott

For six motionless hours we had been sitting in a big kowa tree in the jungle of India's province of Madhya Pradesh. On that chill February night in 1958 my wife and I had been called from our camp to come quickly to the village of Dhega, where a pair of tigers had been killing cattle; we were the only people within 50 miles with rifles. Now, the moon gone, we were still waiting for the tigers to return to a buffalo kill they had made. "We will hear them when they come," said Rao Naidu, our guide. "When I flash the light, you and Mrs. Scott will shoot."

At last the barest scuff of sound came from the darkness. Rao Naidu flashed his light. Directly below us stood, not the tigers, but a large, tawny leopard, eyes shining like topaz as he looked up at us. He had deliberately bypassed the dead buffalo to stalk a fresher meal—us. Growling, he suddenly stood with front paws on the trunk of the kowa tree. My shot hit its mark before the leopard could charge.

That was my introduction to the regal, spotted creature, the prince of cats. Cleverer than the tiger, fiercer than the lion, pound for pound the strongest of carnivores, the leopard is the most beautiful and graceful animal in the jungle. He is also the most dangerous. One seasoned forest officer observes, "A leopard can hide his whole body where a tiger can't hide his head. He can leap on your back from a tree that a tiger or a lion could never climb."

Leopards are not normally man-eaters. Some become so by accidentally killing a human being and, finding how easy it is, concentrate on it. At times, physical incapacity or old age forces the cats to prey on human beings, but usually the leopard is such a master hunter that he has no need or inclination to attack man. Deadliest of all man-killers was the "Man-eating Leopard of Rudraprayag." From 1918 to 1926, in the 500 square miles of Garhwal, India, this fearsome animal killed 125 persons before he was shot by Jim Corbett, the famous hunter.

I had the opportunity to observe that the leopard is the cleverest of predators. Armed with binoculars, I waited several hours a day near a grassy clearing in the Indian jungle to see a sight Rao Naidu had told me about. Often chital, or spotted deer, came here to graze. Then one day I saw something rolling on the ground, playing with its tail like a house kitten. Chital are creatures full of curiosity and, as I watched, three came out to investigate. When one of the deer was within striking distance, the "kitten," a full-grown leopard, was off the ground and on the chital's back so fast that I could scarcely follow the motion.

Like human fingerprints, no two leopard skins are identical in their markings, or rosettes. Coloration varies from the normal buff or straw color with black rosettes to a heavily coated gray in Persia and a rusty brown in Java. African leopards differ from Asian in having slightly smaller spots placed more closely. The Indian jungle animals are the largest, with tawny coats and fewer rosettes. An average male measures about six feet eight inches in length, weighing 110 pounds. But many large cats measure over eight feet and weigh as much as 180 pounds. Since the tail often stretches another three feet, the cat appears enormous. Size, however, has little to do with a leopard's ability. This amazing animal has a variety of hunting tricks. In Kenya, white hunter Syd Downey watched one prepare to stalk a buffalo calf. To disguise his own body scent, the leopard rolled in buffalo dung so he could get close without frightening his prey.

I saw a pair of leopards using perfect teamwork as they hunted langurs in the trees. Almost as agile as these monkeys, the cats jumped from tree to tree, finally herded nearly all the monkeys to a large mahua tree, a giant creeper so isolated that the monkeys had to jump from tree to ground to reach it. As the last

Success as a hunter lies in ability to surprise. The leopard's feet are so heavily cushioned with noise-muffling pads that his movement has been described as "the flowing past of a phantom."

langurs hit the ground, a leopard leaped from the tree and easily killed one. The other cat calmly joined its mate in one of their favorite meals while the terrified monkeys that had escaped sat in the tree, howling.

The spotted cat's strength is remarkable. African safari-organizer Donald Ker told of finding a leopard kill, a 300-pound giraffe, high in the crotch of a tree. Another hunter saw a leopard carry a full-grown donkey almost a quarter of a mile over rocky hill country. Naturalist Dunbar Brander caught a leopard in a trap, but by the time he returned with his men the cat had freed himself, bending the iron jaw back with his free paw in an incredible display of strength.

Nature has equipped the leopard superbly to be the perfect killing machine and the faultless hunter. It has "radar" chin whiskers and bristle tufts on its forearms. These tactile organs instantly flash impressions to the brain. The upright ears are extremely efficient, picking up the slightest airborne sound, and the sense of direction in respect to sound is remarkable. After I had waited eight hours over a bait one night, a leopard approaching cautiously heard me—200 yards away—slip a notebook from my pocket. His head went up, and he bounded off. Yet the person sitting beside me in the tree hadn't heard a sound.

The leopard walks on his toes in the graceful manner of a ballet dancer. This gliding walk is effected by setting the hind feet precisely in the tracks of the forefeet, a perfect method of moving his 150 pounds silently across even the driest leaves.

The leopard's principal weapons of attack are claws —five on forefeet, four on hind feet—and these have an ingenious device which leopards share with most of the cat world and which prevents the claws from blunting by contact with the ground: in normal position the claw-bearing joint lies folded back over the preceding joint, so that the claw is off the ground and completely covered by a sheath of skin. When the leopard extends his paw to strike, a tendon connected to the limb muscles immediately pulls the reverted joint, drawing it downward and forward. Claws emerge instantly.

Even the leopard's strikingly beautiful coat, glowing with "black roses," aids in the cat's profession of killing —and surviving. This spotted hide is such perfect camouflage that U.S. armed forces in World War II copied its pattern for jungle warfare. By repeating broken lights and shadows, the rosettes deceive the eye and obscure body contours.

Yet with all these marvelous physical endowments the leopard's most important single asset is his intelligence, which ranks high in the evolutionary tree. There is evidence that the leopard has the ability to

reason. Dunbar Brander, trapping leopards in India, noted that when other animals were caught in traps they would howl and scream. But when a leopard was caught, the only sound was the closing clack of the trap itself. The cat would silently and intelligently work to free himself, seeming to realize that noise would attract man, his enemy.

A leopard takes only one mate, and the pair show strong affection for each other. A hunter once put poisoned bait out for a female that had been killing a settler's stock. Next morning he found the leopardess dead, her mate beside her, his head across her body. The leopard refused to leave his mate; he stayed there until he was shot.

The young—usually from two to four cubs—come into the world blind, after a gestation period of three months. Home is likely to be a cave, a hidden place under a rock ledge, or a hollow tree. From the time they are weaned at four months, until their death 16 to 23 years later, leopards devote their lives to hunting. The leopardess starts training her offspring in the art as soon as they can waddle. She teaches them to stalk her moving tail. As they attempt to attack the tip of the tail, she quickly flips it out of their way, keeping them at it until they can finally catch it. When the young are about the size of a fox terrier, the mother takes them stalking in forests or rocky areas. An Indian has watched a female with three cubs carefully kill a goral, or wild goat, exaggerating all her movements—the crouching stalk, the leap, the kill— while the youngsters watched attentively.

At the sign of danger, leopards freeze to the ground instantly, never run and expose themselves. An English tea planter observed an Indian leopardess teaching this important lesson. When her cub broke and ran at an unexpected noise, the mother picked the cub up by the scruff of the neck, brought it back to the place where it had started to run, then placed her paw on it, pushing it to the ground. When she removed the paw, the cub lay still, lesson apparently learned.

The dazzling beauty of the leopard nearly wiped out the African cat about 25 years ago. Leopard skins were then so popular as furs that African suppliers could not keep up with demand. In two years the cats were almost exterminated in the Wakamba country and the Kenya lowlands. The British government finally put the leopard on the game license and confiscated all traps. Since then the leopard has made something of a comeback in Africa. But once again his skin is coveted—it is one of the most sought-after furs in the United States. Let us hope that the world's most beautiful four-footed animal continues to survive in spite of his beauty.

Crows are gregarious and sly. They are gifted mimics and have an extensive vocabulary of caw-words for communicating warnings (they can even be taught to talk, like parrots and mynas).

OUR FINE-FEATHERED FIEND

Alan Devoe

Henry Ward Beecher once said that if human beings wore wings and feathers, very few of them would be clever enough to be crows. He might have added that few would be humorous, mischievous or unpredictable enough. For the common crow is a feathered genius and an endlessly astonishing bird.

A lady in Stewart, Ohio, owned one so dainty that he insisted on washing worms before eating them. A Staten Island crow not only could pick pockets but, when he found a pocket empty, would cry "Go

to hell!" and fly away in a huff. One kept by a Georgia moonshiner as a lookout against revenuers would ogle any attractive lady and mutter ribaldly, "Oh-boy-oh-boy-oh-boy!" To be sure, not all crows can talk, but certain ones taken young have been known to learn a hundred words and half as many complete phrases; and there are records of wild crows picking up such expressions as "Giddyap!" and "Whoa!" and "Hey!" which they hear farmers shout in the fields.

The common crow is found practically all over the United States east of the Rocky Mountains, as well as along our western coast line. In Canada he is known even in parts of the Northwest Territories. Because of his pilfering and destructive habits, state and local governments have offered bounties on him for years; but ornithologists wryly agree that there are probably more crows in the United States today than there were at the time the Pilgrims landed.

As crows are rather clannish, there are usually a number of nests—perhaps 50 or 60—within a small area. The birds exercise their sly mischievousness by stealing one another's nesting materials. When a nester flies off to feed, one of his neighbors adroitly removes the choicest moss and rootlets and secretes them in his own nest. Then, when the thief is absent, the recently burglarized bird flies over and regains the stolen goods, plus half a dozen other choice bits.

Being individualists and unconventional, crows in the nesting season sometimes become involved in the eternal triangle. When this happens, fights rarely result; the trio settles down to an unorthodox design for living. Two males have been observed feeding the same brood of fledglings, and I myself have seen two females alternately brooding a nestful of eggs while accepting the attentions of one strutting male.

Baby crows stay in the nest about three weeks, consuming their weight in food every day. Then for several days they practice flight maneuvers and wing drills before the critical elders of the flock, who teach them the rules of the crow community. The youngsters take advantage of their apprenticeship to swindle as much free food as possible. Though perfectly capable of foraging for themselves, they pester their parents with loud and piteous petitionings to be fed and sometimes may even feign illness in order to sponge on them.

A list of the things crows eat takes three pages of fine type in a Department of Agriculture report. The bulk of their diet is vegetables, fruits and nuts, but they can and do eat almost anything else: wasps, rodents, toads, carrion, even poison ivy. A pet crow belonging to a Long Island naturalist once consumed a pint of house paint and survived.

Certain foods are special favorites, and crows' stratagems for getting them are endless. Hunting mice, for instance, is tedious, so a crow sometimes rides on the back of a foraging pig; when the rooting porker turns up a field mouse, the wily bird gobbles it and flaps off with a cackle of mirth. If a crow spies a fox carrying prey, he sets up a tumult that fetches all his brethren in the neighborhood; then they swoop down and pester the fox until he gives up his prize.

All crows have the gift of mimicry. Outstanding geniuses can imitate the squawk of a hen, the whine of a dog or the crow of a rooster to perfection. I have watched a crow, artfully concealed in a chicken yard, clucking and crowing to lure a hen from her chicks. When this failed, the crow strolled forth from concealment and walked maddeningly up and down in front of the hen until she rushed at him, whereupon

he skipped deftly aside, and two hidden crow cronies darted down and seized two of the chicks.

Owls sometimes raid crow roosts at night and kill a sleeping bird. So whenever crows locate an owl in daylight they mob him and thrash him to the accompaniment of a hubbub of imprecations. They gang up similarly on hawks, raccoons, skunks, cats and any other creatures that they know might harm their eggs or young.

Of human beings the wise and wily bird can afford to be almost contemptuous. Crow sentinels, posted in a high tree while their fellows feed, can spot a gun barrel half a mile away, and never confuse it with a fishpole or a walking stick. When they signal that a man with a gun is coming, the flock departs in absolute silence at a speed of 45 miles per hour.

Without serious threat from enemies or starvation, crows enjoy a life-span of about 20 years and are free to spend much of their time in games and practical jokes. One favorite and rowdy game is waking-the-sleepers. On hot noondays they love to fly quietly over the countryside, drop down on a slumbering rabbit and rap him sharply on the skull, or settle silently on the backs of drowsy cattle and start a sudden terrifying uproar. Another sport is hide-and-seek. A young crow hides in a hollow tree and loudly sounds the distress caw. The flock rushes to the spot, hunts vainly and flaps away. This may be repeated a dozen times, after which the young crow pops out of concealment and guffaws. The flock, far from being annoyed, bursts into a cawing of general merriment and approval.

Some crows like to collect white pebbles and shells to use in their version of a ball game. One, holding a shell in his beak, launches out from a tree, and the others buffet him to make him drop his prize. Then another snatches the shell from the ground and flies off, to be set upon in turn by his playmates.

In autumn the small summer flocks of crows gradually merge into larger flocks and presently fly to their great winter roosts, sometimes 1500 miles south of the summer feeding grounds. A Johns Hopkins scientist estimated the population of a roost near Baltimore at 230,000; another near Arlington National Cemetery has held 130,000 crows; one near Peru, Indiana, 100,000. Records show that some of these great roosts have been occupied by wintering crows since the white man first arrived in this country.

Many are the tales told of the amazing doings of pet crows. One crow owned by William Crowder, the naturalist, developed the perilous habit of playing with kitchen matches. Not wanting the house burned down in his absence, Crowder substituted a box of safety matches. On his return he found his pet hurling them out of the window one by one, crying "Ha! Ha!" as he did.

The knowingness of a crow is not the thought-born "intelligence" of man. It is a thing of instinctive cunning and an innate prankish glee—a source of perpetual entertainment and surprise.

HE LIVES BY HIS WITS

Lewis Nordyke

Every device and trick known to man—financed by local, state and federal governments—has been used in an unceasing battle to eradicate the coyote. More than 50,000 are killed each year in the United States. Yet the sly little wolf continues to hold his own. Today he numbers at least two million, and he has spread from his original haunts in the western prairies and mountains to many a new neighborhood.

The coyote could retreat to the uninhabited parts of vast ranches and rough wastelands and live in comparative peace, but that doesn't suit him. Most species seem to delight in living among their enemies, matching wits with them and daringly feasting on the food they produce. A government trapper who found every one of his three dozen traps sprung and robbed of bait remarked: "The coyote is the smartest varmint alive." When a favorite Texas haunt became a practice range for bombers, the coyotes left—temporarily. Soon they were back to investigate. Things didn't look so bad after all, and they stayed. The coyote is a tawny-gray animal resembling a small German shepherd dog. He seldom weighs more than 30 pounds, but he is very fast; his speed has been clocked by automobile at 40 miles an hour. Scientists describe him as an inferior member of the wolf family, but his wits are so sharp that he thrives in regions where the more ferocious lobo has been driven out.

The immortal Reynard the Fox of our childhood literature never used a trick as clever as one pulled by Tippy, a pet coyote reared by a Texas family. Tippy's liking for fresh poultry stuck with him in captivity, and he began catching chickens. The family chained him to a corner of the house and fed him scraps. Tippy promptly scattered the scraps within the length of his chain and retired around the corner. The gullible chickens ventured forth to pick up the scraps; Tippy picked up fresh poultry.

A fat coyote is seldom seen. Regardless of the abundance of food, he stays in top condition for the running and fighting he apparently knows he must do. As a fighter he is quick as lightning and has a devilish trick of dragging his teeth through the flesh of an enemy. But he fights only in emergencies, preferring to use cunning.

The coyote is exceedingly clever at getting his hunting done for him. He will stalk an unsuspecting badger that is excavating a smaller animal's burrow, and quickly grab the rodent unearthed by the laboring badger. He watches birds of prey and takes their kill or the food they find. But he knows how far he can safely go: experienced hunters say they have never heard of a coyote attempting to steal the kill of a mountain lion.

Coyotes scavenge the highways, having learned that travelers toss out scraps and that cars kill rodents and birds. The coyote would prefer poultry or lamb, but does well on any food man produces, and on many that man wouldn't touch, such as snakes, lizards and insects. When he can get it, the coyote eats fruit for dessert. Vernon Bailey, a veteran Wildlife Service naturalist, reporting on the stomach contents of 450 coyotes taken in Oregon, found that 177 had eaten wild rabbits of all kinds, and 137 had accounted for other miscellaneous rodents. His conclusions were that the coyote "may serve a useful purpose in checking overabundance of jack rabbits, cottontails, ground squirrels, woodchucks, gophers, meadow mice and other small rodents."

The coyote lives in a den in a hillside, or under an overhanging rock, or beneath a stump. In most cases there are two dens, one for the mother and the young and the other for the father. Wildlife Service researchers believe that coyotes mate for at least a year and perhaps for life, because they have seen the same ones living together for long periods. And they have witnessed some mighty combats when "bachelor" coyotes attempted to interfere with family life.

The usual method of courting an unmated female is bloody fighting among the suitors. After a short time the female pairs off with one male and the rest depart. The female doesn't always pick the best fighter; sometimes she chooses the male that has received the most decisive licking. The coyote breeds once a year and produces a litter of from 4 to 19 pups. Under no circumstance will pups cross an invisible out-of-bounds line around the den. Snooping biologists have seen the father come trotting along toward home; the pups spy him and tumble over one another running to meet him. But, regardless of how far away the father may be, they halt at a fixed spot, approximately 50 yards from the den.

At about the age of two months the pups are taken out one by one, usually by the father, and taught to hunt. They start on large insects, such as grasshoppers, and graduate to field mice and rabbits. Next the parents watch the pups fight among themselves and occasionally step in to show how it's done. Parents keep their young under close protection until the pups are almost a year old, practically grown. They seem to know something about sanitation. A Wildlife Service observer saw parent coyotes rolling their young in the sand, and noted that the coyotes didn't return to the old den but dug a new one not far away. He investigated the old den and found that it was alive with fleas.

The male will dash almost into the teeth of howling dogs to lead them away from the den. And many a pack of trailing hounds has been confounded by the teamwork of a pair of coyotes. One takes on the dogs for a while, then drops down to rest while the other has his turn. They backtrack, crosstrack and break their trails in brooks and streams. It isn't unusual, either, for a pack of trailing dogs, even well-trained ones, to end by running in circles while the coyotes escape. At times it seems as if the coyotes are simply enjoying a daring sport.

In the open country of the West, trained greyhounds are the coyote's worst enemy; they can quickly dispatch him once they sight him. But the coyote has learned something about camouflage. D. M. Bentley, chasing coyotes with greyhounds in the Texas plains country, once saw coyotes wallow in weeds until their fur was thoroughly stained. When there was a chase, the coyote singled out by the dogs took to the weeds. Often his camouflage completely confounded the greyhounds, who do not hunt by scent. Coyotes have also been known to jump on automobiles and flatcars to escape pursuing hounds. They can be depended upon to develop a new defense for every new attack.

At one time, tourists from eastern states frequently bought or found coyote pups in the West and took them home as pets. The pets usually escaped. By this means as well as through natural migration the coyote has spread far from his natural haunts.

Some dark midnight you may hear a horrible, spine-tingling howl. You needn't worry; the coyote won't harm you. And you needn't get out your gun, for he's farther or nearer than he sounds and you won't be able to find him. But if you listen closely, you may hear faint howls in the distance; the coyotes are relaying the message, whatever it may be. They have a relay system of communication, but no mere man can decode the messages.

MONKEY TRICKS AND TRAITS
Martin Johnson

For many years my wife, Osa, and I have been deeply interested in apes and monkeys and have had several as pets, but we learned most about them at our cabin at Paradise Lake in British East Africa. In this spot, well beyond the haunts of men, the animal life used to be like that which Adam and Eve must have known. Our particular breed of tree folk was the Chacma baboon. This fellow is of an olive-dun color, weighing around 50 pounds. His long hair makes him look much larger. Like other species, he is gregarious. The individuals go about by families; the families, in turn, stick closely to their group or tribe.

From our windows we could always see baboons, in trees or at the lake, and often we have estimated that there were more than 2000 in sight at one time. One tribe dwelt among the rocks near a cool stream that never went dry. Their leafy beds were built on ledges, high out of reach of man or leopard, and we used to watch them moving along their narrow paths so slowly that they seemed to be holding their breaths in fear. Once while watching them on the ground we suddenly startled an old female, who, dashing off with a scream, started a stampede. One little fellow was left behind. Hoping to catch him for a pet, I ran after him. He glanced over his shoulder, squealing with terror, as he saw me overtaking him. Suddenly he decided it was no use, he didn't have a chance. He stopped, lay down on the rock and covered his eyes with his tiny hands. Trembling all over, he lay there, sobbing, just as if he knew I were going to kill him, and couldn't bear to see my hand uplifted to strike.

I picked him up. His heart was going like a trip-hammer. He moved his hand a bit from one eye and peered at me. The sight of my face so close was too much. He pressed his hand quickly back and cried out in desperation. When I found I couldn't soothe him, I set him down and backed off. Again he peeked at me from behind one hand, and gave a sort of gasp —I was too far away to grab him! He moved one foot, then another. Both worked all right. With a yell he turned and ran off to tell his playmates of his frightful adventure with a giant.

A young baboon is a funny creature. His head is too big, his eyes grotesquely large and his stomach all out of proportion to the rest of him. In his first year

The cry of the coyote has many meanings; whether it is a resounding howl of triumph, a call to a mate or a warning of approaching danger, other coyotes get the message.

Baboons are noisy creatures, boisterously gay in their youth, boisterously irritable in their old age.

he is almost as hairless as a baby, and his tail is like a rat's. But to his mother he is most beautiful; she fondles him by the hour. If there is an alarm, the little one takes a running jump to its mother's back and rides away like a little jockey, sitting starkly upright, not afraid now that he has his fingers deep in the fur of the one who protects him. If he gets tired of sitting up, he may lie down and, I believe, even go to sleep. Yet he never falls off, no matter whether the mother is racing wildly over the ground or making hair-raising leaps aloft.

I think most monkey children are disciplined by their elders more severely than human children are. Young monkeys are always getting themselves into scrapes, being cuffed and howling at the tops of their

lungs. If a baby grabs a berry or leaf it is not supposed to eat and puts it into its mouth, the mother doesn't hesitate to pry open the jaws and rake out the forbidden article.

Baboon babies play a great deal. They have a regular game of tag in which one tweaks another's ear or tail and then the whole crowd go after the offender. The old males are most resentful of gaiety among the young. Perhaps a pair of youngsters will be wrestling and rolling about and squealing—a common sight. Sooner or later the fun or the racket gets on the nerves of some old baboon, who interrupts his scratching and yawning to come over and take a wallop at the players. Pretending not to notice them till almost on top of them, he briskly darts out a hairy arm and heavy palm for a cuff that sends the innocents over and over in the dust, screaming bloody murder. The mothers never interfere in such circumstances.

The old males appear to get increasingly irritable with age. At night they make a terrific racket for hours before they are able to get to bed. We slipped up close to them one evening to watch, and found that each old male ranted around until he got just the spot in the tree he wanted. Then gradually the females and younger generation settled down. In about ten minutes the first and biggest old male began to squirm. Perhaps his bones didn't fit the angle he had chosen. Maybe he had rheumatism. Perhaps it was just plain cussedness that wouldn't let him go to sleep without disturbing others. Up he rose, grunting and rasping and blowing. The females lay still, pretending not to notice. The younger baboons made ready to move. Next came an angry bark.

"Why doesn't somebody pay attention to me?" the old scoundrel seemed to say. "Picked that bed yourself!" some daring young rowdy squealed.

Whereupon bedlam broke out while the outraged old fellow threw the nearest female "out of bed." The younger chieftains, seeing by what method dignity and respect are gained, began complaining in their own nook of the leafy apartment house, and not before they were tired out did the barking, clawing, cuffing and general confusion die away to the quiet of the jungle night, broken only by the roar of a distant lion and the *boom-boom* of a prowling ostrich.

In the daytime the "old men" are still overbearing and short-tempered. One wrinkled grandfather used to sit on a rock below us and cuff at every monkey that passed, just for sheer cussedness. Another big and aged baboon we came to call "Mr. Grouch" didn't consort with the rest of his tribe. He used to sit alone, moodily scratching and snuffling. Osa had a blind where she often took her lunch and stayed all day in order to photograph the game that came to the water, and Mr. Grouch finally discovered her refuge and deliberately set about making himself a nuisance.

Day after day he came as close as he dared. Everything Osa did he imitated as well as he could. If she brushed away flies, he waved a hand. If she shook a limb to scare him away, he duplicated the action. If she reached for a rock, he made a pass at the ground. If she clapped her hands, he rubbed his together. If she lost her temper, he'd lose his; and when she rose to chase him away, he'd run a few yards, then turn and chase her back, cursing her roundly in monkey language the whole time.

Again and again she came back vowing that she would shoot Mr. Grouch next time because he scared away the game. Yet I knew she would never bring herself to kill him. Indeed, she finally went so far as to invent games with him, trying motions that she thought he could not imitate. But he never was stumped. And in time his temper seemed to improve till he almost got to like Osa.

People often ask me just how much like a man these creatures are in their native haunts. The answer is that in innumerable ways their personality closely approaches that of human beings.

NOT SO DUMB—
THE WOODCHUCK
Alan Devoe

Nearly all of us who have ever lived in the country know Woodchuck as our number-one nuisance. He hides some of his den holes so completely that the horses and heifers break their legs in them. There is practically nothing in our vegetable garden that he doesn't like, and not much in our flowerbeds; and he will climb the best-made fence, or dig under it, to get the delicacies. Oh, we know Woodchuck, all right. Or do we?

When the heavy frosts set in, even though the golden autumn sun still shines warmly and there is still plenty to eat, Woodchuck retires into his four- or five-month hibernation. His sleeping chamber is far inside his burrow, down under the frost line. For his first few days there he merely naps and nods, sometimes rousing and prowling a little. Then gradually he sleeps more and more deeply.

Naturalists have dug Woodchuck up at every stage of his winter rest and watched him dozing away in special observation boxes, so we know the astonishing thing that happens. His pulse slows from his summer rate of 80 or 90 heartbeats a minute to less than five. Curled up tight, Woodchuck breathes more and more slowly until, when fully asleep, he is drawing only about a dozen breaths an hour. His temperature may go down to 40° Fahrenheit. He sleeps as the trees sleep, withdrawn into a deep life suspension that is very close to death.

Woodchuck's burrow is an engineering masterpiece of safety. For four or five feet he tunnels slantingly downward, throwing the dirt outside to make a mound. Then he takes a gradual turn and pats a hump of earth into place on the tunnel floor. An intruder, peering into the burrow, cannot see beyond this barricade, and Woodchuck uses it as a kind of observation stand. After the hump, he may tunnel another 25 feet before curving upward to an exit, and he may make several lateral tunnels, each leading to other exits. Working carefully from below, he pulls every crumb of earth inward and makes the exit hole as small as he can. Around these exits there is never a telltale mound. Here Woodchuck likes to sit triumphantly, chirping and whistling, while dogs bark their heads off at the earth-mounded burrow entrance way over

yonder on the other side of the field. The entrance mounds may grow higher and higher every year, although as far as we know the inhabitant does no fresh burrowing.

When Woodchuck is making his tunnel, he commonly hollows out a little side room for a toilet, so that the corridors of the burrow are kept clean. After a time Woodchuck brings the droppings to the burrow entrance and piles them into the dirt mound

The hibernating groundhog (or woodchuck) sleeps for months in a burrow ingeniously engineered. Legend says that if he comes above ground on February 2 and sees his shadow, he will return to his burrow for six more weeks of winter.

there. Mixed with earth and disinfected by the sun, the waste material becomes indistinguishable.

Woodchuck's whistle is his commonest utterance. But he growls, too, down inside his burrow when we pass near it. He sounds like a bear fight. He also makes a queer grating, chattering noise by grinding his teeth together. And he makes one more noise, still more astonishing: he sings, trilling and fluting away, very softly, like a warbler. But unless we are ever-lastingly peering into burrows and listening, we are not likely ever to hear the 'chuck's song, or if we do, we are likely to mistake it for a bird's.

Woodchuck has enough curious ways and unex-pected behaviors to keep a home-acre naturalist busy for a lifetime. How does it happen so often that a good terrier goes lolloping down a burrow in pursuit of Woodchuck and shortly comes back empty-handed? A determined dog does not back down from a fight, dangerous though an angry woodchuck can be. The answer is that Woodchuck can throw up an earth-work faster than the best dog can tear it down; and he can pack and ram it to the consistency of concrete. Many a terrier has gone rushing down a burrow and found what seems to be a blind ending. Woodchuck has just that minute made it.

Woodchuck's heavy digging claws are not at all suited for tree-climbing. But Woodchuck, neverthe-less, can go aloft whenever he feels like it. This may occur often or only rarely. Sometimes in the spring he gets a craving for fresh maple sap and goes clam-bering up a maple 40 feet or more. And a final whop-per, but a true one: when Woodchuck makes his descent from these heights, he almost always (un-mindful of the impossibility of doing it) comes down the tree headfirst.

MIGHTY HUNTER
OF THE WILDS

Laurie York Erskine

The gray wolf has an enormous range. In spite of every effort to exterminate him, he persists in most of Canada and vast areas of Asia and Eastern Europe. In the United States he is found throughout Alaska and in at least 14 other states. I would call him the most efficient big-game hunter of all four-footed beasts. Some of the big cats are faster and stronger, but probably no other animal hunts in such uncanny coöperation with his fellows, or is so sure of success. This has not only gained for him a reputation for supernatural cunning, but it has also earned for him the undying enmity of mankind.

In the early days of cattle ranching, many small stockmen were wiped out by wolves. Certain wolves became famous. The Aguila wolf of southern Arizona averaged one calf every fourth night for eight years, and sometimes he wantonly slew half a hundred sheep in a single night. The Custer wolf in the Black Hills destroyed $25,000 worth of stock in seven years; old Three Toes of South Dakota slew $50,000 worth be-fore he was captured after being hunted for 13 years.

We call him the gray wolf, but his coat is often a tawny brown or red. Off-color wolves can be easily mistaken for dogs. Once in Ontario I saw three ani-mals 100 yards away; one was gray, the others were brown, and they stood gazing at me with such friendly curiosity that I took them for Indian sled dogs. But when I stepped toward them they moved off into the woods, and I'll never forget the chill that ran up my spine when I recognized the unmistakable lope of the wolf. Slower than many of his victims, he makes up for this by his endurance. He'll keep up a steady lope of 15 to 20 miles an hour all night if need be.

An average gray wolf is five and a half feet from nose to tail tip, stands 32 inches high and weighs 80 pounds. Seven-foot, 175-pound wolves have been killed. Stanley P. Young, a veteran biologist of the U.S. Fish and Wildlife Service who, with Dr. Edward Goldman, has collected almost everything that has been written about the animal, reports that in Alaska he saw wolfskins eight feet long.

At two or three years of age the wolf finds a lifetime mate. The young are generally born in the late spring. The litter of from 4 to 14 whelps is nursed for about two months, during which the male hunts alone, dragging part of his kill home for his mate. As soon as the young are weaned the mother helps with the hunting, for the whelps are then hungry for meat. If the parents make a kill far away, they gorge them-selves with meat and disgorge it again at the den en-trance for the whelps. In the daytime the male wolf lies down on some high place overlooking the den where he can warn his family of danger. If a man ap-proaches, he may show himself to divert the enemy from his family. When the young ones are three months old the family lives in the open, sometimes roaming a territory of 200 square miles.

Moving always counterclockwise, the wolf patrols his hunting route constantly. He knows every hiding place and lookout, every spot where he can blend his color with the landscape and melt from sight. Along this route the parents teach their young to hunt. A strange wolf enters the area at its peril.

Since the young often stay with their parents until two or three years old, a family may consist of from five to eight full-grown wolves and a litter of whelps. This is the legendary wolf pack. It seldom includes wolves of more than one family, though several families occasionally run together for brief periods.

Few wild-animal families are more devoted. At least one member is always on watch to warn the others of danger. They often risk their lives to protect one another. Once in the wilds of British Columbia I found myself watched by a wolf crouching on a hill near my camp. When I reached for my rifle the animal dashed for cover. As I fired, a second wolf ran openly across the hill, yelping loudly—apparently trying to save his mate by diverting my fire to himself.

Wolves are immensely strong. At the mouth of a den in New Mexico I found the remains of a yearling calf; the head and hindquarters were missing, but the wolf had dragged the rest of the carcass two miles from the nearest grazing land over ridges and through tangled brush that my companion and I had found hard going.

A wolf's long, curved fangs are sharp as steel and he can sever the spine of a calf or break a deer's leg with one bite. Traps have often proved unable to hold him. Few dogs can survive a fight with a wolf.

Much of the wolf's diet is made up of rabbits, mice, gophers, birds and chickens, but he prefers big game, cattle or sheep. In attacking sheep and cattle he is seemingly crazed by their stupidity and defenseless-

ness and slaughters them indiscriminately, killing far more than he needs for food. But when hunting wild game he is a sportsman—and no more cruel than nature itself is.

Wolves scout for prey in packs, and when the deer, elk, caribou or moose is found, one or two wolves will approach the animal from downwind until it is started up. Then the long chase begins. One wolf will follow directly behind the quarry; others take strategic positions and head the quarry off so that it runs in a circle until it tires. Then the pack brings it down by tearing at its throat and hindquarters.

The coöperation of a hunting wolf pack is amazing. They seem to have a system of communication and take their positions like a well-trained team. They will

herd a quarry to the edge of a cliff and run it over, or corner it in a steep ravine. In winter they run a deer onto ice, where it can get no foothold. In summer they cover both banks of a stream and keep the deer swimming until it is exhausted. Bull moose, elk and caribou, however, often kill the attacker with their antlers or powerful hoofs.

Stories of human beings killed by wolves have little foundation in fact. Perhaps in Europe in the old days, when wolves roved near every village, some such cases may have occurred, but all who know the gray wolf of North America agree that he is no man-killer. The Canadian Wildlife Service knows of only one authentic instance of an unprovoked attack on a human being. Even a trapped wolf will seldom fight his captor, but will cringe away in fear.

The wolf has sharp eyesight, a keen sense of smell and good hearing. Hunters in prairie country have declared that wolves learn the range of a rifle and then stay safely beyond it. Men who have set trap guns have found the trigger cords cut by wolves that have stolen the bait.

In outwitting this cunning opponent, expert wolfhunters have succeeded best by taking advantage of his two most dependable habits. His appetite for carrion makes him vulnerable to poisoned bait. In the first great campaign to wipe him out from the cattle ranges, professional hunters killed many thousands by poisoning carcasses with strychnine. In time the wolf learned to avoid such bait. The wolf's second vulnerable habit is one which he shares with the dog. Along his hunting route he has visiting posts, the equivalent of a dog's favorite tree or hydrant. The trapper who can find these posts and conceal his trap close to them usually gets results if the trap has the scent of a strange wolf. Smelling it, a wolf scratches up the area and strikes the trap.

Hunters have tried to rear captured wolf pups with varying degrees of success. Many Indian trappers in the North use half-breed wolf dogs for their sleds, but these beasts can seldom be controlled by anyone except their master.

Thousands of years ago, when the first dog wagged his way into the cave man's heart, the wolf remained true to the wilderness—and he has never changed his mind. No lure of care or comfort will ever tame him, and he will outtrick man's every effort to exterminate him. Indeed, if naturalists have their way, we shall always preserve him in the remoter regions of the world where he can do no harm to man. There he will help maintain nature's control of the wildlife population, and remain the proud and defiant dog which refuses to wear man's collar.

Man is the only animal the wolf fears. A ruthless killer of sheep and cattle, he will approach humans only in the Far North, where few wolves have ever known man's scent.

Chapter five

VILLAINS OF THEIR WORLD

Most animals that kill do so out of necessity, but some seem to revel in a fiendish role. The shrew, the mink, the wolverine—these kill for the love of killing.

The extremists of death are not confined to mammals. Among the insects, there is that airy creature, the vicious dragonfly, specially equipped for speedy murder. An oyster-boring snail is the plague among shellfishes. And jellyfishes are as vulnerable as any human swimmer to the deadly stings of the Portuguese man-of-war. Even the birds have their Cain— an antisocial little monster called the shrike that makes the most objective zoologist shudder before its ferocity.

When a marauder steals out of its den and creeps through the underbrush, a cry goes up among the birds and beasts, warning that a villain is abroad. Killers arouse fear and anger in man and animal alike.

ARCH CRIMINAL OF THE WILD

Leslie T. White

The wolverine, scarcely larger than a Scottish terrier, is a unique combination of viciousness, courage and cunning. A fox, in comparison, is slow-witted and a lion timid. The most destructive of all denizens of the woods, this marauder is held in awe by woodsmen and dreaded by every animal in its habitat. Cougars and grizzlies have been known to relinquish a fresh carcass to him. Even a pack of wolves has given ground to a single wolverine. One specimen placed in a zoo promptly killed a polar bear.

Indians believe that the wolverine is the earthly abode of the devil, for how otherwise can be explained his seemingly supernatural knowledge of man's ways? He ranges throughout the northern woods of North America and Europe, yet because of his cunning relatively few people have ever seen a wolverine.

Usually he weighs between 25 and 30 pounds and, although of the weasel clan, resembles a small brown bear. Short-legged, with a broad, round head and low-hung body, he is incredibly powerful. A wolverine can move a log so heavy that two men would be required to lift it. The only thing weak about him is his eyes, which he has a habit of shading with his paw, as a man does with his hand. This deficiency is offset, however, by a keen sense of smell.

Wolverine fur has little commercial value, but it is the only fur that will not hoar up with frost when breathed upon. It is therefore prized for trimming the part of a parka hood that comes in contact with the wearer's face.

In battle the wolverine is a terror. He has long, curved claws and teeth that are razor sharp. He is absolutely without fear, and as he charges, bent on killing, he grunts and growls as if there were truly a devil under his shaggy hide. Regardless of the odds, he never retreats in a fight with another animal: it is invariably win or die.

The only animal I know of that ever killed a wolverine was, strangely enough, a peace-loving beaver. This little fellow was ambling along the shore of its pond, minding its own business, when the wolverine jumped it. Unable to shake off the assailant, the beaver managed to roll into the water and stayed under until its enemy was forced to release his hold. Though the wolverine is a good swimmer, he prefers to battle on land, and in this case he headed for shore. The mauled beaver, however, came up under the marauder, sank its powerful, wood-chopping teeth in his throat, dragged him under and held him firmly until he drowned.

The wolverine's home is in an isolated cave or crevice, with a bed of grass, leaves or moss. He mates between April and August, and from three to five young are born the following spring. The female, formidable at any time, is especially bold in defense of her young and on provocation will attack an armed man. The young get a brief course of instruction in deviltry until autumn, when the family breaks up and each member goes its solitary, evil way.

When on the prowl, the wolverine is a tireless wanderer and will cruise over an area from five to 60 miles from his den. He usually feeds on small animals, birds or carrion, but often goes after bigger game. *Forest and Stream* reported an authenticated instance of a three-year-old bull moose fatally wounded in a running fight with a wolverine.

Seeming to harbor a grudge against all living things, this scourge of the wilderness destroys for the sheer love of vandalism. No one knows how he acquires his almost clairvoyant understanding of steel traps, guns and other mechanical gadgets. Certainly it is not from experience alone, for wolverines in virgin territory exhibit the same uncanny skill. One of them will often follow a trap line at night, devouring what caught game he desires and maliciously destroying the rest. Sometimes he will follow the man, springing the traps for the sheer sport of it, or carrying them off to hide them miles away.

Some years ago I was visiting the Hudson's Bay Company's factor at James Bay, in northern Ontario, when a distraught Cree trapper came into the post. The factor, a Scot, knew that something serious must have happened to the trapper, for it was the height of the trapping season and the Indian was a long way from his grounds. The Cree lived alone in a small log cabin about 60 miles from the post. He said that in the first few months of the season he had done exceptionally well, and had stored away in his snug cabin a nice catch of marten, ermine and fox pelts. Then a wolverine moved into his territory. After one tour of his ruined trap line, the Cree determined to kill the raider. Suspecting that the modern steel trap was much too simple for his wily enemy, he set out one morning with his dog, a large wolf-husky, to build a line of heavy deadfalls—the swift-death type of log trap used by generations of his forebears.

Several times he crossed fresh tracks of the wolverine. The intermittent growling of his dog told him

The wolverine is a vandal and a murderer. He is sometimes known as the "glutton" because of his insatiable appetite—both for killing and eating.

the malevolent little beast was close, so he kept his rifle handy. While he was eating a brief lunch, the dog flushed the wolverine. Hearing the commotion, the Cree plunged into the thicket and discovered the two thrashing on the ground. The wolverine had the big husky by the throat. Unable to shoot for fear of killing his dog, the Cree used his gun as a club. The wolverine let go and vanished into the brush as the Indian vainly tried a snap shot. The dog died of a severed jugular vein.

More embittered than ever, the Cree worked hard building the heavy traps, but in late afternoon a blizzard came up; so he made camp for the night, hanging his snowshoes on a tree to keep them out of reach of prowling animals. In the morning he discovered that the snowshoes had been cut down, the frames eaten through and the buckskin lacings methodically chopped into short lengths. Without snowshoes he could not wade through the deep drifts, and he had little food with him. So, after hiding his equipment, he floundered off in search of willow suitable for fashioning improvised snowshoes. He was gone less than an hour, but on his return found that his blanket was shredded and the small metal container carrying his matches had vanished. Worst of all, his precious rifle had been dragged away.

Forcing back panic, the Indian set about making a crude pair of circular snowshoes with the willow branches. It was a torturous job, for he had no tools and no fire to warm his freezing fingers, but, salvaging what he could of the old buckskin lacings to make a temporary webbing, he at last was able to set out at dusk for his cabin.

What he found at home was heartbreaking. The wolverine had methodically destroyed the Cree's entire catch of pelts. He had eaten, carried off or otherwise hopelessly befouled all food not in cans. Everything destructible had been ruined.

The sympathetic old factor gave the Cree credit for a complete new outfit of food, blankets, snowshoes, traps and a gun. After the Indian had left to continue his battle with the wolverine, I remarked that never before had I heard such a fantastic yarn. The dour Scot took down from a shelf a small booklet prepared by the Hudson's Bay Company for professional trappers. The passage on the wolverine ends with these significant words: *When the wolverine appears on his line, the trapper has but two alternatives: He must trap the wolverine or give up trapping.*

"Fantastic, aye, that it is," the veteran factor admitted, "yet I have known much the same thing to happen many times. No other creature in the north equals the little fiend."

BUTCHERBIRD
Alan Devoe

As every fiction writer knows, a powerful and clear-minded murderer does not make an effective villain. He may produce a response of plain fright, but he does not "make the flesh creep." For *that* effect we must have somebody twisted and strange, a personality off key. This, no doubt, is why we may be given such an odd feeling by the quiet-colored little bird called a shrike. In popular language its name is butcherbird. It is a good name.

To see a hawk wheeling and crying and peering at the earth far below in search of prey is to see something splendid. We may wince a little as the bird swoops in its tremendous dive, sure and relentless as the angel of death. But there is a cleanness in it. We can exult with a hawk. Even veteran naturalists, however, are moved to an uneasiness by shrikes.

A shrike appears to be—indeed is—a songbird. It is not any bigger than a robin, and it is colored in bluish grays and white, rather like a mockingbird. It sings a pleasant, low-voiced, caroling song full of little chucklings, and its nest is daintily lined with rootlets, feathers and fine grasses. A shrike has the gentle little feet typical of a perching bird. A facial strip of black, like a tiny mask, gives the bird a look of trimness, demureness. This is the way a shrike looks and sounds; and this is what can give a man a "cauld grue."

For a shrike is a bloodier killer than a hawk. It has neither the size nor the equipment for massacre, but it has the will. Only the shrike's beak—hooked, notched and toothed—is serviceable as a death instrument. Its gentle song can change in a moment to a shrill shrieking. It can fling itself upon a bird as big as itself, or bigger, and kill it in a fumbling frenzy. A shrike perches on a telephone wire or in the top of a small tree, twitters its soft little song and watches for the stir of a grasshopper, a mouse or a sparrow or any small bird. If nothing stirs, it may venture on an expert mimicking, and from its throat comes the plaintive, squeaky sound of a baby bird in distress, fetching most of the songbirds in a neighborhood.

Watchful, the shrike eyes them and makes a selection. That plump sparrow, perhaps, over in the maple sapling. Shadow-quick, the shrike slips from its perch and rushes at its prey. A shrike is fast, but so is a terrified sparrow. Hardly ever can a shrike make a

The Dr. Jekyll and Mr. Hyde of the bird world, the demure-looking shrike, turns into the most horrible killer of all.

clean pounce, as a hawk does. There begins a long and terrible pursuit. Having no talons, a shrike must beat its prey to earth. It must catch up with it, rise above it and then come down on top of it and smother it to the ground. The chase has a kind of nightmare quality: so absurdly near the ground, so queerly horizontal and so wildly erratic. The fleeing sparrow twists, turns, dodges around bushes, fence posts, anything. With incredible intentness the shrike follows, rising and putting on added speed each time the sparrow tries to rise, forcing him earthward again. Out of the shrike's throat now comes something not at all like its pretty songbird's song. This is its murder noise. It sounds something like *Keeeeee!*—rather like the thin, shrill blowing of a child's tin whistle.

A final twist and dodge and rush of speed, and the shrike drops on the sparrow with flailing wings, bearing him clumsily to earth. The shrike's weak feet cannot strike a deathblow. There is a tussle, the shrike clubbing the sparrow's head with its hooked beak. Presently the sparrow has been bludgeoned and ripped to death.

The shrike gathers up the body and flies laboringly away to its larder. This is most commonly a thorn tree. The shrike shifts and maneuvers the body against the point of a long thorn. With a heave and a push he skewers the sparrow on it, much as a butcher hangs up a side of meat. The shrike may eat the sparrow at once, or he may only sever the head and daintily pluck out the lungs. Or he may not eat at all. Shrikes kill to store. They also, apparently, kill sometimes just because killing is their life.

Thorn trees are not as numerous now as they once were in many parts of shrikes' territory. But the butcherbird has taken to using barbed-wire fences. When thorns and barbed fencing are both absent, the shrike jams the sparrow between two twigs close together and secures the body by twisting and twining one of the frail legs as a man might twist a wire.

A naturalist knows quite well that all life, without exception, feeds upon other life. The natural world is full of killing, as it is full of birth, play, happiness and fulfillment. There should be no reprehending of shrikes for doing a thing natural to them. All the same, that little tin-whistle cry of *Keeeeee!* is a queerish thing to hear. That funny, fumbling, implacable flight . . . that smothery pounce, the clubbing and beating and tussling . . . all those little impaled bodies, skewered in the thorn tree, with their heads pulled off . . .

It is not too difficult to keep in mind the rightness and soundness of things when it is hawk wings that flash and those sure, strong talons that strike and kill. The test of a philosopher is the butcherbird.

THE FIERCEST ANIMAL ON EARTH

Alan Devoe

When I was a boy I used to wonder, as boys do, what wild animal was the most ferocious in the world. The lion, perhaps? Tiger? Grizzly bear? When I grew up to be a naturalist and learned the answer, I was astonished. The fiercest of all fighters and the most voracious predator is a tiny mammal, the common shrew. You would have to put at least two of them on a scale to register one ounce.

A shrew is so savage that it will attack, kill and devour animals twice its size. It has such a prodigious appetite that it can eat the equivalent of its own weight about every three hours, and it burns energy so fast that if deprived of food it will starve to death in less than a day. There are shrews of one sort or another in most parts of the world—in the tropics, deserts and the arctic. The three-inch-long pygmy shrew, found in Virginia, Maryland and North Carolina, is the tiniest mammal in North America, and another member of the shrew family, the two-inch, fat-tailed variety of Europe, is the smallest mammal in the world.

Probably not one person in 100 is aware of ever having seen a shrew, yet in many countrysides it is the commonest animal of all. It looks much like a wee mouse with a sharp, pointed muzzle, tiny eyes that are barely visible and velvety, dark gray or sepia fur. What we see is just a scurrying little blur as the shrew whisks through the grass in its desperate, ceaseless search for food.

In its grass-roots jungle the little assassin has to rely on sniffing out its prey or blundering upon it, for its pinhead eyes see little. It lifts its muzzle, sniffs, darts around a grass tussock, sniffs again, whizzes off at a tangent through the grass and suddenly makes a springing leap like a tiger attacking its prey. It has found a beetle, perhaps, or a butterfly, slug, centipede or cricket. A shrew will eat almost anything, and it gobbles so fast—all the while shaking in spasms of excitement—that it devours its victim in a few seconds. The fact that it dispatches hordes of insects of

A shrew uses up its life force so prodigally in hunting and eating its prey that it dies of old age at about 16 months.

all kinds makes it one of the most valuable animals.

It is afraid of nothing. When I was a boy I put a shrew in a cage with a young white rat, intending to leave it there for a few moments while I got its own cage ready. Instantly the furry midget reared up, bared his teeth and let loose a high-pitched, chittering squeak of rage and hunger. In panic, his hulking adversary cowered in a corner. Then in a flash the shrew was across the cage, slashing at the rat's throat, swarming all over him. At the end, the shrew gobbled up every last vestige of the rat, including its bones and claws and fur.

A naturalist friend of mine who keeps snakes and feeds them on mice once made the mistake of giving one of his charges a shrew. When he visited the reptile's cage next day it contained only the shrew, racing around in a desperate search for more snakes. It is even fatal to put two shrews in a cage together, for in a few minutes there will be just one, licking its chops and waiting for another meal.

The life of this bloodthirsty creature begins in a loose ball of leaves and grasses usually hidden in a hollow stump or log or the abandoned burrow of some other small animal. In this nursery is born a litter of four to ten pink, crinkly babies the size of honeybees. They begin to creep around the nest when they are about a week old. At three or four weeks their mother weans them, changing them to a diet of flesh —usually earthworms. A few days later she unceremoniously boots them out of the nursery, and each youngster is on his own. Whatever small fellow creature he may meet in his life of less than two years, it will never cross his mind to think, "Is he bigger than I am?" There is just one thought in his tiny skull: "Let me at him!"

What of the shrew's natural enemies? Only a few strong-stomached hunters such as great horned owls, weasels and bobcats will eat short-tailed shrews. For on his stomach the animal carries a potent gland containing a sickening musk that he can loose when overwhelmed by an enemy. The fox that pounces on a short-tailed shrew in the tall meadow grass usually drops his catch in a hurry.

The short-tailed shrew has still another protective device. Tests have proved that its salivary glands contain a venom similar to that secreted by such poisonous snakes as the cobra. When its teeth slash an enemy, the victim grows foggy-minded, then has trouble breathing, then is stricken by a numbing paralysis. As far as naturalists can tell, the short-tailed shrew is the only species that carries such powerful venom. But every shrew carries a ferocious hostility, a ravenous hunger and reckless rage.

TERROR OF THE INSECT WORLD

Alan Devoe

In inaccessible regions of the East Indies, if Sunday supplements are to be trusted, there exists a beast that may with only mild exaggeration be called a dragon. It is quite possibly true. But why go all the way to Komodo to find a dragon? There is one in the neighborhood of your nearest brook or fishpond. And not even the most fantastic tale can produce a dragon more gratifyingly bloodthirsty, or more singular (and even improbable) in some of its ways of behavior, than the dragonfly.

That large and malevolent-looking insect, swift and slim, with gauzy wings and a long body like a stiletto, darts and swoops along the course of country brooks and among the bordering reeds of millponds. It is so startlingly quick and evidently purposive in its aerial darts and rushes that it may give consternation to any beholder unfamiliar with it. Something of this shows forth in the popular names that have been bestowed on it: "devil's darning needle," "horse-stinger," "snake doctor." A dragonfly, so superstition goes, will use its needle to sew up the lips of liars.

A dragonfly in flight has a menacing look. And it is possibly even more disturbing when at rest on a brookside twig, displaying the wicked length of its needle, the queer venation of its flatly outstretched wings, the great mouth and a huge-eyed head which rotates peeringly upon a thready stem of neck. Yet the truth is that this sinister-seeming animal is entirely without ability to do man any harm. Indeed, it is a friend to man, for it slaughters mosquitoes.

In the development of a dragonfly's life there is no stage, as among many insects, of arrest and quiet, no time spent as a pupa between the larval and adult periods. From the time of its emergence from the egg, the dragonfly is active and equipped to pursue its role as the terror of the insect world.

The newly hatched dragonfly, called a nymph, lives under the water: crawling warily through the thick mud of pond bottoms, clambering heavily up the stalks of water plants, retreating during the coldest part of the winter to a torpid near-hibernation in the ooze. Already, as a larva, it has the characteristics of a dragon. Its lower lip is grotesquely huge, hinged, with sharp hooks at its extremity. The young dragonfly can hold back the great lip so that it covers the low-

The dragonfly's "needle" is in reality an enormously elongated abdomen. His head, hollowed out at the back, can rotate, thus giving his large, compound eyes a wide range of vision.

er part of the face like a mask. Masked (and looking something like a miniature caricature of some sort of unearthly bulldog), it goes creeping along the stream bed.

It is indeed ravening for blood, as any greater dragon might. With a halt and a sidle, it abruptly extrudes its gigantic lip, crooks the hooked rim of it upon a beetle larva, whisks back the lip and swallows. Masked, it moves on. It flickers once more and a little brook snail has been trapped. A few moments later the monstrous, curling lip has put an end to a larval mosquito. Eating, swelling, molting, the dragonfly nymph lives out its months of immaturity as one of the most resolute and insatiable carnivores in all its murky world of pond muck. It even makes a meal, when it can do so, of any of its fellow dragonfly nymphs that are less adroit.

One day in spring (or sometimes at other seasons) the dragonfly nymph crawls up a waterweed for the last time. It halts a few inches above the water surface; its nymphal skin splits; and it comes forth to dry the strong, veined wings and the shimmering needle body of adulthood.

A dragonfly can outfly a swallow. It is expert in the sudden halt, the instant takeoff, the abrupt contrivances of banking and veering. It establishes a regular round for itself, a kind of patrol, from this tree to that twig, from this sun-warm stone to that tussock. It is singularly methodical, neatly adherent to a schedule for its round of massacre.

The dragonfly's legs are all bunched at the front. Useless for walking, they serve as a special kind of basket. In full flight the dragonfly scoops and tumbles its prey into the basket of its little bunched-together legs, where it can hold the victims until they are stuffed into the huge jaws. In two hours one scientist fed a captive dragonfly 42 horseflies without satiating it. Others have found that if a dragonfly's tail is bent around and presented to its mouth, the dragon will begin gobbling its own body and continue until it has eaten all of itself that it is able to reach. Remote Komodo has no hungrier dragons, and no odder ones.

TERRIBLE-TEMPERED MR. MINK

George S. Fichter

One winter day years ago I set a trap beside a creek and checked it regularly. It stayed empty for several days and then, on a foggy morning I'll never forget, I saw that it held a small brown animal. As I approached the trap in soft ground, my captive did not hear me coming. He was crouched over, busily gnawing at something. A closer look told me that the animal was a mink and that he was gnawing his leg, trying to get free. Suddenly I stepped on a twig. The mink jerked his head toward me, his beady eyes snapping with rage. Then he screamed and lunged the length of the chain—first toward me and then in the opposite direction to escape.

Bold and defiant, he was ready to pit his smallness

against me. Suddenly I was ashamed. I wanted to set him free. With a sapling I pushed down on the spring that held the jaws of the trap together. The mink attacked the pole furiously, sinking his teeth into the bark and shredding the wood beneath. Even when the trap opened, freeing his bloody leg, he continued his frenzied battle. The moment he realized he was loose he began a limping retreat. Every few feet he stopped and stared back with fierce hatred. Soon he was out of sight. From that mink's fervent desire to live I gained a deep respect and compassion for all living creatures, and I never set a trap again.

The mink is one of the least sociable animals of the woods. He is hostile even to his own kind except in the mating season, which coincides with the late winter thaws. But there is no affectionate courting when mink meets mink. They satisfy this basic urge with the same intense drive which characterizes their entire lives. At such times the males lose much of the caution which ordinarily keeps them out of sight, even occasionally showing themselves in daylight.

If you're lucky enough to come upon one, you'll

A mink mother doles out more love to her young than you would expect from such a murderous creature. Some have even allowed their kits to eat them alive when their milk ran short.

see a sleek brown creature smaller than a house cat, slim-bodied and short-legged. He either hunches his way along rapidly, with his back arched, or glides as gracefully and smoothly as a serpent, his body pressed to the ground. He can slither into view and out again so swiftly that you'll wonder whether you really saw an animal at all.

The female is smaller than the male and seldom roams far from her home, which is usually somewhere along a stream or a pond. When she wants a place to bear her young, the mother-to-be may dig the den herself, but she's just as likely to appropriate a muskrat's quarters. It needn't be an abandoned site, for if the mink wants it she moves in and dispatches the occupant. While she waits to give birth she lines the nest with grass, leaves or weeds and adds to this some soft fur from her body as she sheds her winter coat. Her four to eight kits, born blind and nearly naked, start life an inch and a half long.

In about five weeks the kits' eyes are open and their bodies are covered with fur. Then the mother begins bringing home mice, crayfish and other tidbits for them to test their teeth on. When they are about seven weeks old they are ready to go hunting with her. The mother sets about the task of teaching them to be killers, eager to attack anything which shows signs of life.

Grasshoppers or crickets are good starters for the kits. They may find a bird's nest and eat the eggs or the young birds. Meadows yield mice, and now and then the family raids a rabbit's nest or a muskrat's den. Most of the mink family's fare, however, comes from the water: frogs, minnows, crayfish. Mimicking their mother, the eager little gangsters stretch out full length on a log or a rock on the bank of a stream and watch eagerly for a meal to swim by. Their mother is so quick she can catch a trout, one of the fastest of freshwater fish. Soon the young become keen hunters, sometimes taking on such unlikely customers as snapping turtles.

Before the summer is over, the young mink are able to take care of themselves. Then, with no warning, their mother disappears. Already quarreling and fighting among themselves, the kits soon separate and go it alone. By late fall their fur becomes rich brown, thick and soft beneath and protected by dark, lustrous guard hairs. Beneath their throats the brown is interrupted by a solitary white patch, and there are flecks of white along their bellies. Their bushy tails are a glistening dark brown or black.

Mink are versatile, ranking second in nearly every specialized attribute in the big family of mammals to which they belong. Their musky odor is not as far-reaching or as long-lasting as the skunk's, but it is nauseating if you get a close whiff. And while they are not as capable in the water as the otter, their partly webbed feet equip them for a successful semi-aquatic life. They can climb trees well enough to prey on birds and squirrels. Thus mink are suited for a great variety of life's situations.

In every wakeful moment the fidgety and inquisitive mink is on the move. Follow his meandering tracks in the snow and you'll discover how he spends his time. Sometimes he darts into a woodchuck den, completes his exploration, comes out a side door and hurries on. Or he may make a kill there and bed down for a day or two before hunger sends him hunting again. If he happens by a farmer's chicken house, he may stop in for a meal. One hen would be enough to take the edge off his appetite, but the mink, driven by his killer instinct, goes into a slaughtering rage, often riddling the whole roost. He kills by grabbing his victim's throat and severing the jugular vein with one grisly bite. Then he eats his fill, consuming first the head and entrails.

Scoundrels though they may be, mink rate a pedestal in the eyes of women. Mink coats, which require from 60 to 80 pelts and many hours of skilled labor to produce, range in price from $2500 to $20,000. Before World War II wild mink provided most of the pelts. Nowadays about 90 percent comes from ranch-raised animals. Bred for size and fed a controlled, balanced diet, top ranch mink may be a third larger than their wild forebears. Also, they are pelted when their furs are prime. Geneticists have arrived at a dazzling array of true-breeding mutation colors. Starting with the standard dark mink—the wild type—they have produced a variety of colors, including sapphire, white, topaz, pearl and lavender.

Mink ranchers must keep mink on their minds 24 hours a day to make certain their valuable animals reach the pelting stage in good condition. Tainted meat may set off an epidemic of botulism which can wipe out an entire ranch in a matter of hours. Distemper, highly contagious, can show up suddenly and cause the death of nearly all of the young and half or more of the adults before it can be checked. Because ranch mink will murder each other, the cantankerous cutthroats must be kept in separate cages. And, more costly to ranchers, agitated mink mothers will kill their kits.

Domestication has not altered the mink's attitude toward man. Even after many generations of captivity they remain the same savage beasts they are in the wild. Without so much as giving the food a glance, a ranch mink will gladly bite the hand that feeds it.

PART

5

THE TIDAL FORCES

*Light and darkness and the seasons govern
the lives of animals by day and by year.
Some are sent from one end of the
globe to the other, and some are put to sleep
for months. None could survive if they
did not act according to the calendar
of the Earth and the Sun.*

Chapter one

ANIMALS ON THE MOVE

Ever since animal life began on Earth there has been movement—simple, everyday movement like that of the bee and the ant and the bat, as well as massive migrations of creatures following the sun for warmth and food, or undertaking great journeys to find new homes.

Man has not understood much about animal movement until the arrival of the age of electronics. Then, suddenly, we learned that sonar and computers are primitive instruments compared to the devices the bat uses to fly at high speeds in caves without hitting a wall, or the directional finder of the golden plover which guides it over 2500 miles of ocean from where it was born to its winter home. These are capacities we have yet to comprehend.

Somewhere among the birds and beasts lie complicated answers to all our earthly problems of movement, and when we know how a thousand herring pass so swiftly over the ocean floor without ever touching or colliding, we may even end our traffic accidents.

THE MYSTERY OF PATHFINDING

Alan Devoe

One sunny summer afternoon in 1911 a man crouched motionless in a field, peering at contraptions like sunshades which he had set on the ground near a tilted mirror. Dr. Félix Santschi, a zoologist, was testing a theory about how an ant finds its way home.

Ants that go in groups usually travel along a narrow trail that is chemically saturated by their passing; when one of them comes upon such a trail it is easily identified as the right roadway. Further, the insect can tell which way is "out" from the nest and which "in," perhaps because ants of a group leave a subtly different chemical trace depending on whether they are going hunting or coming home. But how about the solitary ants that forage alone and return home circuitously instead of by a trail? How can they keep their bearings amid a jungle of plant stems?

Dr. Santschi had guessed that ants might be sensitive to the direction of light, and take readings from the sun. An ant was coming now, hurrying as if sure of its direction. Suddenly, as the ant approached the doctor's equipment, it slowed and wavered. It had been receiving sunlight from the west; abruptly the sun had "gone out," because of the sunshades. Instead an eastern sun was shining—in reflection from the mirror. The ant stood still, hesitating, then turned and set off briskly in the reverse direction.

Santschi next tried covering traveling ants with lightproof boxes for various lengths of time. Every time, when freed, the ant would take off on a course altered precisely to the degree to which sun slant had changed during its period in darkness. On moonlight nights the ants responded with the same precision— apparently taking their bearings from the moon. Q.E.D., said Dr. Santschi. Ants *do* take light readings to show them the way to go home.

The gifts by which living creatures orient themselves begin deep down in the chemistry of life. A housefly larva, which must have warmth and moisture for survival, has an inborn tug so powerful that the larva wiggles its way, blind, mindless, inch by inch, in the direction of any warm damp area.

When baby green turtles hatch from their eggs, they must do two things: dig upward through the sand in which the mother deposited the eggs; then head for water. To guide them for the first action they have a built-in urge to go uphill. But then, as a rule, they must go downhill to find water. What cancels Instruction 1 and supplies Instruction 2? Dr. Kingsley Noble and others, testing turtles at New York's American Museum of Natural History, established the answer: light. Water reflects the light from the sky, and it flashes the baby turtle a signal that overrides his uphill orders.

Some creatures' way-findings are not innate but learned. If young bees, for instance, are released half a mile from their nest, they must fly in circles and spirals to orient themselves. Older bees, with a lifetime of scouting practice and stored memories, can immediately fly a beeline for home from release points two miles away. Bees also *tell* each other a direction in which to go. A bee which has returned to the hive from a food-gathering trip performs an intricate round or abdomen-wagging dance. To the bees in the hive the pattern of this dance tells what angle their flight must take in relation to the sun, and what distance they must fly, to find the food source. With the navigational data thus conveyed, the foragers seldom miss their objective.

But it is the wide-roaming creatures whose navigational feats are the most staggering. Consider the salmon, which lays its eggs inland, usually far up some freshwater stream. During their second year the young salmon move downstream to the sea, but when they reach sexual maturity, they head back toward their birthplace to spawn. To reach it they may have to make choices at fork after fork of the waterways. But they get there. How? It seems likely the fish use subtle sensory cues—perhaps chemical sensitiveness to their birth water so keen that they detect even slight traces of it intermingled in other waters. Naturalists have taken eggs from one stream and hatched them in another. The hatched salmon, tagged, return to the "foster" stream for spawning. (For more about the salmon, see page 26.)

For the performances of migrating and homing birds no single explanation is really satisfying. Some naturalists have become convinced that there is an unknown force at work—a force that guides creatures by influences outside the entire sphere with which science ordinarily reckons. Is there really such an un-

known? For instance, dogs and cats are said to have journeyed long, unfamiliar miles to find their masters —feats which would be impossible to explain on any sensory basis. Are these tales ever verifiable?

Dr. J. B. Rhine, famed psychologist of Duke University, whose experiments with "psi" (the symbol for extrasensory powers outside the physical) in human beings convinced a number of fellow scientists that human psi must be acknowledged as proved, came up with startling evidence. Psi may also be at work, he maintained, in some animal way-finding feats. After making a trip to study the facts at first hand, Dr. Rhine told three case histories.

In 1939 young Hugh Perkins of Summersville, West Virginia, son of Sheriff F. C. Perkins, made a pet of a stray carrier pigeon. In April 1940 Hugh had to be taken to the hospital at Philippi, 100 miles over the mountains, for an operation. One night soon after his arrival he saw a pigeon fluttering outside his window, and asked the nurse to let the bird in. "Look at its leg!" he cried. "I'll bet it's my bird—Number 167!" The nurse read the band: AU 39 C&W 167.

And there was Sugar, the cat. He belonged to the Stacy A. Woods family in Anderson, California. When the Woodses moved to a farm outside Gage, Oklahoma, in June 1951, they left Sugar behind with a friend. Sugar stayed about two weeks, then vanished. In August 1952—14 months later—Mr. and Mrs. Woods were in their barn at Gage, milking, when a cat leaped through the open window onto Mrs. Woods' shoulder. It purred and rubbed against her neck ecstatically. It *couldn't* be Sugar! But the Woods family had to believe it, for their pet had a peculiarly deformed hipbone. To feel that strange displacement, dating from kittenhood, is to be convinced that there is only one of him in the world.

There was Tony, who started to be a black cocker spaniel but grew into a distinctive multibreed all his own. Tony was owned by the L. F. Doolens of Aurora, Illinois. When the Doolens and their two boys moved to Lansing, Michigan, in June 1945, they gave Tony to friends in Aurora. He stayed less than a day. Some seven weeks later Mr. Doolen, while walking down a Lansing street, was suddenly pounced upon by a bedraggled black dog, mostly cocker. He bent down, incredulous, and fumbled for the collar. There it was—an odd cut-down collar with a homemade right-angled slot in it. Mr. Doolen would have known it anywhere, for long before, in Aurora, he had cut it down and made the queer-shaped slot himself.

How did the pigeon, Sugar and Tony manage to find their folks across so many miles? Dr. Rhine's theory is persuasive—but nature keeps its secrets.

A green turtle returns to the sea after having laid her eggs in the sand. The young turtles must tunnel upward, then make their hazardous way to the water.

WHY BIRDS GO NORTH
George Dock, Jr.

The great spring flight of the birds, from tiny hummers to giant eagles, each year sweeps in flood tide up the face of North America, sending its ripples into every field and woodlot. Flaming orioles and tanagers from Colombia strike fire in the Vermont maples and Ohio orchards; bobolinks from Argentina bring new life to prairie marshes and meadows. Each year, it is estimated, more than *ten billion* American birds move north, from winter haunts as distant as Cape Horn to summer nesting places that stretch from the Everglades to ice floes rimming the Pole. Barn swallows wheel each spring from Brazil and Argentina across 7000 miles of perilous air to lay their eggs in Labrador or Alaska. Small warblers travel from Venezuelan jungles in February to Yukon forests in June. In autumn Alaskan curlews fly over thousands of miles of ocean to the South Pacific. Each May the *same* Baltimore oriole returns to the *same* elm in Scarsdale, New York, after a 2000-mile cruise from South America.

Most migrants nest north of the equator, in the Old World as well as here. A map tells why—apart from the desire for a comfortable climate. There is more land in the north. Nine tenths of the south temperate zone is covered by ocean, while three quarters of the north temperate zone is land, totaling 50 times the south-temperate land area. Moreover, the lands of the Northern Hemisphere extend thousands of miles farther away from the equator than does any southern land mass, and have their widest expanse nearly two thirds of the way toward the North Pole. The tapered southern continents end halfway to the South Pole.

The importance of living space is apparent when we realize that in the eastern United States only one or two pairs of land birds on the average can occupy each acre. The most favorable territory seldom harbors more than 15 nesting pairs per acre.

Another reason why northern lands attract countless birds at their nesting time, and *only* then, is that the days are longer and more food can therefore be obtained. At the equator the day is about 12 hours long. In June, along the 40th parallel of north latitude, from Salt Lake through New Jersey, central Spain, Turkey and middle China, the sun is above the horizon 15 hours daily. When you strike the 60th parallel—across southern Alaska, northern Labrador, Scandina-

Taking to the air with a burst of feathers, Elegant terns set out from their breeding grounds in Mexico in a peculiar migration—some to the north and some to the south.

via and Siberia—the time from sunrise to sunset is 19 hours on June 21. Between the 40th and 70th north parallels, the world around, the vast majority of migratory birds have their breeding grounds.

A bird must consume an immense quantity of food to keep itself alive: one chickadee ate over 5500 cankerworm eggs daily; a robin found and swallowed 15 worms in an hour; a flicker, the incredible daily menu of 3000 ants. In the nesting season the parents' job assumes formidable proportions, for their young devour their own weight in food each day for the ten days to six weeks they are in the nest. Youngsters that feed themselves from the moment they hatch, like ducklings and quail, grow faster when they have longer days in which to hunt.

But death on a great scale is the price birds pay for

the benefits of migration. Snows, lighthouses, hunters, sudden freezes, gales, droughts, floods, grass and forest fires all take their toll of migrants. Nature offsets the heavy mortality among the northernmost migrants by increasing their output of young. Censuses made by bird-watchers show that a pair of birds of almost any migratory species nesting in the North has more eggs per brood than those in a more southerly area. Mockingbirds and warblers in the West Indies have only two eggs to the nest; those on our mainland average five. Robins may raise two or three broods each summer in the North.

Migration drains the tropics of an excessive number of birds during more than a third of the year, and permits resident tropic species more food and space for their own nesting needs. The greatest density of diverse bird life, however, at any season anywhere on Earth is in Central America and northern South America between November and January. Into that narrow space, averaging 1800 miles across, is packed a fair part of our wintering billions of North American summer birds, stacked upon the hundreds of resident species.

The long-range cruises of the billions of migratory birds are vital to mankind. Their summer occupation of north temperate lands is the principal control that keeps insects and rodents from destroying all plant life during the hot months. As our trees come into leaf, trillions of insects lay their eggs; but swarms of northbound birds devour great numbers of these destructive worms, beetles and grasshoppers. Man could not live if birds did not come to his assistance.

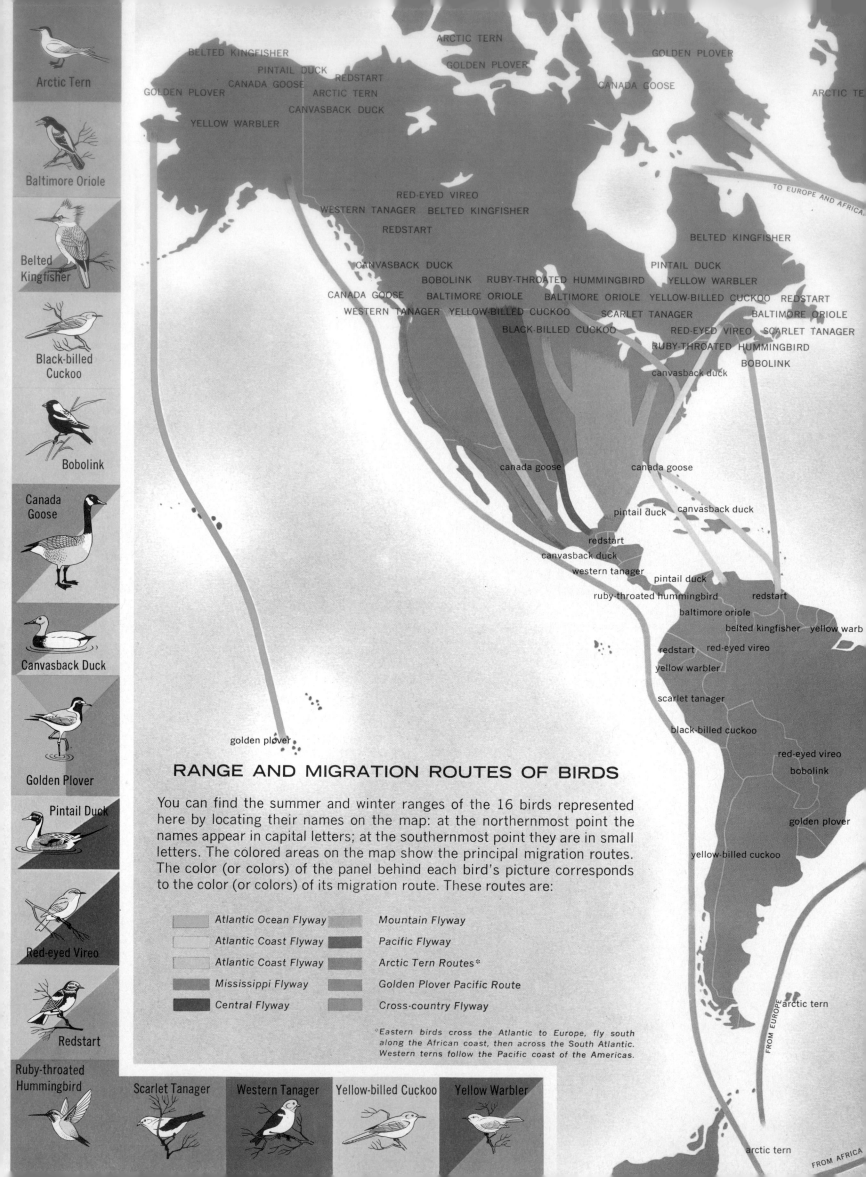

RANGE AND MIGRATION ROUTES OF BIRDS

You can find the summer and winter ranges of the 16 birds represented here by locating their names on the map: at the northernmost point the names appear in capital letters; at the southernmost point they are in small letters. The colored areas on the map show the principal migration routes. The color (or colors) of the panel behind each bird's picture corresponds to the color (or colors) of its migration route. These routes are:

Atlantic Ocean Flyway	Mountain Flyway
Atlantic Coast Flyway	Pacific Flyway
Atlantic Coast Flyway	Arctic Tern Routes*
Mississippi Flyway	Golden Plover Pacific Route
Central Flyway	Cross-country Flyway

*Eastern birds cross the Atlantic to Europe, fly south along the African coast, then across the South Atlantic. Western terns follow the Pacific coast of the Americas.

Arctic Tern

Baltimore Oriole

Belted Kingfisher

Black-billed Cuckoo

Bobolink

Canada Goose

Canvasback Duck

Golden Plover

Pintail Duck

Red-eyed Vireo

Redstart

Ruby-throated Hummingbird

Scarlet Tanager

Western Tanager

Yellow-billed Cuckoo

Yellow Warbler

HOW BIRDS CHART THEIR WAY

Peter Farb

Early one autumn morning we found a yellow-and-black myrtle warbler lying stunned outside our picture window. We put it in an empty cage and offered it food and water. Within a short time it was fidgeting about, hopping from perch to perch, lifting its wings as if to fly. Suddenly, while our youngsters were passing the cage from hand to hand, I was struck by an amazing fact—no matter how the cage was turned, the bird kept pointing constantly southward. Surrounded by noisy, excited youngsters and the trauma of having bumped against a glass window, the bird unerringly kept in mind the direction in which it had been migrating.

Year after year billions of birds uncannily follow trackless highways around the globe on their routes of migration. The springtime arrival of that four-inch myrtle warbler in the treetops may represent the end of a journey of several thousand miles, perhaps from Venezuela or Brazil. Somewhere in its tiny eyes or brain are the equivalents of sextant, compass and clock; and today, with the help of radar and complex electronic gadgetry, scientists stand on the brink of solving the mystery of bird navigation.

"More has been learned during the last decade than in past centuries," states Dr. Jean Dorst of the National Museum of Natural History in Paris. "We now know some of the navigational aids which birds use—among them, the sun and the stars. The future will tell us how birds transform their observations into practical flight directions."

Witness some of the astounding navigational feats of birds. Several years ago Laysan albatrosses which posed a threat to aircraft on Midway Island in the Pacific were removed to other nesting sites. The first of these "gooney birds" taken to the Philippines—4120 miles away—was back a month later. Another, taken in the opposite direction to the state of Washington, returned in a scant ten days, having achieved an average flying speed of 317 miles a day.

Equally astonishing is a feat of bird migration reported recently by Dr. William J. Hamilton III, of the California Academy of Sciences in Berkeley. A female bobolink was captured in late summer near Kenmare, North Dakota, and shipped to him by air. Dr. Hamilton banded her with colored rings on her legs. The bird escaped. The following spring he received a phone call from a woman at Kenmare who had just spotted a female bobolink with colored bands on her legs—the very same bird that had escaped from Berkeley! The bird could not have remained in the United States, for this species has never been seen there during the winter (western bobolinks migrate as far south as Brazil). Nor is Berkeley on any migration path for bobolinks. Somehow the bird was able to compensate for her displacement by airplane from North Dakota, make her way to the wintering grounds and return to her previous home by solving a problem difficult even for a human with navigator's instruments.

Perhaps the most challenging mystery is how birds can find their way unerringly over thousands of miles of featureless ocean. During most of the year a species of shearwater wanders over the Pacific, from Japan to California and northward to the Aleutian Islands. Yet the birds arrive at their nesting grounds off the coast of Australia—millions of them darkening the sky—on the same day every year.

How do they do it? For years ornithologists thought that the birds were guided by prevailing winds, the Earth's magnetic field, or the Coriolis effect resulting from the Earth's rotation. It was once believed that young birds simply followed the older birds. But Frank Bellrose, of the Illinois Natural History Survey, has disproved that idea in several instances. He captured blue-winged teal in Illinois on their southward migration, banded them, released the adult birds quickly and kept the young until long after the adults had flown southward. Recoveries of the juvenile birds, which had never flown south on migration before, showed that they had traveled southward along the routes usually taken by the adults. And so sure were they of their direction that they made amazingly rapid flights—one was shot in Florida only two days after being released.

These birds were not following older birds but a far more ancient guidance system, an instinct acquired in the egg. Was it possible that they were using the sun for guidance, as a human navigator might? Indeed, it is thought that many kinds of birds do. A long series of experiments by Dr. G. V. T. Matthews, formerly of Cambridge University in England and now with the Wildfowl Trust, offers evidence that some birds can navigate by the sun. Any marine navigator knows that the farther north one goes, the lower the sun appears on the horizon. Not only that, but during the day the sun appears to move across the sky at the rate of about one half its diameter per minute. Thus a bird must be able to perform hair-precision reckoning, and it must continually revise its calculations as it flies!

The clue that birds navigate by celestial objects first came from laboratory experiments. Some years ago Dr. Gustav Kramer, of the Max Planck Institute in Wilhelmshaven, observed that captive starlings in early October were fidgety and remained in the corner of their cage pointing southwest, their normal migration direction. The following spring the birds again became fidgety and congregated in the opposite end of the cage, pointing northeast.

It was apparent that the birds were getting their cues from the daytime sky. But many songbirds and waterfowl migrate solely at night. Another German scientist, Dr. Franz Sauer, thought that night-flying birds might use the stars for navigation. Dr. Sauer took caged European warblers to the planetarium of the Naval School at Bremen. There, on a dome 20 feet across, he was able to produce a facsimile of the star patterns at any latitude, longitude or time of night. For example, when he presented the birds with an artificial springtime sky, the warblers immediately went to the north-northeast corner of the cage, their normal flight direction at that season of the year. When he changed the position of the planetarium stars to represent the pattern at a point on the way to the warblers' winter quarters in Africa, the birds almost immediately changed their direction and headed "south."

Final confirmation came by a field experiment. At the start of the migration period in the autumn, the birds were flown to Southwest Africa, where they normally winter. When their cages were uncovered, their first instinct was to fly southward, as they would have from Germany; but as soon as they glimpsed the African sky, they settled down again.

In the last few years an electronic tool new to ornithology—radar—has been applied to study night-time migrations. When radar was first used during World War II, occasional bright spots of mysterious origin, known as "angels," were seen on the screen. Not until 1957 were these angels proved to be blips caused by night-flying birds. Since then, radarscopes around the world have been trained on the night sky during migration and new facts have emerged. For example, migration occurs in much greater volume at night than ever before suspected, and far beyond the range of the human eye (some birds fly as high as 14,000 feet). Radar has also disproved that night-flying birds follow coastlines or great river systems, as was once believed. Radar readings filmed at night by Dr. William H. Drury, Jr., of the Massachusetts Audubon Society, show that the birds pour over the Atlantic coast with little reaction to the configurations of the coastline.

Great use of radar has been made by Frank Bellrose and his associates in Illinois. With their radar-equipped truck, they follow migrations along the Mississippi that were formerly invisible because of altitude, distance, clouds and darkness. On a heavily overcast night I sat with Bellrose watching the "angels" of migrating waterfowl. Because of the overcast many of the birds seemed to be twisting and turning as if bewildered. Nevertheless they were somehow able to keep to their ancestral paths.

To increase the efficiency of his radar, Bellrose is experimenting with placing aluminum foil "vests" over captured birds to increase their reflective surface so that they can be tracked farther. An even better method has been found by Bellrose and William Cochran, of the University of Minnesota, who has devised a tiny radio transmitter, smaller than a box of wooden matches, which will be attached to migrating waterfowl. The signals sent out by the transmitters will carry up to 40 miles, allowing Bellrose to plot exactly every twist and turn taken by the birds in determining their direction.

Now the tracking of bird migrations over *thousands* of miles is looming as a possibility. Ornithologists have suggested sending aloft a "bird satellite" that would circle the Earth, receive the pulses sent out by the transmitters attached to the birds and then relay them back to Earth. With this satellite in orbit, answers could come quickly to such puzzles as the routes taken around the globe by the wandering albatross, the travels of the Australian shearwater, the sky paths of the Canada goose.

Already, however, there is one important overall finding about bird navigation: it is a far more complex phenomenon than anyone thought a few years ago. Until recently it seemed that someday a single, simple answer might emerge. Now it appears that birds are capable of not just one method but an astounding number and combinations of methods. They use visual landmarks in the vicinity of their home territories. On migrations, besides the sun and the stars, it is possible that there are other navigational aids such as air masses of different temperature and humidity. Recent experiments show that birds may even be capable of sensing radio waves.

At the present pace of research, the complete answer to how birds navigate will probably be available in the next few years. But even after the mystery has been solved, there will always remain the greater marvel that birds were navigating by the sun and the stars long before man ever appeared on the Earth.

MIGRATING MAMMALS, INSECTS AND FISH

Ivan T. Sanderson

All over the world men have from time to time encountered vast armies of animals—not only birds—advancing across the face of the Earth in countless millions, often without apparent cause. The commonest example is probably the locust, a perennial scourge in many warm lands. One swarm in the Red Sea area covered 2000 square miles. In the north of Canada and in Norway vast numbers of little ratlike animals known as lemmings pour down from the uplands from time to time and, after crossing the coastal plains, plunge into the sea and disappear. In the years before springboks were drastically reduced in numbers, millions of these graceful little antelopes, pressed shoulder to shoulder and reaching in all directions as far as the eye could see, roamed across South Africa, many of them to be drowned in the Orange River.

These unexpected eruptions of animal life occur in almost every country. I once walked for an hour through a continuous carpet of little hopping frogs in the grass fields of West Africa. Hardly a summer passes without a swarm of insects being reported in New York. One year the Bronx had two—green flies that appeared from nowhere and huge cockroaches that appeared out of drains. Such phenomenal appearances of animals should properly be described as emigrations, in contrast to seasonal migration. Migration makes possible the continuation of the species, while emigration invariably ends in mass suicide. Yet these two marvels have some features in common.

Norwegian lemmings live in colonies on mountain uplands above the tree line, where the main vegetation is grasses and lichens. Every so often the number of lemmings in one of the colonies increases tremendously. They begin to produce larger litters at shorter intervals. The animals that prey on the lemmings—owls, foxes, weasels and hawks—also begin to increase and become bolder and more voracious. The process goes on until there is hardly standing room for the animals. Finally when the pressure of numbers becomes intolerable, hosts of lemmings pour down the mountainside into the woodlands, followed by swarms of their enemies. On they go, a vast moving blanket that creeps across the

Earth, spreading in all directions. They are devoured by the thousands, are drowned in billions while crossing rivers and fiords, or wilt away from starvation. Caught up in a mass hysteria, the animals have lost all their natural sagacity.

The basic causes of both emigration and migration are the same—food and water—but, whereas emigrating animals disappear, migrating animals (or their offspring) always return to the place where they began their journey. For most of them, migration is seasonal; they move from north to south or from the mountain heights to lower ground for the winter. But for others the degree of movement can vary greatly. Elephants sometimes perform migrations that take nearly ten years to complete. Troops of some kinds of South American monkey migrate back and forth between two areas of forest every few weeks.

A most astonishing sight is the migration of land crabs on the island of Jamaica. These creatures, which dwell in rock crevices, descend at the same time each year to certain beaches for breeding purposes. They invariably do this by following the straightest line possible, and as a result they scramble over any obstacles, even houses, that happen to be in their path.

One species of aphid spends part of the year on apple trees and part on the stems of grasses. These insects, used by certain ants as we use cows, are herded and protected and "milked" by the ants of a honeylike fluid which exudes from the aphids' bodies (see page 48). Having discovered that the aphids have to migrate, the ants carry them down from the apple trees and place them on the grass stems or take them from the grass up to the apple trees, as the season may demand.

The amazing behavior of Atlantic eels is unique (see page 97). Eels spend many years of seemingly contented life in the ponds and streams of Europe and North America. Then suddenly they leave their homes, go down the rivers and head out into the Atlantic until they reach a great deep in the Atlantic Ocean south of Bermuda, where they sink and disappear forever. Later an eruption of tiny, transparent, threadlike creatures with bulging black eyes comes welling up to the surface; spreading out like an ever expanding mushroom, they stream off in two groups—one heading east for Europe, the other going west to America. Both shoals—by now grown into young eels—swim up the rivers of their respective continents until they reach the abodes whence their parents started out.

This phenomenon has a fascinating theoretical explanation based on what is known as Wegener's theory of continental drift. Alfred Lothar Wegener, a German geologist, pointed out that the Earth was once covered with an outer crust less deep than the oceans. At some point in time about half of it flew into outer space, however, and the remainder broke into pieces and drifted to the present-day positions of the continents. As evidence, he cut out maps of the continents and showed that they can be fitted together. The east coast of North and South America fits almost exactly into the west coast of Europe and Africa. A current widely accepted theory gives a different explanation: it holds that the Earth has expanded at the rate of one meter every thousand years. Hence the continental crust has been *forced* apart, rather than drifting as Wegener maintained.

Now if the eels originated in the sea-filled crack between the Old and the New Worlds when they lay close together, and spent their time between breeding seasons in the ponds and rivers of the nearby land on either side of the crack, they would have had to make longer and longer journeys to their breeding grounds as the continents separated, until it eventually became impossible for them to make the trip every year. Thus they would have to spend a longer rest period in fresh water and go less frequently to breed. By carrying this process to an extreme, it will be seen that their behavior would eventually become what it is today, whereby they spend their whole lives resting and storing up energy for their great adventure and then set out to the ancestral grounds, now thousands of miles away, where their eggs are laid. The effort now entailed so entirely exhausts them that they never survive to make a second trip.

Migration is a major life process of the animal world. The many varying kinds are unified only by their object and result: survival. Without migration, a great part of our animal life would probably have long since disappeared from the face of the Earth.

THE SPREAD OF MAMMALS

From its beginning, the face of Earth has undergone immense changes. It was once possible for animals to spread, by age-long migration, across a land bridge where the Bering Strait is now. Such avenues of migration, as well as barriers to them, have been appearing and disappearing since mammals first evolved. At present, mammals are grouped in six main regions, each of which is bounded by natural barriers — mountains, deserts or seas. These areas are shown on the map to the right.

Animals of the **Nearctic** Region (North America) and the **Palaearctic** Region (Europe, North Africa and most of Asia) have so much in common that it seems likely that, up to recent geological times, the two areas were joined at the Bering Strait. The American buffalo is very like the European bison; the moose closely resembles the elk; the North American caribou and European reindeer are virtually identical. Among medium-sized mammals, the foxes, otters and beavers of the **Nearctic** and **Palaearctic** Regions are so alike that some experts regard them as races of a single species. Smaller animals, particularly rats and mice, because of their rapid reproduction, have evolved with marked differences.

In the **Palaearctic** Region many species of mammal range almost unchanged from the British Isles to Japan. The typical carnivore of the region is the wolf, and the cat family is represented by small and medium-sized species, such as the wildcat and the lynx. Deer, too, are common, and bears are more characteristic of the **Palaearctic** and **Nearctic** Regions than of any other parts of the world.

Equator

The similarity between the marine animals on either side of the **Central American Isthmus** suggests that here the sea, at one time, was unbroken. Wide rivers across the isthmus now form barriers to the migration of land animals, but the nine-banded armadillo, typical of the South American fauna, has continued to spread northward. Gulping air to inflate itself, it can float across the rivers.

CENTRAL AMERICAN ISTHMUS

NEO

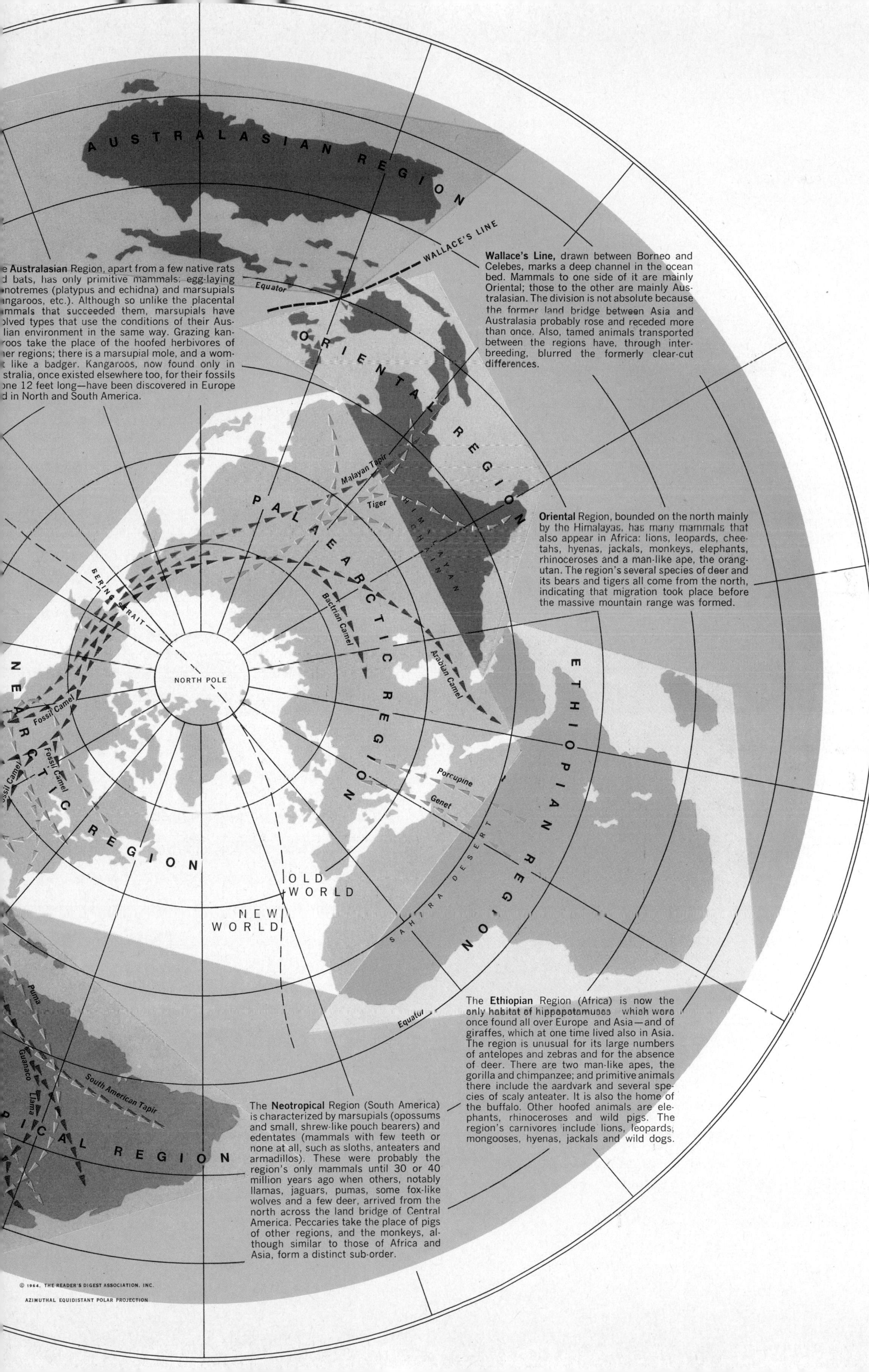

AUSTRALASIAN REGION

The **Australasian** Region, apart from a few native rats and bats, has only primitive mammals: egg-laying monotremes (platypus and echidna) and marsupials (kangaroos, etc.). Although so unlike the placental mammals that succeeded them, marsupials have evolved types that use the conditions of their Australian environment in the same way. Grazing kangaroos take the place of the hoofed herbivores of other regions; there is a marsupial mole, and a wombat like a badger. Kangaroos, now found only in Australia, once existed elsewhere too, for their fossils—one 12 feet long—have been discovered in Europe and in North and South America.

WALLACE'S LINE

Equator

ORIENTAL REGION

Wallace's Line, drawn between Borneo and Celebes, marks a deep channel in the ocean bed. Mammals to one side of it are mainly Oriental; those to the other are mainly Australasian. The division is not absolute because the former land bridge between Asia and Australasia probably rose and receded more than once. Also, tamed animals transported between the regions have, through interbreeding, blurred the formerly clear-cut differences.

PALAEARCTIC REGION

Malayan Tapir

Tiger

HIMALAYAN

Bactrian Camel

Arabian Camel

BERING STRAIT

NORTH POLE

NEARCTIC REGION

Fossil Camel

Fossil Camel

Fossil Camel

Oriental Region, bounded on the north mainly by the Himalayas, has many mammals that also appear in Africa: lions, leopards, cheetahs, hyenas, jackals, monkeys, elephants, rhinoceroses and a man-like ape, the orangutan. The region's several species of deer and its bears and tigers all come from the north, indicating that migration took place before the massive mountain range was formed.

ETHIOPIAN REGION

Porcupine

Genet

SAHARA DESERT

OLD WORLD

NEW WORLD

The **Ethiopian** Region (Africa) is now the only habitat of hippopotamuses—which were once found all over Europe and Asia—and of giraffes, which at one time lived also in Asia. The region is unusual for its large numbers of antelopes and zebras and for the absence of deer. There are two man-like apes, the gorilla and chimpanzee; and primitive animals there include the aardvark and several species of scaly anteater. It is also the home of the buffalo. Other hoofed animals are elephants, rhinoceroses and wild pigs. The region's carnivores include lions, leopards, mongooses, hyenas, jackals and wild dogs.

Equator

Puma

Guanaco

Llama

South American Tapir

NEOTROPICAL REGION

The **Neotropical** Region (South America) is characterized by marsupials (opossums and small, shrew-like pouch bearers) and edentates (mammals with few teeth or none at all, such as sloths, anteaters and armadillos). These were probably the region's only mammals until 30 or 40 million years ago when others, notably llamas, jaguars, pumas, some fox-like wolves and a few deer, arrived from the north across the land bridge of Central America. Peccaries take the place of pigs of other regions, and the monkeys, although similar to those of Africa and Asia, form a distinct sub-order.

African cattle egrets, snowy and exotic, are newcomers to North American pastures.

WILDLIFE IS
ON THE MARCH
Peter Farb

Three Massachusetts naturalists, out checking the arrival of bird migrants one spring morning in 1952, suddenly stopped in their tracks, astounded. For there, darting between the legs of a herd of grazing heifers, was a large alabaster bird, stabbing at the ground with a long yellow bill. Improbable as it seemed, they had spotted a cattle egret—a bird never before reported on this continent.

This magnificent member of the heron family has long been a familiar sight in southern Asia and Africa, where it lives with water buffalo and elephants as well as cattle, feeding on the insects which the animals' hoofs stir up in the grass. The species was totally unknown in the New World until about 30 years ago when one turned up in British Guiana —nearly 2000 miles from the nearest point in Africa.

Ornithologists at first refused to credit the Massachusetts find, arguing that the bird might have escaped from a zoo. Soon, however, more sightings of cattle egrets were reported: two at Cape May, New Jersey; ten at Florida's Lake Okeechobee; one near Chicago. Today the egret has fanned out over North America and is now found in at least 15 states from Maine to Texas. There is no doubt that the cattle egret will eventually become familiar over much of the United States and Canada.

This is just one aspect of an extraordinary explosion of wildlife that has been taking place all over the globe. Everywhere birds, fish and four-legged animals have been on the march—moving into new areas, amazing naturalists by unexpected appearances. Before 1875 there were few moose in northern Canada; now they occupy practically all of that area to the tree line, and much of Alaska, too. Denmark reports at least 25 bird species unknown there before 1900. Octopuses have strayed from their Mediterranean grounds to the waters of Britain. The fantastic spread of the North American muskrat over Europe and Asia began with the escape of five muskrats imported by a Czech in 1905. Today they inhabit Europe in millions and are an important fur animal in Siberia and northern Russia. Whether by man's doing or by changes of temperature over a long period, a new tide of animal life is emerging.

"We must make no mistake," says Oxford University's Dr. Charles S. Elton, a world authority on animal populations. "We are seeing one of the great historic convulsions in the world's flora and fauna."

If John James Audubon were tramping a southern New England woodland today, he would miss many birds and animals he knew—the flocks of passenger pigeons, the ravens and bears. But he would rub his eyes in amazement at some of the things he did see. On a recent field trip on Long Island, for example, practically within sight of the Empire State Building, I saw mockingbirds, those symbols of the southern plantation. Forty-five years ago these birds rarely ventured north of Maryland; today they can be found in gardens along the Canadian border.

In 1960 I drove from New York City to Canada.

Beside the highway I saw a gray-clad 'possum, for centuries almost exclusively southern in its range. A neighbor later complained of 'possum thievery in his garbage dump. That wouldn't have happened a few decades ago, when the 'possum was unknown this far north; now these animals have nearly reached the southern end of Hudson Bay. Nearing my summer cabin a short way north of the city, I spotted tufted titmice, cardinals, cowbirds, a turkey vulture. All these birds are recent immigrants to the area. As I drove through New England I was—believe me!—in coyote country. The coyote, the very symbol of the western range, has spread across the northern shores of the Great Lakes, then southward. Coyotes have been trapped in Connecticut, Massachusetts, in the Adirondack and Catskill Mountains of New York and in nearly every Vermont county.

As I passed lakes and marshes, I often had to remind myself that I was in New England, for I saw king rails, fish crows and water thrushes—birds that once were more commonly found in the South and Midwest. This countryside had seen the invasion of some 15 southern bird species—and another dozen which, in our grandparents' day, one would have had to travel west of the Mississippi River to see, including the prairie horned lark, the western meadowlark and kingbird.

Vast changes are also apparent in the life of the sea. Early settlers of New England were impressed by the abundance of cod from Massachusetts to the Grand Banks of Newfoundland; it was not seen farther north. But by early in this century Greenland Eskimos found cod so plentiful in local waters that they switched from seal-hunting and became de-

pendent on it for food. Iceland, too, is now reaping a rich cod harvest, and other fish that once lived exclusively in southern waters are visiting Iceland—sharks, sunfish, tuna.

What is the cause of this sudden spread of wildlife? Biologists offer various explanations. The late ornithologist Ludlow Griscom thought the cattle egret's expansion was due to an innate vigor of the species—"biological ginger," he called it. He noted that this species has been multiplying extraordinarily in its old areas as well as moving into new ones. Other wildlife experts point to climatic change. Weather records from around the world indicate that temperatures in the Northern Hemisphere are rising at an average rate of three degrees a century, more in some places. The Gulf Stream along the U.S. coast has warmed up about five degrees in the last 60 years. Farmers in Canada, Scandinavia and Siberia are now plowing land which has been frost-bound in living memory. In eastern Canada the tree line, slow to react to climatic change, has nonetheless advanced northward two miles in the last 30 years. All such changes affect living conditions for wildlife, as well as the distribution of specific food plants, and so inevitably alter its range.

As another explanation for the spread of land animals and birds, scientists point to man's alterations in the face of the land. They have seen prairies broken in the Midwest, giant reservoirs built in formerly arid areas. Forests have been logged over in the East, new forests planted in the South. A forest bird may now be able to leapfrog from one new tree plantation to another across what was formerly a "fence" of meadowland. It is believed that the western deermouse, native of grasslands, has spread eastward by following the grass shoulders on new interstate highways.

One of the most extensive treks by any American animal in recent years has been taken by the armadillo. Until about 40 years ago this strange mammal was restricted in range to southern Texas. But then the Texas forests were cleared and stockmen killed off the coyotes, bears and bobcats which had previously preyed on it. With these barriers eliminated, the armadillo fanned out over Texas and on into Oklahoma, Kansas, Arkansas, Louisiana, Mississippi and Alabama. Its push to the Atlantic Ocean was aided by escaped pet armadillos in Florida. This obscure animal now promises to become one of the most common mammals in the South.

Thus, while man ponders his chances of colonizing space, many forms of wildlife are reaching out to find new habitats on this old planet of ours.

Chapter two

NATURE AT REST

Among the birds and beasts, rest is more diverse than in the human world. It can be short—catnaps. Many animals sleep awhile, then stalk awhile. It can be long—hibernation. Bears and woodchucks will hibernate where the winter is severe, living off the fat they have stored in preparation for a long rest. But some creatures merely retire to winter quarters—the beehive or the burrow—and live off the food they have stored.

During the midsummer heat there are those which snooze and those which go into the deep sleep of estivation. There are also the drought sleepers. Lungfish retire to escape death when their ponds have dried and the water of life is gone. Down in the mud they drowse sometimes for years, waiting for the rains to come and awaken them.

Animals have their own sleep habits. In various ways they are similar to humans—some insects stretch and yawn, and mammals no doubt dream as well. Chipmunks, squirrels, sheep and goats go to bed at sunset and get up with the sun. Others reverse the hours, sleeping by day—the owls, cats, wolves, skunks and weasels. The shy ones—deer and rabbits—move abroad by twilight, sleeping both during the midday hours and the darkest dark.

CREATURES OF DAY AND NIGHT

Lorus J. and Margery J. Milne

Snug in our houses after dark, we seldom think of the millions of creatures outside our door for whom each night is a challenge and an adventure.

The busiest hours in the world of nature are those at sunset and sunup. At dusk the day-feeding birds of the open fields fly to the topmost branches to spend the night in greater security. At the same time other birds and animals desert their woodland sanctuary to forage in the fields and beside streams. Now deer and red foxes, striped skunks and banded raccoons begin to move about in the open. During these minutes of twilight almost every individual is alert and active, but in the confusion of transition the quick-eyed predators snatch many meals.

Along the water's edge, the raccoon thrusts down its handlike forepaws, feeling for a crayfish; it manipulates its catch underwater as though to scrub it clean, then tears it to shreds. Where the reeds and cattails are spaced out by shallow water, ducks tip and dive to reach the vegetation along the bottom; long-legged herons and other wading birds stand like sentinels, ready to spear a passing fish.

Animals of the night have special knowledge of their whereabouts based upon habitual use. They learn that a tree is three jumps in one direction, the burrow four in another. Wherever they go in familiar territory, they remain oriented by their own muscular movements. Six leaps and a twist to the left; three more and a sharp right turn—with these instinctive moves they race to safety.

A surprising number of daytime animals return to the same site to sleep each night. The sleepers may make no bed, but each has a "bedroom." The bumblebee may be found in the identical hollyhock from the day of the flower's opening to the day it closes for the last time. A butterfly may select an area of bark as a clinging place and arrive there at dusk each day after seemingly aimless flitting over the countryside. In the stone wall a few wasps hang inverted from the underside of the paper nest in which their young develop; others have found crannies safe from wind and lie with their antennae curled, their legs folded in repose.

Birds commonly use the same roosting site for sleep, even though they have constructed an elaborate nest somewhere else. A nest is not a home but an egg-hatching device and nursery pen. Unless there are eggs to incubate or young to protect from the chilly dark, the nest-makers sleep elsewhere—usually in the tree branches.

By sunset birds of many sizes have wrapped their toes firmly around a twig or branch. From a muscle in each thigh a strong tendon runs over the knee, down the shank, around the ankle and under the toes. In settling for the night, the body's weight pulls taut this tendon and ensures a grip that no wind will loosen. Sometimes not even death will dislodge the birds.

The majority of small migratory birds of North America travel by night, and this in itself is remarkable, for most birds appear helpless without light to see by. The dark hours seem to be used for flying because these birds need the daylight hours for feeding. Alighting toward dawn, they can alternately rest and feed until dusk before starting onward again. On the other hand, night-feeding insectivorous birds, such as the nighthawk and whippoorwill, migrate by day. Bats, whether they migrate by day or night, feed while flying.

During the darkness preceding morning twilight, many creatures behave as though they knew how long it would be before sunup. On an overcast morning as well as when the sky is clear, a robin hesitantly begins a lonely predawn solo; speckle-chested thrushes

COMMON NORTH AMERICAN MOTHS

1. *Underwing moth—drab front wings cover the colorful hind wings for camouflage.* 2. *The leopard, introduced to this continent from Europe.* 3. *The beauteous io moth with its dramatic eyespots.* 4. *White-lined sphinx moth, an important pollinator of flowers.* 5. *The matchless luna.* 6. *The cecropia moth.* 7. *Close-up of a male cecropia; his feathery antennae enable him to trace the female's scent.*

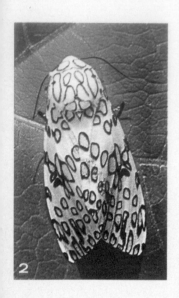

start up; bluebirds lisp and warble. As the clover leaves unfold and the growing light reflects in each dewdrop, the bat hurries to find its cranny, the owl its tree hole, the nighthawk its rooftop. Worms draw back into the soil and beetles retire beneath stones and logs. By the time the deer have settled in the thickets, the rabbit is in its burrow, the raccoon and opossum and porcupine are in their favorite trees. The beaver is asleep in its thatched castle.

As the sun appears, the birds leave their perches and their notes die away like a conversation when dinner is served; the songsters are busy eating, breaking the night-long fast, gathering food for their young. In the rhythm imposed by the spinning Earth, the world of darkness has yielded and the creatures of the night have made way for those of the day.

THE MARATHONS OF SLEEP
Archibald Rutledge

The phenomenon of hibernation is one of the most mysterious in nature. Millions of mammals, reptiles and insects slumber all winter long, with the functions of some bodily organs entirely suspended, and with other organs so slowed down that their action is hardly perceptible. Instinct, that voice of nature whispering down the ages of the things that are safest and sanest, leads them to prepare for this strange winter sleep even before autumn sets in. Bears, for instance, lay up excessive stores of fat on which to live during the winter. A lean bear in late fall is usually dangerous; feeling that he has not supplied an urgent need, he becomes irritable and often savage.

During this suspended existence the hibernator's temperature may drop to almost half normal. The heart slows down and all functions of alimentation and excretion cease. Respiration is faint and in some sleepers appears wholly to cease. An English scientist kept a hibernating marmot (an English woodchuck) in pure carbon dioxide for four hours without apparently affecting it adversely. A hibernating bat was submerged in a bucket of water for an hour; when taken out, it was still asleep and still perfectly normal. A hedgehog survived a 22-minute immersion. A hibernating dormouse, curled up in a hard little ball, can be rolled across the floor and still will remain sound asleep. Mysterious changes take place in the powers and relationships of various organs. For instance, the brain and spinal cord were completely removed from a hibernating marmot, and the creature's heart continued to beat for ten hours longer.

Hibernation is obviously one of nature's experiments in helping wild creatures survive the rigors of winter. Birds can speed south before the blizzards come; moles can keep up their tunneling at levels below the frost line, and many animals simply continue to prey upon one another. Bees do not hibernate; they have honey to live on, and they keep up their own temperatures by closely clustering and constantly vibrating their wings to raise the hive temperature. Of those animals that do become dormant when it's cold, bears are the most consistent, though raccoons, skunks, and badgers sleep through the worst of the winter. Chipmunks and squirrels, near relatives of the woodchuck, alternate sleeping spells with occasional feasts on the food they have stored.

The long sleep does not affect all the members of one species; the black bear will hibernate in the North, but not in the far South. Invariably the female bear retires first. As places for hibernation, bears choose deep holes at the bases of huge old trees, cavities under old log piles, or caves. Snakes may hibernate in hollow logs or perhaps under stumps. I once saw some timber cutters rouse a big rattler in late winter from his den beneath a huge log; in his slumber he had so far used up his surplus fat that his skin hung on him almost as loosely as it appears to hang on the sides of an elephant. From the mud along the edge of a ricefield ditch I have seen workmen dig out both bullfrogs and moccasins. And I have known hibernating copperheads to be plowed up in an open field. Farther north, snakes seem to choose rock dens; I know of one in the Pennsylvania mountains where almost 200 hibernating rattlers and copperheads were found. One naturally wonders why these sleepers ever awake. It seems that when the hardly-alive functioning of heart and lungs has used up all surplus fat, the creature's temperature will drop; and when it does, he wakes up. If he did not awake then, he would die. One will occasionally see abroad in the winter a skunk, a raccoon or a badger. The chances are that he awakened hungry and has come out for a good dinner before he embarks upon another period of napping.

We do not usually associate hibernation with marine creatures; but the so-called saltwater terrapin buries himself in the mud for the winter; and his shore neighbors, the sandcrabs and fiddlers, do likewise. Toads and frogs regularly hibernate, the latter in the mud beneath their favorite waters. I remember an old toad who was so shrunken as to appear almost mummified, and even after two hours of baking

Left, a trapdoor spider at the entrance of his burrow with the hinged door propped open; right, the spider in his burrow. The trapdoor, which seals the burrow, is made of silk and earth.

in the sun he still retained an air of colossal ennui.

Dormice and hedgehogs (the latter holding the record both for duration and intensity of sleep) hibernate in captivity. Reptiles and tortoises commonly do not, nor does the bear, though there is on record one case of a captive bear in South Dakota which dug a deep hole, entered it in December and did not emerge until March.

Some creatures hibernate when their prey hibernates. Those bats which do not migrate retire for the winter when the insects on which they feed have either perished or gone to sleep themselves. While most hibernators sleep curled up, the bats are unique in that they hang in their customary head-down positions for months at a time. Most spiders remain awake during the winter months and may be found at any time in crevices or under rubbish. Lack of food does not trouble them—they can go for months without it. But the marvelous trapdoor spider does hibernate, first sealing his little doorway with a blanket of silk.

Where winter and summer are very definite periods, hibernation goes on with the precision characteristic of a system of nature. But in climates where the demarcation of the seasons is not radical, all kinds of queer things happen. There is a Line of Hibernation, more or less movable, depending on the severity of the winter. Near Charleston, South Carolina, where I long lived, it was impossible to *count* on a sleeper's staying asleep. There, snakes and other reptiles are supposed to hibernate; but on a warm January day I have heard a bull alligator serenading his ladylove with his dreadful bellow as if it had been April; and on a mild day in late December I have found the lordly diamondback rattler far from his den, searching for food. It was formerly believed that bats were perfect hibernators in north temperate climes, but they emerge in the winter when the weather turns soft. Is it not possible that when the temperature of the weather rises, the depressed temperature of the long sleeper rises with it, thus awakening him? And when he finds that he is hungry, he naturally begins his search for food.

The sleep of birds, most of which do not hibernate, presents a curious study. We describe them as generally sleeping with the head under the wing. As a matter of fact, they only thrust the beak among the feathers between the wing butt and the body. What induces this particular position is a mystery. But not all birds take this posture. My tame pheasants sleep on high perches with their heads sunk between their shoulders. Coveys of quail always roost on the ground, forming a perfect ring, with all their tails together. A good many birds, especially the waders, sleep standing; storks and herons often sleep while poised on one leg. African mousebirds crowd together in dense, ball-like masses. Owls sleep by day, but never very soundly. Ducks sleep both on land and on water; on the former they often drowse while standing on one leg; on the latter they frequently keep lazily moving with one foot. Wild turkeys, which prefer high, bare trees for roosting, apparently sleep through the wildest blast.

Among the higher insects Julian Huxley says that ants, at least, require sleep. "They may choose a depression in the soil as bed, and there lay themselves down, with legs drawn close to the body. When waking (after some three hours' rest), they behave in a way startlingly like that of our proud human selves. The head and then the six legs are stretched to their fullest extent, and then often shaken; the jaws are strained open in a way remarkably reminiscent of a yawn." Animals and birds in sleep manifest in various ways that, like human beings, their rest is not perfect. They start; they turn; they moan; they snore; birds, especially robins and field sparrows, often sing. Unquestionably many of these creatures dream.

SUMMER SLEEPERS

John and Jean George

Hot day piled on hot day that August in New York's Hudson River Valley. As we sat on our lawn in the shade, lazy with the heat, Jean tossed peanuts at a fungus-freckled stump under which lived the chipmunk we had befriended. Suddenly she stopped and sat up alertly.

"Where's our chipmunk?" she said. "John! Listen to the silence—not a bird singing, not a frog calling, not a squirrel scolding."

"It's August," John said. "That means heat and dryness—and quiet. Water tables have sunk; ponds and wells are going dry. It's a difficult month for most living creatures, and many of them have the good sense to husband their energies by 'retiring.'"

That conversation launched us on what became an annual quest for the "sleepers" of summer. Everyone has heard about hibernation, an escape from winter cold. Its summer counterpart, estivation, is an escape from prolonged heat and dryness. Estivation is total with some creatures: their bodies function at a greatly reduced rate. Others awaken from time to time, but usually stay in their burrows. Which animals estivate, and how deep is their torpor?

We began our study with our own chipmunk, which is a partial sleeper, not an estivator. Digging into the soft earth under the stump, we found the little fellow slumbering soundly in a leaf-lined bedroom. "Your chipmunk isn't eating," John said. "Digestion begets more heat. He's saving his life by snoozing, and he probably won't show himself for two or three weeks. In the cool earth he doesn't need water, and his body temperature drops." The chipmunk's small body was cool to our touch. Roused by our intrusion, he shuddered with the agonies of coming out of his comfortable sleep. Then he scolded us and disappeared into another part of his burrow. We restored the insulating earth. Three weeks later our peanuts were disappearing again and the chipmunk's flagpole tail was raised over the rocks and leaves at the edge of the woods.

The ground squirrel goes the sleep of the chipmunk one better—he estivates. Out west one July the burrow of a ground squirrel near our cabin popped with activity. In and out the golden animal went; sharp notes filled the air; legs scurried. Then, in August, the burrow was as still as a deserted city. We carefully dug back the earth, following the neatly packed tunnel to the ground squirrel's grass-lined sleeping chamber.

Unlike the chipmunk, this sleeping beauty did not wake. Jean was sure there was no life in the tidy ball of fur. The head was curled down toward the groin, the tail wrapped close to his ears. The body was cold and would not be uncurled. We carefully repacked the ground squirrel, feeling all the while that we had witnessed a facet of life so strange that it was scarcely life at all.

Other animals of the world, of varying sizes, go into this deep sleep of estivation in time of drought. The sleepers include some microscopic animals, as well as the lungfish of Africa, the yellow-bellied marmot of our West, alligators and certain freshwater fish in the tropics, and mud minnows, snails, frogs and toads over most of the United States.

On an August day in Poughkeepsie, New York, John was cleaning our basement window wells when, lifting leaves and twigs, he discovered five toads pressed against the earth. Each had scooped itself a little pocket. John picked one up. Its legs did not thrash as a toad's legs do when the animal is picked up in June. Instead the toad held them close to its body and sat quietly on John's hand. It finally made an instinctive response to danger and flopped back into the leaves. A few struggling moves and it was under cover, pressing itself against the moisture held in the earth by the decaying leaves.

We spent a hot afternoon at a woodland pond looking for frogs in their summer quiet. The water, so alive with eggs and polliwogs and fairy shrimp in spring, was gone. We dug into the mire and finally came upon a frog—motionless, buried alive. We carried him home and put him in an aquarium. In a short time he became active and swam about—not with the energy of spring, however, but with slow, gliding movements. And he uttered no sound even when we pinched him behind the forelegs, which almost always makes a male frog croak.

These sleepers of summer give August its siesta quality. Yet under this cessation of activity is the atonal chorus of the insects: the rasp of the katydid, the crackling flight of the locust, the monotonous shrilling of the cicada. Many insects revel in August because they can tolerate more heat than most forms of life. They rarely need more moisture than the dew or the water in their food. And so August is a festival month for the insects.

What of the birds in this sleepy season? At four one morning in the hottest part of August, Jean went to the area along the fence row that belonged to the towhee, vocalist of the vibrant song: "Drink your *teeee.*" At the same time John took to the deep woods to spy on the ovenbird that rends the air of spring and early summer with the piercing call: "Teacher! Teacher! Teacher!" The towhee was singing, but not as loudly as in spring. He soon stopped and sat quietly, opening his beak from time to time—a bird's way of cooling off. A month before, we had heard five ovenbirds singing at that hour in the woods. Now, not a chirp from them. August had brought a sudden halt to their concerts. But soon the heat would go, the rains would come, and another season would be on the land.

During estivation—the deep sleep of summer—breathing and heartbeat become slower, though not as slow as in hibernation. Shown here, a ground squirrel asleep for the hot, dry weeks.

Chapter three

MAGICAL LAWS OF NATURE

Wild animals have lived so long with the ferocity of the sun, the frigidity of the winter wind, with predators and hunger, that their bodies have changed greatly to protect them.

Slowly, over aeons of time, the walrus could adjust to the sea by changing his feet to flippers, and by accumulating fat for a warm insulating coat. The grouse has thrived in the forest because he matched his colors to fallen leaves and the decaying logs. A small crab found a way to live among the deadly tentacles of the sea anemone by developing immunity to the flower-animal's poison, and there it hides protected from its enemies.

Adaptation turned the nose of an elephant into an arm, his ears into fans and his teeth into spears. And when an appendage becomes a liability, like the tooth of the saber-toothed tiger, the animal will vanish.

Changing form is not the only means of survival. There are acts of instinct or of will which the creatures of the wild perform repeatedly. Some, like migration and mating, are triggered by the light of the sun. Others, like healing a wound or coping with the winter cold, come from an age-old wisdom born into the birds and beasts or taught to them by parents.

NATURE'S MARVELOUS ALARM CLOCK
John George

The dreary month of February descends. The wind rattles the windows. The snow deepens on the land. I go to my study window and look out across the raw, gray world, depressed by the everlastingness of a northern winter. Then I hear it! The resonant love call of the great horned owl booms across the forest. The biologist in me exults, for I know, despite the weather, that the countdown to spring is under way. That call means the female owl will soon be sitting low on the nest, warming her white eggs as the snow drifts across her head and back. For the owls must time the arrival of their young to the arrival of the bird migration and the appearance of young, awkward mammals.

The owlets will hatch in March, just as the red-winged blackbirds arrive in numbers. At a time when the young must be fed their weight in food each day, the owl parents will need only to dip into the fields and marshes to supply the ravenous mouths. Later, when it seems impossible to find enough food to feed the owlets, most of the migrating birds will be coming through the forest and fields, noisy, conspicuous and easy prey. This migration, in turn, has been triggered to reach its destination about the time that insects, other foods and shelter are abundant. And the insects will awaken in time to gnaw on the opening leaves or, in the case of insect parasites, upon their hosts.

This hair-trigger timing is wondrously planned. Each species of plant and animal is different, but

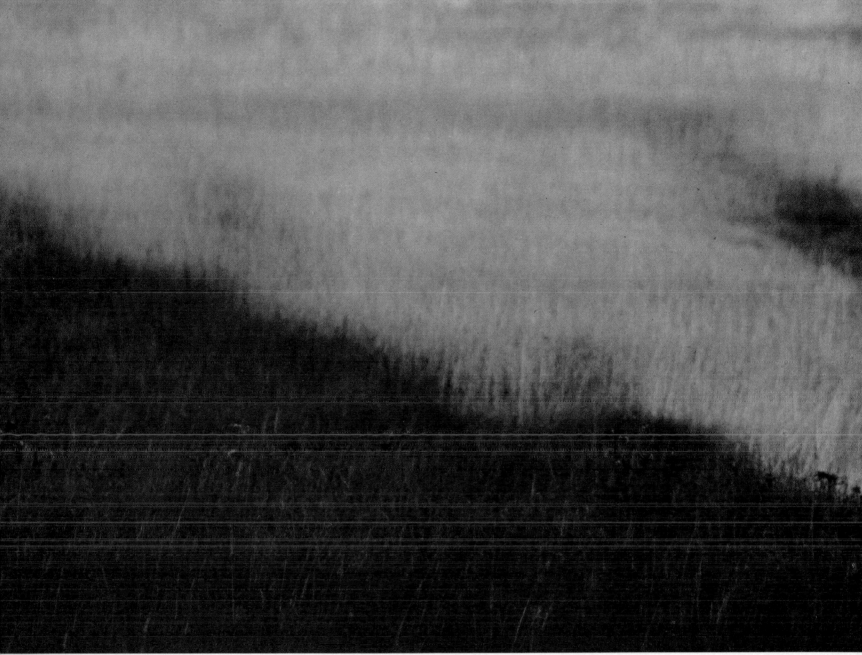

Light, the length of day, is the master signal of animal life. It heralds the seasons of migration and of mating. The sky informs the elk when he should move to winter quarters.

all respond to a special touch. For years scientists and laymen believed that the touch was heat alone —the return of warm weather. Only within the last generation have biologists proved what the main timing device really is: light. Temperature is fickle; it varies from day to day, year to year, as often unseasonable as not. But light is reliable; every year, on a given day, the light duration is the same and has been for millions of years.

Biologists noted that some plants and animals bloom or breed in the spring, as the daylight increases. Others bloom or breed in the autumn, as the daylight decreases. Then there are still others that are "day-neutral"—that is, they bloom or breed regardless of the length of daylight. These observations prompted scientists to test the effects of light on living things.

Starlings were used in the first bird experiments. These birds are spring breeders. But the scientists showed that light, not heat, is the external conditioning factor in their breeding cycle. When caged in winter, in a room warmed to summer temperatures, the starlings did not come into breeding condition. They mated and bred in April—just like their wild cousins.

Then the scientists changed the light duration. In December, when the sun set early, they turned lights on the birds. Within a few days the males began to molt their winter plumage and to take on the colorful feathers of their breeding raiment. They courted their females, and at the end of December— four months ahead of schedule—the females were ready to lay eggs. (Poultry farmers use this knowledge to control egg production by lighting chicken coops after dark.) Next, light was broken down into its separate colors, and groups of starlings were kept under red, white, violet and green lights. The results were startling. Under red light the birds rushed into breeding condition—even more rapidly than under white light. Under violet and green, however, they remained sexually dormant.

Why? Physiologists reasoned that the red component of light must stimulate the pituitary gland to send out a hormone which activates the development of the sex organs. In the case of a heavily feathered bird, light could enter the system most easily through the eyes. To prove this the scientists blindfolded a group of young birds and, sure enough, they did not mature as long as they could not absorb light through their eyes.

The reaction of birds to light inspired tests on other animals. Ferrets, raccoons, squirrels and many others breed in the spring. When scientists put ferrets under lights in the autumn, the animals began to breed months earlier than usual, and, as with the starlings, it was red light that produced the change. Goats, sheep, deer, among other animals, mate in autumn. Knowing this, sheep breeders who want early spring lambs now bring the adults into dark sheds before nightfall in July and August, thus starting the fall process in summer.

Toward the end of February every year I wait for the last signal that winter is done, that the light is lengthening the day and breaking the grip of winter. This signal is the first rain after the first spring thaw. When this occurs my wife, Jean, and I round up boots, lantern and raincoats; then in the darkness of the night we go to the vernal woodland ponds to see the nuptial dance of the salamanders. These amphibians are aroused from their sleep by the lengthening day and pattering rain, that they may lay their eggs in the spring ponds. Later, when the summer sun dries these ponds, the young will be air breathers and will no longer need the water. They are timed to outgrow their watery world when that world is gone.

In the darkness and rain we see them, looking ancient, prehistoric, turning time back millions of years—to the days when the amphibians were the dominant form of life on Earth. We are cold, the air and the land are cold, the water is icy; but before our eyes life begins. The males lay little white spermatophores—like collar buttons—on the leaves. The females twist gracefully and settle over them. It is done! Just before dawn the tiny old creatures crawl back through the rain to their dens. The next night there are salamander eggs attached to the sunken twigs in the pond. We look at this new life and know that it is light that has summoned it into being. And we know, too, that in that icy February pond, spring is waiting.

CAMOUFLAGE— THE CALL TO COLORS
Donald and Louise Peattie

Most of the color that floods the world seems to man to have no purpose at all. It is sheer, delightful superabundance of life's energy. But for countless animals color is a master weapon in the great game of survival. The camouflage of nature is better than any that man has ever devised, and when animals perfectly match their backgrounds, they are both safe and alert to attack their own prey. Mr. Toad looks like a lump of the earth he squats on. Agile Mr. Frog is as green on top as the scum of the pond where he floats, but underneath he is pale as light seen through water. The polar bear and snowy owl are white as the arctic wastes. Brilliant tropical fish hide amid the bright-colored coral of the reef.

The plover's pebble-dash eggs, laid just above the highest wave mark on the seashore, blend with the shingle. So does the dappled fawn, lying motionless, blend with the forest floor. And the underwing moths, probably common in your backyard, look so like the bark of the trees where they alight that they are as good as invisible. But give one a poke, and it flies off displaying the brightly patterned underwings for all to see.

Some creatures camouflage themselves with material from their surroundings. One larva uses lichen, another dead ants. Masking crabs have horny bristles on which they hang disguises of algae or sponge. The sponge crab cuts out a colorful sponge mask, just the right size to fit, and holds it in place over its back with a special pair of legs. As for the squid, it can eject a small cloud of ink, roughly the shape and size of itself; then it slips away while the enemy is distracted by the ink cloud.

Quaint and curious are some of the efforts to avoid detection. Certain tropical mantises are colored like the flowers of their favorite tree. In South America is found the glass-winged butterfly, so transparent you can see through its wings—and so perhaps not see it at all. And the dead-leaf butterfly resembles a bit of old foliage not only in color but in delicate venation and ragged outline. Even its slow, swirling flight is like that of a falling leaf.

In our own country we have the walking-stick insect, which looks exactly like a twig not only in color and shape but even in the angle at which it

Creatures with protective coloration, like these 13 Texas lizards—known as horned toads—can escape the watchful eyes of their enemies, yet be in plain sight all the time.

perches on the branch. Touch it, and it will continue to play 'possum, but if too much annoyed it will put out the legs it has held close to its body and stalk away with an air of offended dignity at having had its disguise penetrated.

The ability to behave so that the color camouflage is nearly perfect is familiar to us in the case of the American bittern. This slim bird of stripy plumage will stand perfectly still among reeds with its bill held almost straight up, the better to merge with its background. Moreover, when a breeze blows the reeds, the bittern has been known to sway accordingly. Certain tropical insects gather together,

heads all one way, to form a pattern resembling the flowers of the tree on which they rest.

The bright plumage of the male bird may well appeal to his lady. But it also serves to attract attention away from the female's quieter garb, thus keeping her the safer. A male bird may also display some brilliant coloration to frighten a rival, as in the case of the Chinese ring-necked pheasant, now common in this country. On the side of his neck the male carries startling red pouches, which he can puff out in an encounter with another male. This immediately reduces a challenger's confidence; he may even skulk away without a fight. If, however, you dimin-

ish the apparent size of the victorious bird's pouches with black water color, the challenger advances with such confidence that the champ will retreat.

When we think of an animal quick-change artist, we usually think of the chameleon, which by doing a sort of slow burn can match a new background. But far more astonishing color changes are found among fish, frogs, squid, crabs and shrimp. A young prawn can change color completely, sometimes in a few minutes, and has a wonderful repertory of tints: green when in seaweed; violet, brown, red or blue-green as it moves among colored algae; transparent blue at night. A flounder has both eyes on one side of its head, but even lying flat and looking up it can note changes on the sea floor and modify its colors accordingly. Placed above squares of patterned linoleum, it will adjust itself to match, all the while waiting for dinner to pass by.

Another meaning of color is that shown in the fantastic relationship between some birds and bees and their favorite flowers. The liplike lowest petal of certain orchids bears a yellow marking strikingly like a female wasp. The male wasp alights there eagerly, and by the time he has discovered the deception two tiny pellets of pollen, connected by a springlike band, have been clamped on the side of his head by the plant. When next he visits such a flower the pellets are hooked off by the orchid, which thus achieves pollination.

Many creatures are color-blind and see the world as though it were an untinted photograph, in grays and blacks and whites. But even a color-blind enemy can be deceived by the kind of protective coloration called disruptive. This is the marking or mottling that breaks up an otherwise identifiable outline. A snake motionless in the grass is often missed because of the pattern on its back. Spotted giraffes and striped zebras are hard for the hunter to see, even at fairly close range, in their native veld. A partridge or quail on the floor of the woods may not be seen because of its mottled feathers.

Since there is no outline harder to conceal than a circle, even a wary eye can give its owner away. But Brother Raccoon wears markings like a black mask that divert attention from his pupils, and many a bird has a black or white streak through the eye, or a patch around it, to draw attention from that bright jet gaze. More than one fish goes so far as to display a "false eye" in its tail. Thus you may be fooled as to which is head and which is tail.

These devices, and thousands like them, are not casual happenstance. They are an irreplaceable part of nature's grand strategy for the game of life.

BEATING THE WINTER COLD
John and Jean George

On a crackling-cold evening in Pennsylvania we stood at the edge of a frozen pond and watched some ducks. All around them the world was buttoned up with ice and snow, for it was well below zero; but the ducks were splashing and swimming busily in a patch of open water. "How *do* they keep the water open?" Jean asked.

"Those ducks are applying one of the simplest laws of water," John answered. "When they paddle their feet, they roil up the warm water from the bottom of the pond to the top so the patch won't freeze over. The ducks use the opening primarily to forage for food, but it helps to keep those bare feet warm too. For though the air is eight degrees below zero, that water must be 38 or 39 degrees above—else it would be ice."

Instinctively the ducks were doing what needed to be done for survival. Many birds and animals keep warm in winter by using—instinctively—just such simple physical principles. Human beings use many of the same principles, but approach them through the slower processes of thought.

For thousands of years we have known that fingers, toes and ears freeze first. But it has been only within the last 200 years that we have understood that this is due to the ratio between the amount of body surface through which heat can be lost, and the body's bulk and heat supply. (This explains why mittens are warmer than gloves; the fingers of a glove have more radiating surface than the mass of a mitten.)

About 100 years ago physicists working on the kinetic theory of gases found that heat travels very slowly through still air. Applying this knowledge of dead-air space to our cold-weather clothes, manufacturers have developed coats and jackets with light, airy padding. But deer have been using this principle for thousands of years. With the first autumn frosts, they shed their cool summer coat and grow a special one for winter—each hair of which is hollow, like a small tube sealed at the outer end. Covered with this air blanket, deer can walk the winter wilderness needing no more shelter than the lee side of a log or the windbreak of a hemlock.

In autumn the squirrel builds a loose ball of a

Coping with the cold is sometimes a matter of anatomy, sometimes of instinct.

Climate determines the size of a jack rabbit's ears—the colder it is, the smaller the ears, because there is less area to lose body heat. The giant-eared creature at the left lives in warm Arizona.

One of the most charming sights in nature is a perfect circle of bobwhites. Facing outward, they fit their bodies together (as in the lower picture) to share the warmth.

nest, using dry leaves and twigs. Curled inside this airy mass when the snow flies, he becomes his own furnace, heating the still air around him until he is locked in comfort. We watched a woodpecker one winter go to his nightly roost in a cozy hollow of our apple tree. Inside, surrounded by wood and out of the wind, he fluffed his feathers—nature's most remarkable insulating material. Wrapped in motionless air, he needed to heat only himself, a very economical arrangement. We took temperature readings on him one zero night, using a thermocouple with two long wires that touched him but did not waken him. The outer feathers were cool, but within that quilt the temperature was 104 degrees.

But what of the rabbit's great ears, which certainly violate one of the cardinal rules of conserving body heat? Even these have evolved according to nature's ingenious plan. The jack rabbit of Oregon has ears only half the size of his enormous-eared kin from warm Arizona. And the arctic hare of the windswept tundra has very small ears, just large enough to catch the sound of the arctic fox breaking trail in the snow. In many other birds and mammals the cold makes tails smaller, legs and necks stockier. Indeed, the farther north an animal's habitat, the shorter his extremities, and these changes can take place within a generation. Mice raised in a laboratory at 90 degrees grew fine, long tails and were slender and long-legged; those raised at 60 degrees had shorter tails and were grosser.

In addition, almost all northern members of a warm-blooded species, or related species, tend to be chunkier and bigger. Witness the bear family: the Goliaths—the polar and Alaskan brown—are confined to the cold northern end of the globe while the medium-size black bear is an inhabitant of the north temperate zone. This tendency applies even to man. Studies show that men of the polar areas have longer trunks and shorter legs and are heavier than their southern cousins. There is good reason for these plans in nature: the denser and larger a body, the more slowly it loses heat. But even with more density and less surface, animals of the North need a good furnace. Consequently the heart is generally bigger.

Color is one more natural device by which animals fight off cold. Many northern species turn white in winter—the weasel, the snowshoe hare, the ptarmigan. This was long thought to be solely protective coloration, but now biologists believe that an important function is warmth. Since white repels heat, black would seem a better color for warmth, but more important than absorbing the scant heat

outside is the problem of holding the heat the body generates. And white does just this.

The U.S. Army teaches its mountain troops and pilots who might be downed in tundra country to imitate the humble igloo of the cottontail rabbit. We knew why one morning when a cottontail, frightened by our approach, burst out of a snowbank. Stooping down, we found a cavelike niche in the snow where the rabbit had pressed his body into the powder and let the wind pack the drifting snow around him. Sealed away from the wind, his own body heat warmed the cavern. The troops find that a small cave in the snow—perhaps only a foot bigger than a man and sleeping bag—will keep its occupant as warm as a rabbit.

Cold is a severe problem for all living creatures, but the combination of cold and wind can be killing. It has occurred to everybody facing gales on a cold winter day that the thermometer is wrong. Bare faces and hands ache when the official temperature reads only 34 degrees. A wind-chill chart compiled by the Army's Surgeon General Office gives the reason. On such a day, with a wind blowing at 20 m.p.h., the effect on your exposed flesh is the same as at 38 degrees *below zero* with no wind. Even on a relatively balmy day of 55 degrees a 15-m.p.h. wind makes your face and hands as cold as if it were 11 below.

We discovered a nuthatch that knew all about this. On windy days he came and departed from our feeding station by a devious route. Dropping below the slope of the hill, he crossed the open yard at an angle and swooped up to the station from about a foot above the ground. "That bird reminds me of swimming across a swift river," Jean observed.

This statement made John wonder if the bird was not purposely maneuvering himself in a river of wind. So, wetting his hand, he walked the bird's route, then tried other routes. This satisfied him that the nuthatch was staying out of the wind. When the bird had to cross the blast of air that funneled through the yard, he did not go broadside to it, but dropped into it and angled across like a good swimmer, letting the push and pull of the current carry him.

That afternoon we bundled up our family in unfashionably warm dead-air-space clothing and took off across the winter landscape. We followed the footsteps of deer up the windless side of the mountain and explored the snow tunnels of the rollicking mink. We saw how the mammals and birds had solved the physics of wind and low temperatures. Then we came home, exhilarated and bright-cheeked—and turned up the thermostat.

A pair of scorpions engage in a life-and-death struggle, the poison-filled stingers of their tails arched menacingly over their bodies, ready to strike.

ANIMAL POISON

H. Munro Fox

Poisons are produced by many different sorts of creatures. Scorpions, bees and snakes have glands which prepare the poisonous liquid, and they have tubes to conduct it to sharp spines or teeth for inflicting a wound. Other animals, which have no offensive weapons, derive protection by pouring out a poison on the skin. A toad, for instance, does this.

The skunk sprays a poison gas, a stuff chemists call mercaptan, which contains sulfur. This is a curious example of how an unusual chemical substance may be found in widely different groups of animals. The purple dye used by the ancient Romans for the togas of their nobles was derived from a shellfish— a sort of sea snail. Newly dyed togas always had an unpleasant smell, for the smell of the purple was nothing more or less than mercaptan.

In some cases we know that poisons play a role in the functioning of the body of the animal which manufactures them. In many instances this may be the real *raison d'être* of the venoms, quite apart from any protective value. The poisonous spittle of snakes, for example, has work to do in the digestion of the snake's food; and a most extraordinary case is presented by a green marine worm, a creature the size of one's thumb, which may be said to be the most extreme and most successful feminist in the sea. The male is microscopic. Like all sea worms, the young of this feminist creature at first swim about, settling down later to staid adult life. If these swimming young settle anywhere on the ground, they grow into the fat female worm; but if they happen to fall upon the skin of their mother, quite another fate befalls them. Part of the worm's skin is covered with a slimy stuff which is poisonous to many animals that would like to eat the succulent worm; but if the minute young settle down on the skin this same stuff, far from killing them, causes the young to change into the microscopic and retiring males of the species. In short, young which would otherwise have grown into fat females are changed by the poison into diminutive males.

One of the most fascinating chapters in animal poisons is the subject of natural immunity, the fact that some animals are immune to the poisons of others and remain unhurt if stung or bitten by the poisonous animal, whereas all other sorts of beasts succumb. The desert fox, the kangaroo rat and other inhabitants of deserts where scorpions abound are in this happy position. Their cousins, living far away from the desert, would be seriously injured by a scorpion's sting, but the desert breeds remain unhurt. It is to be supposed that in the far distant past, before the desert animals had this complete immunity to scorpion venom, those which were stung and could not resist died, leaving no offspring. Their luckier brothers, who happened to have a hardier constitution, survived and left behind them a resistant race of descendants.

Another bizarre instance of this same phenomenon is provided by certain crabs which carry on their backs a kind of sea anemone. The sea anemone is a plantlike animal with the power of stinging like a jellyfish. Minute capsules, each with a needle for penetrating the skin of the victim, are shot out in uncountable numbers when the sea anemone is attacked, and as the poison is very harmful, few enemies venture to attack the happy creature. Consequently the crab walks about with a sea anemone on its back for its own protection, and the anemone enjoys the advantage of sharing the crab's meals by stretching down its food-catching tentacles to the crab's mouth and stealing bits of food.

We now come to the most curious part of this story. How is it that the anemone's batteries of poison capsules do not injure the crab? True, the crab has a thick armor, but the poison, one would think, should injure the crab by way of its mouth. In fact, research has revealed that if the poison is extracted from the anemone and injected into any ordinary crab by means of a hypodermic syringe, the crab very rapidly dies. The effect is most striking when the poison is injected into a crab's leg. Within two seconds of the injection, the crab, following the Biblical injunction, twists off its poisoned member; but if the poison is injected with a syringe into a crab which bears an anemone on its back, no effect follows at all. The creature does not even notice the venom. In other words, the crab with the anemone is immune.

Research revealed one further chapter of the story. Unlike the desert fox, the crab is not born into the world immune to the poison which it will meet later on. The young crabs are all of them vulnerable, but when one of them adopts an anemone as a permanent guest, it gradually becomes immune to its visitor's poison. Every time a fish or other creature pushes against the anemone, it shoots out a cloud of poison capsules. The crab is thus often forced to swallow a number of these ejected venom capsules and—as it has to do this day after day—gradually ceases to be affected.

NATURE MEDICINE
Archibald Rutledge

As a plantation boy, I kept many wild creatures as pets. One of these was the fawn of a whitetail deer. One day a barbed-wire fence tore an ugly gash in its side. I cleansed the wound with carbolic water and bandaged it. But my patient pulled the bandage off and carefully licked the hair away from the injured place, exposing it fully to the air and sunlight. He took entire charge and shortly healed himself.

Birds and animals appear to know just what herbs will cure what ills. The Indians and our pioneer ancestors learned the rudiments of medicine by observing what plants were sought out by animals suffering from wounds, fever, alimentary disturbances; by watching a bear grubbing for fern roots; by noting how the wild turkey, during a rainy spell, compels her babies to eat spicebush leaves; by seeing a wolf, bitten by a rattler, chewing snakeroot.

We may wonder why carrion birds are not infected by their food. But nature has supplied the vultures with heads that are practically featherless; they scrupulously clean their huge beaks; and, further, the vulture will select a high place exposed to the sun and sit there with wings extended for the purpose of cleansing his feathers. The manner of his life calls for special caution in sanitation, and he takes it.

Both birds and animals bathe regularly, and these baths are of many varieties—water, sun, mud, dust. In the Yellowstone, old grizzly bears use the hot sulfur baths, which may alleviate the aches incident to age. It is almost a daily habit of such game birds as the quail, ruffed grouse and wild turkey to take dust baths to discourage insects.

Birds and animals that are injured are inclined to act swiftly and unerringly. A muskrat will completely cover a wounded part with hemlock gum, thus excluding dirt and germs that might lurk in the water in which he swims. Bears also smear their wounds with spruce or hemlock resin, and occasionally with clay. But I never knew a muskrat to use the latter. He knows that water would wash it off. A wounded orangutan or gorilla will attempt to stanch the flow of blood with its hands, and will then close the hole with packings of astringent aromatic leaves.

I used to have a flying squirrel in a big cage. One night she caught her foreleg in a crack, and in her frantic efforts to escape she broke it. For several days she lay with her injured paw in the same position. She who had been vividly active suddenly became passive, intent on the one great aim of healing herself. And this she did by being absolutely quiet.

When a wild creature is injured, it first seeks solitude and complete retirement. Then, besides giving scrupulous attention to its external wound, it takes internal care. It may induce vomiting; it will almost certainly take a laxative. Members of the canine and feline families, when below par or in physical distress, eat green grass. An animal with fever hunts up an airy, shady place near water and remains quiet, eating very little and drinking often. On the other hand, a rheumatic animal seeks the sunlight and soaks up all the heat possible, as this relieves its pain.

With the changing seasons, when their systems require certain adjustments, some instinct causes birds and animals to change their diet. For example, in the South, where there are great dredge cuts left by phosphate mining, buck deer will travel miles to drink that water, which is rich in lime. They need lime for antler growth. All female birds need lime to form eggshells; and it is a common thing to see pet birds eating cuttlebone. When sick or wounded, wild creatures resort to the ancient remedies of nature: medicines, pure air and complete relaxation.

In a "resort" on Lake Amboseli in Kenya, elephants bathe in the rusty-colored waters, spattering their hides with red mudpack that will rid them of parasites.

PART 6

THE SOCIABLE KINGDOM

*Their languages, their rules for the common good,
their pleasures, courtship and family life:
these are the most advanced of animal ways.
By instinct and habit and learning, they have
built the herds, swarms, flocks, tribes—
the animal societies—without which they
could not have survived.*

Chapter one

ANIMAL LANGUAGE

That the song of birds is the loveliest of all languages is felt by everyone. But whoever walks into a yard or park soon becomes aware of other tongues being spoken all around. The chattering of a squirrel is an angry cry of alarm and fright, and the hysterical "chip, chip" of an adult sparrow is the sound of a protective parent.

Animal language may also be utterly voiceless. Chemical signals from the female moth bring males flying along miles of invisible trail. The delicate garden snails speak through postures and movements to announce that the mating hour has come. The mere tensing of a mother duck tells her ducklings to crouch like rocks on the path to a stream.

Animal language is song and noises, poses and scents, movements and touch. It is innate in all beasts in some form, even in those which lead almost solitary lives. Much of what the beasts have to say has been discovered by students of their ways. You and I can learn it, too.

What can be more intriguing than the sight of a flock of snow buntings speeding over a field, then suddenly alighting on a spot agreed to by all through some instantaneous and remarkable language!

The catbird mews angrily when startled, but usually sings beautifully, often imitating the finest songs of other birds.

Born poor singers, the young male chaffinches form choirs and improve greatly with group practice.

The nightingale: his song is the most glorious of all.

Song sparrows have many "dialects," singing different melodies in different parts of the country.

THE MYSTERIOUS MAGIC OF BIRDSONG

Donald and Louise Peattie

It starts with the earliest light, like hope itself. A bird voice finding its way through the thinning darkness, from some central source of joy and ardor. Song, original and sure, and then another birdsong, and another, until the coming day is alive with an uplifted chorus. There is no sound more welcome than the song of birds. This is not only because of its varied beauties but for a deeper reason. Birdsong is a language—one without words, but with a meaning. We cannot understand it, but one thing within the mystery of birdsong we can be sure of. Its magic comes bubbling out of the deepest sources of springtime well-being. It is a yea-saying to life.

As to *how* birds sing, it might almost be said that they were made to, having a unique apparatus for their melodies. Whereas we humans have a larynx for our vocal utterance, birds have a syrinx, a tiny, delicately articulated voice box which can produce the rolling trill of the canary, the elaborate arias of the mockingbird or the pure, perfect notes of the hermit thrush. For the *why* of their singing, science has a few answers, too—but none of them complete. One of the most precisely assured is that a bird sings in order to stake out a claim to his bailiwick for nesting. The migrating males, arriving first in the springtime, proclaim each a certain territory as his own.

In some sunny, reedy swamp you may have heard the chorus of the red-winged blackbirds—those handsome, dark-uniformed birds with red-and-yellow epaulets—loud in song before ever the streaked females appear on the scene. "Konkeree!" they whistle, and it might be translated, at that moment, as "Here am I! Here I stay! This is mine—this patch of reed and sun and water." Other males may be singing in competition with him, but it is a good guess that the most valiant singer wins the area.

As the females come winging from the south, the males announce with their songs that they are owners of territories, ready to set up housekeeping. The male sings through the nesting season, perhaps to please his lady, certainly because he is so full of the vernal surge of life that it just naturally bursts out in birdsong. This is proved by the fact that a solitary captive, unable to win a place to call his own or to draw to himself a mate, will in the springtime sing on in his prison, day after day. The spring is within him, and that is reason enough for song.

With the hatching of the nestlings, song lessens. As breadwinner and grub gatherer, the father bird has less time for operatics. Certain species may rear a second brood and thus renew their musical efforts into midsummer. But this song lacks the fullness of the spring singing season; indeed, it is sometimes sung almost with closed bill, so that only the nearby listener can catch it.

The time of day, as well as the time of year, influences birdsong. The coming of the light seems to prompt singing in most of our familiar winged neighbors. But if you listen to a dawn chorus, you will note that each kind of bird sings at his chosen moment. Again toward late afternoon there is an impetus to song, softer than the daybreak music. And certain birds, like the vesper sparrow, are drawn to sing with the coming of dusk. Others, like the whippoorwill, are vocal only at night. Still others, most famed of them the nightingale, sing both by day and by dark. And the chimney swifts mount out of the darkness of the city's chimney pots at an early hour and rise high into regions where there is light that has not yet arrived on the ground. There they sing as though they had come together to praise the Lord.

The marvelous spontaneity of fine birdsong is a mystery. Was the wild torrent, like musical laughter, from the canyon wren's throat once packed away, an inherited gift, in the egg from which he broke? Did the brown thrasher come by his lovely melodies the same way? Careful studies by ornithologists, using tape recorders and electronic devices, give us a paradoxical answer. It has been concluded that, generally speaking, the simple call notes of a bird are born in him when he is hatched, but that true song may be partly inherited and partly learned, or entirely learned.

A group of English researchers under W. H. Thorpe at Cambridge University, for example, have found that when a young chaffinch is taken from the nest and reared alone, it sings but a poor and restricted version of the song of its kind in the wild. This, they suggest, may be taken as the basic inherited song pattern. But give the prisoner in solitary confinement a fellow chaffinch, and his song improves as he listens to his companion. Song, in short, stimulates song.

The chaffinch students supply a further chapter of interest in their study of isolated birds. In the developing songs of an isolated *group* it became almost impossible to distinguish the song of one bird from another. The group song became quite as complex as that of a chaffinch in the wild. But it had almost no resemblance to the usual wild chaffinch singing!

And, the Cambridge ornithologists found, it's what the bird learns in its youth that sticks. Among the chaffinches it was during a brief and critical period of about six weeks, when the bird was a little less than a year old, that the singer developed finally its song pattern. It did not seem to matter what the chaffinch heard thereafter. The song it learned as a youngster was fixed for life.

As a result, a neighborhood of songsters sometimes develops a local variation of its own. In the Midwest we once lived on the fringe of a garden where the song sparrows were loud with their usual song, to which a fitting lyric has been written: "Maids, maids, maids, put on your teakettle -ettle -ettle -ettle!" That summer, when we went to Massachusetts, we encountered a bird of the same species which sang quite a different air. It had a refined Boston accent, and the song contained no boisterous cheer about maids and teakettles at all.

Some birds incorporate in their singing the songs of other species. The jay and the mockingbird, to name two, have a reputation for imitation. An old gentleman we knew raised blue jays in cages in his office, to see what they could be taught. His prize pupil was one that imitated perfectly not only the squeak of his office chair and the family whistle for the dog, but also the sound of the children knocking at the door and calling to be let in.

Through the years, in many places, runs a musical thread on which dear memories are strung. There were skylarks once at Stonehenge, so high above the prehistoric shrine in the spring sunshine that they seemed to make the air glisten with their twinkling voices. On a Provencal hillside there was a cuckoo, regular as a clock every springtime. And there the nightingale, supreme of singers, lifted his voice to a pinnacle of ecstasy; and then, when the sustained enchantment seemed almost too great to endure, raised it to a yet higher, purer note that throbbed out across the moonlight in nearly unbearable loveliness.

There is the ultimate mystery of birdsong—not just the incomprehensible communication between feathered singers, but the wordless and magical meaning brought to the wondering human senses by a wild, sudden beauty that lifts the heart.

THE NATURAL ART OF COMMUNICATION

Alan Devoe

Three fox cubs were playing while their mother eyed them contentedly from their den entrance. Suddenly one of the youngsters started to trot off across the pasture. The vixen stood up, "pointed" with her sharp muzzle in his direction—and stood rigidly still and silent. She made no sound I could hear from where I was hidden, but in a few seconds the cub began to slow down. Turning around, he looked straight at his mother. She kept her gaze on him. As if pulled by an invisible thread, the little fox hurried home. Years later I found an identical episode recorded by a well-known naturalist, and subsequently similar observations have come my way. That little scene of inaudible communication at the fox den started me investigating that endlessly amazing thing, the language of the wild.

Some animals communicate with one another by a kind of Morse code. I have "listened in" on conversations taking place without any detectable sound or action. Some animals express themselves through gestures. When a worker bee finds a flower full of nectar, it flies back to the hive and begins a peculiar hovering dance in the air, fairly shimmering with its urgent message. One by one, other bees join in and presently troop eagerly to the source of nectar.

Rabbits thump their hind feet sharply on the ground to convey messages of anger or alarm. The tiny white-footed mouse uses a similar means. When trespassing mice invade the patch of land he has staked out as his own, White-foot warns them off by a staccato "No Trespassing" message.

When any menacing creature, such as man, appears in the animal world, the alarm is passed along in a dozen ways. Perhaps a blue jay first sights the danger and gives his sharp "Beat it!" cry. Instantly other birds and squirrels relay the message over the woods wireless. A female wild duck transmits the danger signal to duckdom by uttering a harsh cry and sailing suddenly aloft. A partridge makes a short, swift flight from tree to tree with loudly whirring wings. A mother bear brings her cub scrambling down from a treetop by thwacking the trunk. Over in the pond an alert beaver slaps his heavy, flat tail with a tremendous *whomp* on the surface of the water.

The ways in which wild things talk to one another

Prairie dogs, among the most sociable of animals, post sentries that broad-cast—by sharp barks and thumping—an enemy's approach to the colony.

are almost as varied as the creatures themselves. A doe says "Follow me!" to her fawn by flirting her brushy tail suddenly upward to show the white underside. The so-called "death watch" beetle raps out its announcements by tapping its hard snout against the walls of its dark burrow in the wood.

A male hummingbird addresses the female in a language that is pure poetry of motion. On quivering wings he swings before her in an aerial arc, like the swing of a pendulum. More and more passionately he "speaks," the two ends of the arc-flight rising higher and higher, until suddenly he shoots straight upward in an "exclamation mark" that may carry him zooming 60 feet. An instant's hovering at that great height, and then abruptly he plunges down and hovers suspended, glittering, in the air before her.

One of the queerest of animal communications takes place between the little African bird called a honey guide and the ratel, or honey badger. The bird loves the grubs of bees and wasps; the badger loves honey. But the honey guide cannot deal with thousands of infuriated bees; and the badger has such short legs that he cannot make the long investigations needed to locate the hives. So the honey guide flies around the forest until he finds a bee tree, then whizzes to the placidly waiting badger and

dances over its head, speaking in shrill cries, *Cherr! Cherr!* The badger lumbers after the fluttering bird. Safe in his stingproof hide, the badger rips the hive to pieces; and bird and beast settle down to feast.

Arboreal ants in the tropics "talk" from tree to tree by tapping on the bark and leaves so vigorously that it sounds like a rain shower. Through an elephant herd there ripples a perpetual murmur of talk and signaling, a sign language conducted by ears and trunks. Jack Miner, expert on wild geese, knew their "honk talk" so well that his friends said he could call a wild flock down from the sky by "telling" them, gander fashion, of a good pond and corn supply where he was hiding.

Other naturalists have learned to talk with bears, moose, owls. I know one veteran woodsman, now living in the city, who amuses himself occasionally by leaning out the window and "wolf-talking." In a twinkling all the dogs for blocks around shed their centuries of domestication and stand tensely alert, shivering with excited response to the old language of the wild. Incredible? Fantastic? Perhaps. But there is so much we do not know about what goes on in the senses and psyches of animals that no experienced naturalist ever closes his mind too firmly to the language of the wild, whatever it may be.

Chapter two

THE WILL TO LIVE

Living from day to day is ferociously earnest for most animals. The mouse lives in fear of the stalking weasel; the killifish zigzags in desperation to keep away from the feeding haddock and herring.

No matter how frightening the world may be, there is not a beast that will not attempt to stay alive. Fleeing from danger is the simplest way to save oneself. A butterfly sees a child's hand coming toward it, and it flies away. A rabbit runs before the hound. Even a worm hears the fisherman's spade and slides swiftly down its hole. But flight is not the only means of attaining safety. The opossum plays dead to stay alive.

From the instinctive order of the insect world to the intelligent social actions of higher animals, survival is a matter of coöperation. Flocking birds such as crows place themselves on tree or fence to call their warnings to the others, and grazing animals take turns as guardians of the herd.

The bravery of animals on the defensive is very great, and their cunning in outwitting their enemies, especially man, has been a mighty asset in the struggle for existence.

SENTINELS OF THE WILDERNESS

Archibald Rutledge

Behind the dense boughs of a low-hanging cedar, I once watched two full-antlered white-tail bucks feeding in a swale. At first I was fascinated by the patrician elegance of their bearing, but soon I noticed a peculiarity of their behavior: they were feeding alternately. While one was cropping grass, relaxed and at ease, the other—with head held high, eyes sweeping the sea marsh—stood on guard against enemies. Not for a moment, during the half-hour I spied upon them, did they relax their teamwork vigilance.

Another time, at the edge of an open glade, two great stags lay back to back, each on his right side so that their heads faced in opposite directions—a perfect scheme for guarding themselves against danger from any quarter.

Many wild creatures, especially those that travel in groups, protect themselves by having one of their number act as sentinel. The only occasion on which I ever saw several deer without a lookout was when I observed five of them feeding on high-bush blueberries. All their heads were well up, and there was no need for one to act as guard.

The bison that roamed the great plains of the West always had sentries. So do wild cattle now, and wild goats, mountain sheep, moose, elk and prong-horned antelope. Animal sentinels use special sounds of alarm which are instantly heeded by their fellows. The deer snorts, the crow puts into his cawing a loud minatory note, the gray squirrel barks in an angry tone.

Wild turkeys always put out a patrol to scout the country on all sides, and while some members of the flock eat, others warily look and listen. I once saw a magnificent gobbler standing guard while another dusted himself in a sand hole, fluffing out his plumage, and then lay on his side, blinking drowsily in the sun, his big legs extended with comical awkwardness. Presently he waked thoughtfully, righted his majestic bulk, shook from his regal person a cloud of dust, preened himself and then took over the position of watcher. His companion was soon enjoying *his* dust bath, assured of a lookout who would not fail him.

Carl Akeley, the African explorer, told me that herds of African buffalo always post patrols; that the kudu, a large antelope, posts lookouts on the highest hillock in the neighborhood so that they command a wide sweep of country. He said that a gorilla family is invariably protected by one or two members whose business it is to broadcast an alarm in case of danger.

In Africa certain small birds of the starling family spend most of their time on the back of the rhinoceros, feeding on the vermin that are attracted to these huge creatures. Their massive hosts tolerate the birds not only because they eat insect pests but because they warn the rhinos of the approach of danger.

Occasionally a wild sentinel is delinquent in his duty. The goose that flies at the apex of the V not only governs the flock's speed, direction and height from the ground; he is also the chief lookout and is expected to avoid leading his fellows into danger. One day as a great V of migrating geese passed overhead

I saw the leader descend and the flock pass low over a barnyard, whereupon the farmer ran out and shot at the birds. Immediately the flock set up a great clamor as if berating their discredited leader, and he was quickly displaced by another gander.

Indian guides in Canada tell me that beavers usually post a sentry, especially when at their noisy work of tree felling. Prairie dogs, chipmunks and marmots also set watches. I have often concealed myself to watch this technique. One marmot would slowly come out of his hole, scouting the country with his beady, keen eyes. When he gave a little grunting call to reassure his fellows, they would come forth and begin to feed; but at least one, selecting an elevated vantage point, would act as sentry. So long as he was quiet, the others went on feeding. But if I showed myself, a short bark from the watchman sent all of them scurrying pell-mell into their dens.

One day in the wilderness, hearing a little rustling in some bushes ahead of me, I sat down to see what might emerge. Presently a huge wild razor-back sow waddled into an open place in the pine forest. There she stopped, uneasy, intently alert, and gave a low grunt—whereupon nine tiny pigs came out in single file. She had caught wind of me, but did not know just where I was. When the sow's comical and precious children came up to her, all of them (to my delight) imitated her wary posture; and when she put her long tail straight up in the air, the piglets followed suit, though they had very little to show in the way of tails. Finally, having made up her mind where I was, she gave a grunt of alarm and plunged off, her youngsters following manfully. She tempered her own speed, however, to her young ones' ability to follow. Delay might mean death to her, but she delayed—a true sentinel of the wilderness.

Animals that graze on the open prairie are highly visible prey and depend primarily on fleetness for safety. To outwit enemies, a sentinel is posted. Here a pronghorn (American antelope) stands guard, his sensitive nostrils "feeling" the air.

RULES AND REGULATIONS

Max Eastman

In recent years biologists have discovered that we human beings and the animals with which we share life on Earth have many things in common. Such traits as the disposition to form societies, the desire for property and status, love of home, and homesickness are now found to be basic attributes of practically all vertebrate life. These discoveries have upset so many established notions as to constitute what Robert Ardrey, in the book *African Genesis,* calls a "revolution in the natural sciences."

A first step toward this change of view, or a kind of premonition of it, was a book by British ornithologist Eliot Howard. Up to his time everybody had accepted the commonplace assumption that male birds fight over females. What they actually fight over, Howard observed, is real-estate holdings. Each male bird stakes out his own piece of territory with singing, and defends it ardently. If he can manage to keep his holdings secure, he has small trouble getting a discriminating bride to join him. The fighting over her is negligible.

Birds post their property by singing, but most mammals, since they live in a world of smells rather than sounds, do it by "demarcating," which means depositing a characteristic scent at the boundaries of their domain. Lions and tigers perform this function with their urine. Other animals have a special gland designed for this sole purpose. Among some deer and antelope, a gland above the eye produces a strong-smelling oily substance which, rubbed off on twigs and branches, impregnates the whole dwelling-place with a notice of ownership.

Captive wild animals demarcate the cage or area in which they are confined. After that it is home to them, and at times they can be more concerned to keep you out than to get out themselves. I saw an example of this in the zoo in Zurich, Switzerland. Dr. Heine Hediger, the director, led me to the cage of a little ring-tailed lemur. As we drew near, the lemur dashed across his cage, climbed up the grill and placed his mark on a bar exactly opposite to where we stood. He could hardly have said more explicitly, "Can't you see this is private property!" Having said that, he retired to his high shelf and looked at us with an expression of happy proprietorship that made us laugh.

"In the jungle," Dr. Hediger told me, "you will find many quite elaborate homes. They don't have roofs and walls, but they are divided like ours into separate compartments: a dining room, a sleeping room, a nursery, sunbathing terraces. Unless there is a public bath in the vicinity, each home will contain a bathroom. For in the cleansing and care of the body, there is hardly a wild animal that is not more elegant than the average man."

People with a strong property sense are usually pretty touchy about social status, and this is true of a majority of mammals. It is true even among certain kinds of fish. Just as hens in a henyard establish a "pecking order," so do the little red fish called swordtails. Each one in a tankful finds out which others he can dominate and which he must submit to. A high social status gives him many prerogatives—access to food, to females, to an undisturbed corner of the tank. He defends his corner with great belligerence. An experiment described by Robert Ardrey proves how profound this instinct is. "Let the water in the tank be gradually cooled. The time will come when the male will lose all interest in sex; but he will still fight for his status."

We think of a wolf pack as one of the wildest and most undisciplined things in nature, but wolves have a social ceremonial and a system of caste which make our own look amateurish. It took 33 pages in a scientific journal to describe all the ceremonial attitudes and symbolic gestures of a pack of wolves in the zoo at Basel, Switzerland. The attitude of the head, the ears, the bristling of certain portions of the fur, the wrinkling of the brow, the degree to which the teeth are bared and, above all, the way the tail is held are strictly prescribed. If a low-ranking wolf approaches the big chief with her tail in the air, she is just as likely as not to be put to death. Her tail must stay under her belly as though it were glued there! A middle-class wolf may let her tail hang down freely in the presence of the chief, but woe to her if, through ignorance or delusions of grandeur, she lifts it above the horizontal.

Baboons are even more conscious of caste. Aside from lovemaking and rearing their young, one of their principal social activities is grooming one another. As a rule a mature female may groom the big boss with both hands, but a male, even if listed in the Social Register, normally may use only one hand. The lower-class citizen, if male, may use only one finger. And very young males may only *look at* His Majesty's fur. The regulations are obeyed with a punctilio that it would be difficult to find outside the court of an Oriental potentate.

When you study baboons on their native heath, you realize how important these social niceties are. Baboons are among the most helpless of animals, for they live on the ground, yet have no claws. They make up for this by facing their enemies not as individuals but as a troop. The strict regimentation of the troop, the emphasis on status, is not snobbery but simply good army discipline.

The late Eugène Marais, a South African naturalist, observed an act of soldierly self-sacrifice that, if human, would deserve a monument. The troop slept in an almost inaccessible cave high up on a sheer cliff. The way to the cave was a ledge about half a mile long and, in places, no more than six inches wide. Marais would watch with wonder the perfect orderliness with which at nightfall the entire troop made its way along this ledge.

One night just as the baboons were approaching the cave, a leopard emerged from the forest below and began to reconnoiter the terrain. Marais saw two baboons leave the troop and make their way back along the ledge. The leopard, his attention fixed on the frightened troop in which he was going to make his kill, did not notice them. The two baboons dropped on him from above. One bit at his spine, the other at his throat. The leopard caught with his jaws the one on his back, and with a stroke of his paw disemboweled the one hanging to his throat. But the stroke came too late—the baboon's sharp canine teeth had reached his jugular vein. Both baboons died; but the leopard died, too. The troop above them crawled into their cave in the usual good order.

The idea that all nervous and mental disorders have their source in sexual preoccupations now seems even more extravagant than it did when Freud insisted on it. The animal in us, Freud thought, was continually striving against the demands of social life. But now we find that in animals the demands of social life are often as strong as, and sometimes even stronger than, those of sex.

The idea that all political troubles began in the "human" institution of private property also looks a little naïve in view of this more balanced view of Earthly life as a whole. This idea lay at the base of the whole socialist movement. But it was not man who first introduced the institution of private property; it was and is to be found among practically all the higher animals.

We come back, then, with our Western fact-finding science to what was given us by the contemplative wisdom of the Orient—to a sense of the unity of all Earthly life. We are all more closely akin than we thought we were.

THE COURAGE OF HEROES
Joe Austell Small

One of the most fascinating things about animals is the wonderful courage which the weak often display against the strong. In my years outdoors I have witnessed almost incredible examples, and from fellow outdoorsmen have come other stirring stories.

While studying deer which were grazing on a ranch, H. C. Hahn, Texas state biologist, heard squeaks of terror nearby. He turned and saw a five-foot racer snake gliding up a low tree; in its mouth a tiny field mouse struggled vainly. Suddenly another mouse ran up the tree and attacked the reptile. Hahn watched, spellbound. The second rodent bit into the snake's body several times, then got a firm grip and hung on grimly. The snake squirmed and feinted savagely, but could not bite the second mouse as long as mouse No. 1 remained in its mouth. So the snake dropped its victim and turned to settle with the little tormentor who was biting into its back. The brave ruse worked. Instantly releasing its grip, the attacking mouse sprang to the ground and ran to safety with its rescued mate.

I like to recall a remarkable exhibition of courage by two Canada geese in a marsh near my home in Burleson County, Texas. A hunter's shot had injured the hen's wing, preventing her from returning to the Canadian nesting grounds. Geese mate for life, so the gander stayed with the hen, and the pair raised a family in the marsh.

One day when I was in the vicinity of the nest I heard wild commotion. While the gander was away, a fox had attacked the hen and was dragging her off. Summoned by the hen's frantic cries, the gander rushed to her aid, his bill popping angrily. Tearing into the formidable attacker, the big honker dug out pinches of fur, beating the fox about the head with his powerful wings, and clawing. The din was terrific.

In a moment the hen got loose, but, instead of retreating, the weakened mother conquered her terror and attacked the enemy. Even both birds could have administered no serious damage to a fox, but a valiant heart counts for much in the wild, and the culprit turned coward and slunk away into the brush.

There are few wild creatures which, in exceptional circumstances, may not summon up heroic courage. A mother skunk has been known to battle a flooded river, rescuing her trapped babies, one by one, from

Animals living in groups, like these Sykes monkeys, have rigid training. From babyhood on, each must learn his status in the social levels of the tribe.

Even the meekest animals may turn on a dangerous foe, especially to defend their young. Here a rabbit delivers kicks powerful enough to send a raccoon sprawling.

their inundated burrow. A hummingbird will attack and successfully chase away an eagle that has trespassed on its territory, and the naturalist Alan Devoe once saw a rabbit give a terrier the surprise of its life when the dog blundered into her nest of young. Instead of running, she turned and piled into him with her hind legs kicking like pistons. The terrier emitted a yip of amazement and ran.

My favorite story of animal courage describes a duel between a powerful plains wolf and a female antelope that fought for the life of her tiny kid. The encounter was witnessed by Leonard C. DeWitt, partner in the Ox-Bow Ranch near Walsenburg, Colorado.

One May afternoon DeWitt was riding the range when he noticed puffs of dust rising from a small cactus flat some distance away. Raising his binoculars to his eyes, the rancher beheld stark drama. A large timber wolf was running around in a circle, pursued by an antelope doe. DeWitt realized that the wolf had evidently tried to capture the doe's kid and had been attacked by the infuriated mother. The wolf, knowing that he could not outrun her to the distant timber, and not relishing close encounter with the antelope's sharp, flaying forefeet, tried to discourage her by running around and around a cactus.

Excitement mounted in the rancher as he saw a little antelope kid arise, stretch and take several faltering steps toward its mother. Fear for her baby drove the doe to redouble her efforts. Her forefeet struck the wolf's hind legs, and he went down. He was up again instantly, but his hindquarters were bleeding and he limped. In desperation, he turned on her, his jaws slashing. The rancher held his breath. A timber wolf is a terrible adversary; his curved fangs can slit the toughest hide, and he can hamstring a racing ram and cut its throat in two deft movements.

But their first contact had left the wolf a sorry sight. His teeth were knocked out. This eliminated his lethal power. Bedraggled and beaten, he now sidled slowly off, his head held at an unnatural, sidewise position. Then the doe went in for the kill. Hurdling some cactus in her way, she came down squarely on the wolf. Her legs were battering rams that pounded and slashed, raising a cloud of dust that hid the grim finish from the rancher. After the dust had settled, DeWitt saw the antelope prance back and forth for a moment before the lifeless body of her conquered foe; then she went to her kid and nuzzled it gently. Her valiance had triumphed over one of the most formidable adversaries in the wilds.

ANIMAL INGENUITY
Archibald Rutledge

When their own lives or the lives of their young are in danger, creatures of the wild show a wiliness and resourcefulness akin to the ingenuity and courage of human beings. On my southern plantation lived a famous buck—Old Roland—so huge and superbly antlered that he had become a legend among local hunters. One winter, after the hunting season, I was talking with an old workman named Steve. "How come nobody hunt Old Roland this year?" he asked me. "Everybody hunted for him," I said, "but nobody found him." Steve doubled up with laughter. "That old buck's been sleepin' close by my house all winter," he said.

In the broomgrass, not 50 feet from his cabin, Steve pointed out where Old Roland had slept. While the hunters had ranged the distant woods for him, he had couched here in safety. Instinct must have told the buck two things: first, that the old man was no hunter; secondly, that no one would dream of looking for a wary old stag so close to an inhabited cabin.

An animal or bird caught flat-footed and unable to hide will often feign ferocity or madness, or simulate death. Such antic behavior suggests hydrophobia, which animals know and fear, and usually delays an enemy's attack or may even scare him away. The puffing adder inflates himself fearsomely until almost twice his natural size and blows in a terrifying manner. This serpent can put on the most convincing and appalling of all dying acts, a truly gruesome pantomime of suffering. The opossum also feigns death convincingly—his eyes even roll back and his mouth falls open. The more harmless a creature, the more defenseless he is; therefore in a crisis he is likely to imitate one that is highly dangerous. Innocuous snakes will vibrate their tails like rattlers.

Some animals and a good many birds try to hiss like snakes. The best of these imitations is given by the wild-turkey hen when brooding eggs on her nest in the underbrush. On several occasions I have leaped away from what I thought was a snake, only to find that I had almost stepped on a turkey nest.

The fox's shrewdness is most acute when he is attempting to escape from hounds. One afternoon I was sitting on a stump near a stream when a fox hove in sight. Not far behind him a pack of hounds was baying, and I could see that the fox had grown tired. Across the stream an old tree had fallen, and the fox started across this log. What he did next was one of the most sagacious feats in wildlife that I have ever observed.

Halfway across the stream he paused, turned sideways and peered down. Below him was a tiny green island. Down to this the fox leaped. I expected that he would then jump across to the farther bank; instead he jumped back to the side of the stream that he had just left and ran off. When the hounds came up they followed the trail to the middle of the log, then crossed to the farther side of the stream. But no scent awaited them there, and for many minutes they vainly cast about to pick up the trail. Finally they gave up the chase.

I have seen a good many thousand deer in their native wilds, and can testify to their alertness and resourcefulness. A most appealing performance occurred one day in the pinelands near the humble home of a backwoodsman. I had met him in a forest path, within distant sight of his house. He had been rounding up some hogs in the woods, and these, 20 or more in number, were in the pathway ahead of us, slowly making their way toward the barnyard.

As we were talking we heard a solitary hound and were almost certain that he was bringing a deer in our direction. We sat down together on a log and did not have long to wait. Running perhaps a half-mile ahead of the hound, a beautiful buck appeared. He was plainly tired. Both seeing and winding the hogs, he stopped. For at least three minutes he stood motionless and thoughtful; then he stole forward toward the path, where he deliberately fell in with the hogs and began to walk with them toward the barnyard. This strange behavior had in it wild intelligence and the deep design of high strategy. The buck knew that if he mingled with this drove of swine, his scent, for the pursuing hound, would cease to be solitary and compelling.

Within 30 yards of the stable lot the buck left the path, stealing away through the woods. By this time the hound was within sight, and we watched to see whether the buck's ruse would outwit him. It did. Coming to the path, he fell in behind the hogs, ran them full cry and chased them into the barnyard.

All wild creatures, when disabled, resort to amazing stratagems. Once in the woods at twilight I saw a regal wild turkey in a pathetic dilemma. One of his great wings, broken by a hunter or by some accident, was dragging on the ground. Night was coming on, and it was high time for the gobbler to be in a roost far up in a moss-shrouded cypress or lofty pine. He could not fly to a roost, yet if he stayed on the ground a fox or wildcat would surely catch him.

Nearby was a tree that had been broken 20 feet from the base. The break had not been complete, and the top half leaned over until it touched the ground. The old gobbler walked slowly up this incline until he reached the top. He knew he would not be safe there: a wildcat might follow his steps. So he took a mighty leap and, beating with his one good wing, landed in a nearby oak. Here he should be safe. And he was, for I saw him afterward while his wing was healing and finally had the satisfaction of watching him fly 70 feet up to a gnarled limb in a lordly yellow pine.

The ability to remain motionless until danger has passed is a favorite ruse of wild creatures. This habit goes deeper than dependence on mere protective camouflage; it requires something very much like character to let an enemy come perilously close and yet make no frightened burst for freedom. Oddly enough, the deer, almost the fleetest of animals, often takes refuge in utter immobility. I once saw what appeared to be antlers protruding from behind a fallen pine. I stood motionless and watched for 20 minutes. They did not move, and I concluded that they were bare branches of the dead tree. But as soon as I moved they proved to be real antlers after all; the crafty buck

had been watching me and had at first decided that standing still was a better idea than running away.

Another time I saw a doe in a greenwood with her tiny fawn. Like a statue the mother stood looking and listening, but the baby wanted to play and kept running around her on unsteady legs. At last the doe raised her forefoot, gently but firmly set it on the fawn's back and pressed her baby down into the grass, thus hiding him and keeping him still.

One of the most ingenious acts of a wild creature I ever saw was that of a snowy egret which I spied knee-deep in a sea marsh. Every few minutes it would dart its javelinlike beak into the water. Fishing was good. Its appetite satisfied, the bird lifted its wings to fly away. But its efforts were unavailing. Plainly in distress, it struggled to free one leg. Just as I was about to go to its aid, the egret managed to lift itself into the air. Dangling from its left foot was a huge clam, closed like a vise. I watched, curious to see how the bird would meet such a dilemma. Flying off-balance, the egret alighted on a nearby fence post. For a moment he teetered on one foot; then, lifting his imprisoned foot high, he began to whack the clam against the post. Soon the shell broke, and the clever egret, freed once more, calmly preened its feathers as if such a misadventure were all in the day's work.

Superb in flight, a master at every ruse, the fox often makes a sport of eluding his pursuers. He is just as cunning when he is the hunter.

Chapter three

ZEST FOR LIFE

Fleeing and stalking are only part of life in the wild. Almost all animals
devote countless hours to sheer pleasure—to sunning, resting,
bouncing, frisking, playing. A mother fox brings her kits into the spring
twilight to roll and tumble with them in obvious enjoyment; a cardinal
takes off several hours every day just to sit in a bush.

There are trees to play in, and every bear, raccoon and squirrel at one time
or another runs up them in a joyful excess of spirit. There is water
to dive into, and otters, mink, beavers spend as many hours splashing
and blowing it as they do hunting and working in it. Even the lowly
sea urchin has moments of high spirits as its spines dance to the coming
and going of sunlight and shadow.

The zest for life trembles through every activity of the animal world—
the almost human-seeming politeness and loyalty, the courtship
songs and dances and giving of gifts, the lessons and games which
mothers use to teach their young. All the dangers of
the wild cannot repress the love of living.

ANIMALS HAVE THEIR FUN!

Alan Devoe

It was a bright moonlit night on the lonely Argentine pampas. The English explorer, sleeping on the ground, had been wakened by the cry of a puma. In the glimmering light he now saw four of the great cats coming toward him. Tense, terrified, he waited, motionless. Then suddenly he was swept by almost incredulous relief. The pumas weren't going to kill him. They were *playing*. He was merely their audience. Calling to one another, the pumas scampered and raced like kittens in a game of hide-and-seek. They rolled and tussled together. While the explorer held his breath, the great cats took turns leaping directly over his body. At last they trooped away into the night.

W. H. Hudson, the great English naturalist, told that true story. Every naturalist can match it with stories of his own, for the fact is that all the higher animals play. A charging grizzly bear may look like the grimmest of brutes, but he loves to slide down hills in the snow. A grizzly will clamber laboriously to the top of a good snow slope again and again for the joy of whizzing down like a small boy playing shoot-the-chute.

Black and brown bears amuse themselves by rolling downhill, end over end, tumbling and somersaulting. Enos Mills, the naturalist of the American western parks, told of a black bear cub that climbed into an open barrel by a prospector's shack, lurched and rocked until it had overturned the barrel, then rolled uproariously down the mountain.

A young hippopotamus, born in the Amsterdam Zoo, devised his own way to have fun. A maple leaf drifted into his tank one day. The hippo eased his vast bulk gently into the tank and swam under the floating leaf. Then he emitted a fine snorting blast that blew the leaf into the air. When it came down,

the hippo blew it up again. Hour after hour the outsized beast raptly played his solitary leaf game.

Young raccoons often play with a small piece of wood until they have worn it smooth. Fox and coyote cubs toss a bit of moss or bark into the air and catch it again. They shake it, "worry" it and play stalking and pouncing games with it. Even the bloodthirsty weasel has been known to play solitary games with sticks and stones.

There isn't a stodgier animal in the American woods than a porcupine, but porkies wrestle, somehow managing not to stab each other. Swatting with their formidably spined tails is "no fair," no matter how strenuous the match. Howler monkeys wrestle while hanging upside down from a branch by their tails. Young 'coons and badgers box.

Even birds become caught up in the spirit of group fun. Flocks of rooks mount high in the air together, then close their wings and zoom down as near to earth as they dare, opening their wings to break the fall only at the last second. They repeat the maneuver over and over, like daredevil children.

Deer have their own version of tag, very similar to the game children play. When the deer that is "it" succeeds in overtaking another deer, it actually reaches out and tags the other with its hoof.

On a bridge over the Hudson River a row of gulls was seen perching on the bridge rail. As a small vessel approached, they plummeted down and landed on it. They stayed aboard while the ship steamed under the bridge, and then, as it came out on the other side, they flew up to the bridge once more, clattering and crying, and perched on the opposite rail from where they had started. Now they waited for a ship coming in the opposite direction and repeated the whole stunt in reverse.

Animal group play duplicates children's games amazingly. Many deer play a combination of tag and hide-and-seek. They stalk one another around a hill, and the great trick is to see which deer can most adroitly double back to deceive the pursuers. The practice gained in these games undoubtedly has saved many a deer's life.

Carl Akeley, the African explorer, once cautiously approached a group of young elephants in the jungle. The beasts were milling around, thudding and thumping, but did not seem alarmed or angry. Akeley crept closer. When finally he caught a glimpse of the tusk-ers, he was spellbound. The elephants had a ball of sun-baked earth about two feet in diameter. With trunks and feet they whacked it along the green trails for half a mile.

Among young animals, play is training for life, but adults play as well as youngsters. Gray old otters go whizzing down their mud slides as delightedly as the littlest nippers. In the prairie-dog "towns" of the American West, the dogs play by the hour their own version of prisoner's base. One dog runs toward the burrow of another. A third tries to scamper into the first one's hole before he can get back. The game spreads until the whole village is in a wild excitement of dartings, cross-runnings and tactics of blocking and interference. The prairie dogs' whistling and squealing rise to an excited uproar like the tumult of a baseball park.

What urges animals everywhere to these bursts of happiness and play? Perhaps Novalis, who wasn't a naturalist but a poet-philosopher, said as much as we can say about it. The play of the animals, he said, is just their way of uttering the glory of God.

COURTSHIP AMONG THE INSECTS

Max Eastman

We all know that the cricket sings on the hearth, but few know that their song changes when they are in love. They have a file and an edge, or scraper, on each wing cover, and their song is made by rubbing the covers against each other. In his every-day song the male (who is the only real singer) uses about 47 percent of the teeth on his file. But when he is in love, this percentage rises to about 89, and the song becomes so irregular that you can't tell the temperature or anything else by it, except that he is courting.

While he is singing, the female lingers near and gives him an encouraging nudge from time to time. Finally he stops scraping his wings together and lifts them both up. If she has been sufficiently moved by the song, she climbs on his back and proceeds to eat out of a cuplike gland, placed just behind the joints of his wings. This gland secretes a substance which she finds delicious, and may be compared, perhaps, to the gift of a box of chocolates. This process of singing and nudging, giving and receiving, sometimes continues for about half an hour before the female is satisfied and the male becomes silent. Then the nuptial union takes place.

There is often a connection in nature between sex and the pleasures of eating. A mixture of love and nutrition is the practice pursued by some species of the empid fly, who hunt up some tempting morsel, possibly a smaller fly or perhaps the petal of a flower, wrap it in delicate silk strands spun from glands in their forelegs, and formally present it to their chosen females. Some biologists suspect that the industrious little fly adopts this manner of wooing in order to avoid being eaten by his mate, for he doesn't wait for the lady to exclaim over the delicacy of his gift but proceeds to mate with her in something of a hurry while she is busy unwrapping it.

The grayling butterfly puts on an act that seems to require solemn music. He alights in front of his inamorata, displays his beautiful wings and waves his antennae until she is *almost* in the mood of consent. Then, at the critical moment, he dips his head in a courtly gesture and enfolds her antennae in his wings. He carries a sort of sachet bag on one forewing, and during this ceremony a bit of the per-fume is brushed off on her sensitive antennae. This delicate gift of perfume overcomes the last remnant of her coyness. The courtship is over; impregnation follows as a matter of course.

It was long thought that the colors of moths, their tiger hues and the great luminous eyes painted on their "deep-damask'd wings," were designed primarily for courtship. Experiments have shown, however, that it is largely the moths' vivid sense of smell which brings them together in the mating season. In species where the female has a scent gland, a female visible under a bell glass is of small interest to the males in the vicinity, but a female in a less than airtight container will, if she is a virgin, bring males fluttering to her through the dark from almost incredible distances.

The males of the emperor moth are thought to be able to find females of their species from distances up to three miles. Forty or 50 males will often assemble, as though out of nowhere, around a latticed box containing a lovelorn female. The female's scent gland is especially designed for attracting suitors. She "calls" by raising the tip of her abdomen and vibrating her wings so rapidly as to drive the air over it and disperse the scent in all directions. Her instincts are so precise that she never calls except when weather conditions are suitable for a wide dispersal of the scent. About her lovers she shows less discrimination than about the weather; it is a case of "first come first served." This indifference to the suitor's appearance has been a surprise to those biologists who had assumed, along with Charles Darwin, that the gay colors of many male insects were developed through the ages of evolution by billions of discriminating choices on the part of the female.

Sight *is* involved in one of the most human-seeming of all modes of courtship among insects—the communal song and dance. The dance of the midges and mayflies inspired these three lines of one of the most beautiful poems in English literature, John Keats' "To Autumn":

> *Then in a wailful choir the small gnats mourn*
> *Among the river sallows, borne aloft*
> *Or sinking as the light wind lives or dies.*

The scientists cannot make you see and hear this happen, as Keats does, but they have a more romantic explanation. "In due season, and at certain times of the day," says Maurice Burton in his *Animal Courtship*, "mayflies [and midges] swarm over or near rivers. Their dancing consists of a quick fluttering ascent followed by a more leisurely descent, repeated again and again. The dancers are almost entirely males, and they are joined every now and then by one or a few females. Each female becomes paired with a male, and the couples fly away."

So it is not the light wind, after all, but love that puts on this rhythmical pageant. Some biologists, of course, will shudder at the use of the word "love" in discussing the behavior of the simpler forms of life. But in studying the courtship of insects you will find examples of every mode of amorous behavior known to man: bowing, curtsying, kissing, snuggling, fondling, embracing, giving of presents, seducing with perfume, serenading, dancing—even rubbing of noses and brazen exhibitions of sex appeal. The slender damselflies link themselves together and fly around tandem for an hour before mating; they continue long afterward, the male bringing the female along behind him as though on a flying bicycle-built-

The female praying mantis sometimes devours her mate after he has wooed her. The mantis is the only carnivorous insect of its order.

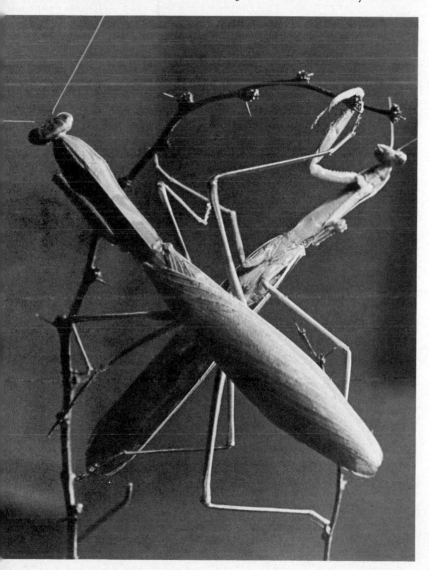

for-two until she has laid her eggs on the leaf or stem of some plant growing in the water.

We'll probably never have any scientific knowledge about the conscious feelings which may accompany these activities, but no scientist can stop us from enjoying the poetry in them!

ANIMALS IN LOVE
Alan Devoe

It's queer the way we use the word "beastly" as an adjective for the gross and degraded, the sort of thing we rightly call "dirty." To a naturalist such talk sounds strange. Actually, love among nature's creatures is no mere brutal carnality. It is a thing of a thousand graces. It expresses itself in lovely and amazing gestures of courtship, in deep devotions, in tender ways.

Even lowly creatures conduct courtships. A fiddler crab waves his great, bright-colored claw and dances for his lady. Many male spiders pour out their love in intricate waltzings and pirouettes. A scorpion extends his "hands," takes the female's littler ones in his and, walking backward, leads her on a promenade. Love songs aren't just for human singing; they reach far down into primitive animal life. When he's in love, the crayfish sings a grunty little serenade by rubbing his feelers against his beak. Even lobsters in the glee of courting time snap their "fingers."

Among the higher creatures, of course, courtship comes into fuller development. There are no more delicate and dazzling wooings than those of birds. The male wren deposits twigs in all the tree holes in his territory, interrupting himself to fly beseechingly to his demure Jenny, vibrating his wings and pouring out a tumult of rapturous melody. The female bird watches his activities, finally chooses one of his sites and makes a nest of the scrambled twigs he has placed there.

A waxwing is likely to do his courting with cherries or similar small fruits. He slips a cherry into the female's bill—perhaps another and another. Presently, if she has been won, she accepts a fruit but does not eat it. She slips it back into her suitor's bill. The two little birds settle down side by side on a branch, passing the love gift delicately back

The satin bower bird woos his lady with gifts of blue to match her eyes—pebbles, feathers and anything else of the desired color. He even paints the bower with blue juice pressed from a berry.

and forth between them. Bower birds have the most amazing courtship customs in nature. The males build elaborate "cottages"—structures sometimes several feet long and up to four feet high, all bedecked alluringly with bright flowers and berries—to which they invite the hen birds of their hearts' desire.

The concentrated love expressed in courtship and mating is not the only kind of affection exchanged between nature's creatures. In their lives, as in our own human lives, there is the quiet, steady joy of togetherness. There is tenderness, steadfastness, devotion unto death. One of the best rough-and-ready naturalists in the Canadian north woods is a former trapper called Long Joe. One day a she-bear was caught in Long Joe's trap. When he got to the trap, the bear's mate was there. The big, shaggy brute had his arms around her, hugging her and sobbing. Woodsmen aren't sentimental. But there is that about love, St. Francis said, that touches the universal heart. Long Joe has never trapped another living thing.

Wild wolves and some foxes mate for life, and every experienced dogman knows that the same capacity for devotion can show up in the blood of dogs. There

was the no-account female "houn' dawg," for instance, that fell into a rock crevasse in Tennessee. Her crony and husband was an equally disreputable-looking hound named Pete. He saved her from starving, during the ten days before searchers found her, by eating only a few nibbles of his supper every night and then streaking off with the rest of it and dropping it down the crevasse.

Love? Dogdom is full of it. Darby and Joan were a pair of Belgian shepherds who endured the London blitz together. When the siren would sound, Joan would run whimpering to her sleeping box and cower there. Wherever he might be, Darby would come tearing home and fling himself shelteringly across her trembling body. The two dogs were lying like that when rescuers dug them out after a hit. Joan had pulled through all right. Darby's big black body, still now in death, had taken the shock of the blast.

It is dangerously easy to sentimentalize animals, to make the mistake of reading human thoughts and feelings into their actions. But it is just as easy to err the other way, forgetting that all creation is a brotherhood and that something of the same mind and heart dwells in all of us.

"Honeymoon" might seem an overromantic word to use in talking about birds. But even the severest scientists, studying egrets, have agreed that it is the right one. When the egrets reach Louisiana from their South American wintering place, the flock breaks into pairs. Each pair chooses a nesting site and withdraws to it. But the couples do not start raising a family immediately. First there is the honeymoon. It has such qualities of passionate happiness and devotion that when it was first witnessed by Dr. Julian Huxley, the English scientist, he could scarcely believe it to be a regular practice in these birds' lives.

For days the two egrets are always together. They perch motionless by the hour, the female on a branch just below her mate's, her head pressed against his flanks. Every so often, as quiet delight surges into ecstasy, both birds raise their wings, stretch up their long necks and then, with an outburst of love cries, intertwine their necks together. The egrets' necks are so long and supple that each of them actually makes a complete turn around the other. The birds are locked together in a true lovers' knot.

Then each of them takes the fine plumes (the famous "aigrettes") of the other in its beak and nibbles them lovingly, giving each plume a long sliding "kiss" from its base to its tip. As the egrets' love play subsides, they untwine their necks and relapse once more into quiet happiness—side by side, always touching. The honeymoon often lasts as much as four or five days.

Human love isn't based on beauty or sexual attraction alone. Romance has mysterious ingredients. It has among animals, too. Boo-Boo, a chimpanzee in the London Zoo, was a winsome young ape, and the authorities were anxious to secure a mate for her. They presented all the available male chimps to her. Boo-Boo would have none of them. The directors of the Zoological Society widened their search. They got her suitors from private zoos in other parts of England and from abroad. Boo-Boo contemplated each one coldly. As a last resort the zoo at Bristol was permitted to send a seedy-looking male chimpanzee named Koko. Koko was middle-aged and paunchy, and he had scraggly hair that stuck up on his head like a bristle brush. But when he shambled in, Boo-Boo took one look and a light kindled in her eyes. It wasn't long before they had their arms around each other. The next year Boo-Boo produced a bouncing baby, Jubilee, the first chimpanzee ever born in captivity in London.

CREATURES OF COMPASSION
Jean George

Infinite care has been taken by scientists in the past half-century not to ascribe human attributes to birds and beasts. They warn us not to read into the conduct of animals our own thoughts and feelings. Yet, when the day ends and the logs in the fireplace are lit, I have seen many a renowned biologist shake his head in wonderment as he tells some tale that breathes of human dignity in a bird or beast.

Investigators have found that the actions of birds, for example, are primarily instinctive. A nestling sees its parent and automatically opens its mouth. In autumn a young bird migrates to its winter home, and in spring returns and builds a nest, all without being instructed. So far as science is concerned, the bird is reacting rather than thinking, and it has no depth of feeling. This every ornithologist knows. Yet an ornithologist told us how he had been baffled by the actions of a sea gull which—and here he hesitated—had seemed to show real compassion.

In a summer camp where our friend was teaching, the cook was given a gull egg. The following day a wet young bird emerged from the shell. The sea gull looked about and quickly accepted the cook as his mother, the children as his siblings, the camp as his rookery. Thus organized, he happily reported to meals at mealtime, played games with the children and went to sleep on bedposts. There were no other gulls in the mountain camp, and the few birds he saw made no impression upon him, so thoroughly had he fitted himself into the world of man.

About mid-July a woodpecker arrived, also a pet, but caged. It spent most of the day drumming a lonely tattoo on the bars. The sea gull came and stood for a time on the shelf nearby, then suddenly ran over and sat down beside the cage. The woodpecker stopped drumming. Soft noises came from speechless throats as, bird-mewing, the gull and the woodpecker shared their lonely isolation from their kind. The ritual was repeated every day. Each time the woodpecker would stop his sad hammering and, in the words of the ornithologist, "become relaxed and at ease beside the compassionate gull. I know I am reading too much into that gull," the narrator added quickly. "But the more I live with birds, the more human qualities I see in them."

Many a small bird, such as this British hedge sparrow, has had her eggs pushed out of the nest by a European cuckoo, who then lays her eggs and departs. So the little mother raises the big baby cuckoos as her own.

My husband, himself a scientist, came in from a bird-banding study one evening, puzzled. "Would you believe," he said, "that a highly developed, almost human form of foster parenthood can occur in the wild?" Then John told of a nest of young savanna sparrows. Both parents were color-banded, so he was absolutely sure of what occurred. Soon after hatching her eggs, the mother was killed by a snake. The father wasted no time in attracting another female to help him feed the ravenous young. Several days later the father was also killed. The foster mother now proceeded to lure a second male to the nest, and the orphaned young birds were raised by these two strangers.

Another time wild birds helped our own young pet owl. We were traveling west, camping out at night with the owl leashed to his perch near our sleeping bags. One morning before feeding him we noticed that his crop was already full. We assumed he had caught a mouse. However, two nights later in Ohio, lying awake on a rocky camp site, we saw what the owlet was up to. He gave his "hungry owlet" call, a stone-grinding sound. Like silent black shadows, two enormous owls winged out of the night. They dropped to the ground near our orphan pet, stuffed mice in his open mouth, then flew away. Apparently they could not ignore the cry of the hungry youngster, even though he was a stranger.

I know that according to scientific precept a bird cannot "love," nor can it be "distressed" except for its own suffering. And yet an incident with our pet crow forces me to wonder. Our son Craig went to bed one summer day with a high fever. Since the boy was not the one who fed the crow, the bird was in no way dependent on him. Nevertheless he sat on a limb outside Craig's window and cawed the "alarm" cry of the crows. Wild crows from miles around answered, flew in to look for the owl or fox they had been summoned to harass. Seeing nothing more than our distressed pet crow, they finally departed in confusion. Three days later Craig was up and out, and then the bird stopped his alarm cawing. He ran after the boy, sat down when he sat, rested his beak upon his knee and swayed in some ecstasy of bird feeling. What feeling? I call it love.

I have heard biologists say that such qualities as courtesy do not exist among animals. But one evening in Pennsylvania, we saw a raccoon start across one end of a log bridge while a 'possum trotted onto the other end. The raccoon was the larger, and certainly able to do in a 'possum—angry 'coons have been known to kill even dogs. The two wild animals advanced toward each other; but, just before they met, the raccoon swung himself under the log, let the 'possum pass, climbed back and went his way.

Animal behavior has come in for some intense study in the past 20 years, and with each investigation it becomes more apparent that either the birds and the beasts do have some human traits—or we have animal ones. Certainly, of all forms of life on Earth, man is the most adjustable and intelligent. There are obvious differences between him and the birds and beasts—but the similarities, too, are large. Aware of them, we gain a more vivid picture of ourselves, and a more certain knowledge that the same laws of life have shaped us all.

MOTHERS OF THE WILD
Alan Devoe

In the fragrant summer dusk, I had twice seen a rabbit come hopping cautiously to the same spot among the tall grass stems. On her first trip she had remained there, nearly invisible, for an hour. The second visit was shorter, but long enough to make me positive about the guess I had made. There must be a nest of baby rabbits there. But how could there be? After seeing the rabbit's first stealthy visit, I had crossed and recrossed that area of the field, but had found nothing.

Now, marking the point with my eyes and never losing sight of it, I again began slowly combing the tall grass. Suddenly, in the dim light, I saw a tiny stir of motion, as if a patch of earth beside a tussock had moved. I bent down. What had seemed to be only a bit of grass-grown earth was actually a tiny, soft, felted blanket. Gently I lifted the little coverlet. Tucked under it were four rabbit babies.

I had learned the mother rabbit's secret. The blanket was a quilting made of her own fur and matted wisps of grass. Every time she left her youngsters in the nest after a feeding, she pulled this warm, soft covering over them, leaving them perfectly hidden and secure against the evening chill.

This practice is only one of many wonderful devotions and ingenuities by which mothers of the wild bring up their little ones. Nature's simplest

Young hippos learn to swim before they can walk; many are even born in the water.

The mother rhino steers her baby with a nudge of her horn.

After leaving their mother's pouch, the whole brood of young opossums travels on her back.

The young capuchin can use his tail as a fifth hand in hanging on during his travels.

The baby Emperor penguin journeys on its mother's foot, tucked in a fold of flesh.

nurseries are "built-in" ones; the body pouches of marsupials. Kangaroos and opossums (see also pages 120 and 76) belong to this company. Tiny and undeveloped as they are at birth, marsupial babies instinctively head for the nursery pouch. The mother animal watches intently, ready to give a fondly helping nudge. With her brood safely cradled, she uses special muscles to pull the pouch closed.

Animal mothers that do not have "built-in" nurseries make many kinds of nest and den to give their babies security. When ready to give birth a mother bat hangs upside down and spreads her wings and body to make a receiving cradle. While her baby is still helpless, she carries him everywhere with her on her flights through the darkness. He holds tight to the fur of her breast with his milk teeth.

Mother gorilla builds for herself and her baby a tree nest of leafy boughs which father gorilla can keep constantly under watch from a shelter he constructs at the base of a nearby tree. Mother polar bear tunnels out a nursery in the snow. At the end of the tunnel she scoops and shapes a comfortable cub room, as secure against the arctic blasts as the inside of an igloo. Mother coyote takes over the abandoned burrow of a badger, woodchuck or some other digging animal, and renovates it specially for her babies' needs. She cleans it out, enlarges it, equips it with an air hole for cross-ventilation.

One of the most delightful nurseries is the work of the common white-footed mouse. Mother mouse gathers fine grasses, rootlets, shreds of soft leaves, strips of pliable cedar bark. Working and reworking the material, she weaves an almost perfect sphere. At one side she leaves an opening just large enough for her to squeeze through. Darting in and out, she performs innumerable turnarounds, hollowing a cozy chamber in the center of the ball. She lines it with the softest materials she can find, bits of moss, wisps of plant down. The finished nest is at last given a final extraordinary detail, a door stopper—a tight little plug of grass inserted in the doorway, closing it against any intrusion of foes.

A heroic chore of many animal mothers is the task of moving the family. Squirrel mothers often decide they must leave a frail old hollow tree when they sense a bad storm coming. One by one the youngsters are picked up, mother squirrel slinging them upside down under chin. With her teeth she grips them by their stomach fur, and the difficult trek is made to a new and safer location. When a mother bear must transport her cub, she seizes the young one's entire head in her mouth, but so gently that she does not harm the baby.

Animal mothers often impart to their babies lores that we may imagine to be inborn. Baby seals, for example, have to be taught to swim. Pleading, persuading, enticing, mother seal generally ends by pushing her reluctant young one adrift. Mother otter, too, must induce her offspring to learn the art of their "native" element. She often resorts to trickery. With a youngster on her back, she swims out into the stream and then suddenly submerges.

Mother flying squirrel often pushes Junior off a tree branch to get him to learn gliding. Mother cat boxes her kittens' ears for slowness and inattention in the art of learning. Kittens are not mouse catchers instinctively; they must learn it. Animal mothers teach chiefly by drawing their youngsters into creative play. Mother lioness twitches the tip of her tail to induce her children to pounce on it. Mother raccoon flips frogs and crayfish to her young ones, making a game of what will later be serious business.

Perhaps the most moving of all such devotions is the superb courage of mother animals in giving protection when emergencies arise. I have seen a mother woodchuck, when a farm dog was pawing furiously at her family burrow, throw up earthworks as fast as the big, powerful dog could dig. Down would go one barricade. Within seconds she would fling up another. Then another and another, yielding the tunnel only inch by hard-fought inch. I thought her heart would burst, but it was the dog that grew exhausted first and went off defeated. I have seen a white-footed mouse mother smaller than my thumb, whose nursery in an old birdhouse I had inadvertently disturbed, make six laborious trips, within two feet of me, carrying her babies one by one to safety. She was shivering with fear; but there are things even in a mouse's world that are greater than fear.

We talk of valor that is like that of a tigress with her young. Actually that same blaze of heroic devotion burns in many a mother of the wild, even the least.

ANIMALS FROM A TO Z

By Jean George

The bobcat is a flesh-eating mammal; the chipmunk is a gnawing mammal. Such terms describe where every beast belongs in the Animal Kingdom. They appear in parentheses after the names listed in this supplement and in the index. Using these terms, you can locate every creature's place on the chart on pages 314-315, which also includes the Latin names.

Drawings by Lowell Hess

AARDVARK *(aardvark)*   This homely animal is the only mammal of its kind. It is an order, a family and a genus all by itself. Hump-backed and rabbit-eared, the long-snouted aardvark lives on ants and termites in the African wilderness. A pair of powerful front feet, designed to tear the earth, and a long ant-catching tongue may not add to its beauty, but certainly enhance its standing as a biological wonder.

ADDAX *(even-toed, hoofed mammals)*   An African antelope, the noble addax wears its handsome rippling horns high over its head. Both male and female have horns. Grayish-brown in color, it has a white mask, laid like a wet towel across the nose just below the eyes, which makes this shaggy-maned antelope appear distinctly different from all other species.

ABALONE *(mollusks)*   Encased in a single large shell, the edible abalone lives in the waters of the Pacific and Indian oceans. Its shell has an unusual row of rounded openings through which it breathes. Beautiful and shimmering, the shell is used for attractive jewelry.

ADDER *(reptiles: snakes)*   The adder is any of several snakes, but especially the common venomous viper of Europe. In North America the hog-nosed snake is a nonpoisonous adder, commonly called the checkered or hissing adder. The stout-bodied hissing adder has a wide head and a turned-up snout. It hisses loudly, terrifying people, but this is usually bluff. It very rarely bites.

See also *Index*

AGOUTI (*gnawing mammals*)   The rabbit-sized agouti is a nocturnal rodent, an odd tropical one that inhabits Central and South America. Its eyes are large and soulful, and its legs so slender as to seem barely capable of supporting its body.

ALBATROSS (*ocean-dwelling birds*)   Largest birds of the ocean wastes, some with a wingspread of 11 feet, albatrosses are unsurpassed in flight. They come to land only to breed and rear one youngster per year on remote oceanic islands.

ALPACA (*even-toed, hoofed mammals*)   The alpaca is the member of the camel-llama family that inhabits the bleak regions of South America, particularly the high country on the barren slopes of the Andes. The alpaca is a domesticated breed of llama raised for its soft wool, which covers the animal from head to ground like a huge horse blanket. Smaller than the llama, it comes in black and brown and white and has a supercilious expression that endears it to all who see it.

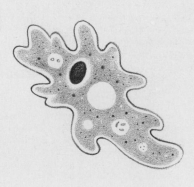

AMOEBA (*single-celled animals*)   Lowliest of animals, the microscopic amoeba has no skeletal structure, no legs, no eyes, no tail. It propels its entire mass forward by throwing its interior fluid in the direction it wants to go. It reproduces by dividing. Some amoebas live in salt water, some in fresh water, others in the soil. Still others inhabit man's intestines as parasites.

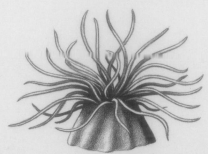

ANEMONE (*sac-like animals*)   This beautiful but voracious carnivore is a relative of the jellyfish and coral. Circular in shape, the anemone seizes worms and fish with its delicate tentacles, each armed with nettle cells which explode on contact, driving a paralyzing thread deep into the body of the prey. Anemones lay eggs, but can also bud a new animal. Most are an inch or two across, but some grow to 3 feet.

ANHINGA (*fully webbed birds: all 4 toes*)   This bird is also known as the snakebird because of its long, weaving neck. It swims with its whole body, except the head, submerged, and darts underwater after prey, impaling fish with its needle-sharp beak. It closely resembles the cormorants and is found in the southern United States, southward to Argentina and in parts of the Old World.

ANOA (*even-toed, hoofed mammals*)   Also called the pygmy buffalo, the anoa lives only on the island of Celebes and is a small, strongly muscled wild ox, no bigger than a newborn domestic calf. It is a dangerous beast, using its spearlike horns to fend off man and animal foes.

ANTEATER (*toothless mammals*)   No beast looks less like a mammal than this one. There are several varieties. Pictured above is the great anteater. About the size of a small bear, it is tube-headed and has no teeth. The animal's mouth is so tiny that a man could not get his finger in, but from it a tongue 2 feet long whips out to snare a meal. When attacked, the animal rears and slashes with the strong claws developed to tear open anthills. The anteater ranges over Central and tropical South America.

See also *Index*

ANTELOPE *(even-toed, hoofed mammals)* This group, related to cattle, sheep and goats, includes the gazelles, the chamois, the addax, the oryx and pygmy varieties like the dik-dik. They range from 12 inches to 6 feet in height. True antelopes are found only in Asia and Africa, but, in spite of its beard, the Rocky Mountain goat is closer to the antelope than the goat. Antelopes have unbranched horns—straight or delicately curved—and, like sheep and cattle and unlike deer, they keep them for a lifetime. Most prefer open country.

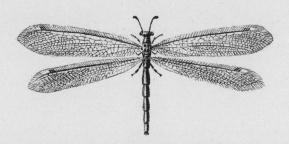

ANT LION *(net-winged insects)* The larva's clever strategy gives this insect its name. The squat, fat larva digs a cone-shaped pit in sand or dust, just below the surface. It then lies concealed at the bottom of the pit with mouth open. The ant or other insect entering the pit rarely succeeds in escaping the larva's greedy jaws. The adult resembles the dragonfly.

ARMADILLO *(toothless mammals)* The armadillo is armed with bony plates, anchored in its skin like hair and consisting of a front and back shield with movable bands between them. Armadillos prowl at night in Florida, Texas, Arizona and southward to Brazil. Unknightly in their armor, if frightened they roll into a ball, bone-hard and impenetrable.

AUK *(shorebirds and gulls)* The flightless great auk became extinct in 1844, when the last of a once prolific species died, presumably at the hands of a feather collector. However, there are 23 kinds of auk alive today, including guillemots and puffins; some look like tiny penguins.

AVOCET *(shorebirds and gulls)* This attractive wading bird has an unusual "language" of head movements which is used in its remarkable courtship ritual, when 10 or more males and females dance around a flat stone. The 17-inch-long avocet of the American West has a white body, black wings and a long bill with which it combs shallow water for food. It builds its nest on the ground near water and lays 4 eggs.

BADGER *(flesh-eating mammals)* The low-slung American badger has relatives around the world. It is remarkably strong, fond of battle and easily able to catch small animals for food. Its long claws enable it to burrow a tunnel—in next to no time—deep into the earth, where it makes its home, hibernating there in cold climates. Badger hair is used in shaving brushes.

BARNACLE *(crustaceans)* This is a complex fleshy creature within a hard-crusted, mound-shaped covering. It lives in salt water, breathes with gills and catches food through the hole in its mound with its feathery arms. Barnacles are found around the world, permanently attached to ships, piers, rocks and shells by barnacle "cement," which they secrete.

BARRACUDA *(fishes: true-bone)* These challenging game fishes with sharp teeth and carnivorous tastes are salt-water versions of the freshwater pike. They attack other fishes and some also attack man. Growing to 6 feet in tropical waters, they provide fine sport for Florida fishermen.

See also *Index*

BASS *(fishes: true-bone)*   The bass is eminently North American. Durable and plucky, it fights fishermen throughout the United States and in most of Canada. Freshwater varieties include the black, the white and the Kentucky bass. The salt-water favorite is the delicious striped bass. Among its relatives are the sunfishes, perches, bluefishes, snappers, porgies and puffers.

BEE EATER *(kingfisher-like birds)*   As their name indicates, these birds of the warm regions of the Old World eat bees and wasps. They wheel gracefully in flight and bore tunnels, sometimes more than 7 feet long, with their bills and nest in them. Their hoarse chucklings sound like people at a party.

BEETLE *(insects: beetles)*   These are insects with 4 wings, like the ladybird and Japanese beetle, heroine and villain of the garden. The outside, thicker wings meet in a straight line down the back and act as armor. The soft second pair, used for flying, lie under them. Beetles are the largest order of insects. North America alone has 28,000 species. The boll weevil is a beetle whose larva feeds on the cotton boll.

BIRD OF PARADISE *(perching birds)*   Found in New Guinea and Australia, these beauties come in costumes with capes, plumes, trains in startling colors. After nesting, the males of some species take no further interest in family life, which is unusual among birds.

BITTERN *(stork-like birds)*   This marsh dweller lives all over the world. It is shy, has feathering of excellent camouflage and "throws" its voice like a ventriloquist. Instead of flying away when danger threatens, it freezes in imitation of a reed.

BLACKBIRD *(perching birds)*   This big New World family includes such diverse creatures as bobolinks, cowbirds, grackles, orioles and meadowlarks. A familiar American blackbird is the redwinged (shown here), a bird of the marshes whose wings are really red, yellow and black. One of the first migrants to come north in spring, the red-winged blackbird performs a quaint and ardent courtship dance. The blackbird of Europe is a species of thrush.

BLACKSNAKE *(reptiles: snakes)*   Large but nonpoisonous, this snake prowls stone walls and meadows in search of mice and frogs. It is a satiny black above, dark slate gray beneath, and may grow to 6 feet in length. The blacksnake is fast and active, and often vibrates its tail in the dry leaves to sound like a rattler. Lurking enemies retreat rapidly.

BLUEBIRD *(perching birds)*   This beloved flash of color has been seriously declining in eastern North America, probably because its tree holes are disappearing. Therefore nest boxes are important for the survival of the eastern bluebird. If these are not made with proper drainage, the young will drown. A western species is the mountain or arctic bluebird, ranging in the Rockies.

BOA *(reptiles: snakes)* Boas are the big snakes of the New World, while pythons are the big snakes of the Old. The anaconda or water boa of South America (shown here) is said sometimes to grow to over 30 feet. The constrictor is a handsome boa, slimmer and shorter than the anaconda. Boas and pythons kill by squeezing their prey, but boas, unlike pythons, bear their young alive.

BOAR *(even-toed, hoofed mammals)* Related to the pig, the wild boars of Europe and Asia have long been hunted. Vicious, dangerous beasts that root about in forests, they are bristled, have tusks and long snouts. The warthogs of Africa are close relatives, and the peccaries of the Americas very distant kin.

BOBCAT *(flesh-eating mammals)* This 3-foot-long bob-tailed cat hides in forests all over the United States, even in the suburban woods near New York City. The bobcat hunts mainly after dark and on the ground. It feeds on small mammals, especially rabbits. Like the house cat, the bobcat loves to toy with small victims.

BORER *(scale-winged insects)* There are many thousands of moth species whose larvae feed on plants in various ways. The borers, particularly the corn borer, are destructive to American agriculture. Other moth larvae with similar habits are the leaf miners, the tent caterpillars (which attack mainly cherry trees) and the worms which get into fruit of all varieties in orchards.

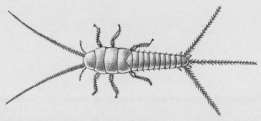

BRISTLETAIL *(insects: bristletails)* Their tails are indeed bristled. One species of these most primitive of all insects is the silverfish, sometimes found in old books or wherever there is glue or other starch. Bristletails have an aversion to light and are always found in dark places—many under stones or logs in forest debris.

BUNTING *(perching birds)* This is a popular name given to some of the finches and sparrows. The best-known bunting in the United States is the indigo of the forest edges; the male is bright blue, the female drab. The painted and lazuli buntings also live in North America. Old World buntings are similar to New World sparrows. The junco is a relative.

BUZZARD *(daytime hunters)* Birds of prey, buzzards soar endlessly on high currents of wind looking for carrion. The turkey buzzard of North America, a vulture of 2 or 3 pounds, has an ugly crimson head, dead-white bill and flesh-colored feet. It nests in hollow stumps on the ground, laying 2 eggs.

CADDIS FLY *(insects: caddis flies)* This insect is best known in its larval stage, when it lives as a small worm in a tube of sand and sticks (or other materials) in streams and brooks. When it is hungry, the larva opens a stone trapdoor at the end of the tube and snatches food from the water. An order of insects by itself, the adult fly has delicate translucent wings.

CANARY *(perching birds)* A small finch, native to the Canary Islands (but native elsewhere as well), the canary is the common cage bird of the world. Wild canaries gather in flocks at the end of the breeding season. Their backs are dull olive, their breasts yellow, and they do not sing as richly as the tame birds do. The tame ones have been bred for generations to perfect their yellow color and melodious song.

CARACARA *(daytime hunters)*   A subfamily of the falcons, the caracaras are black-and-white birds of prey found from the southern United States to South America. About 2 feet long, they have partially naked faces, are good runners and subsist on carrion as well as the small animals they catch alive. They are often seen with vultures.

CARDINAL *(perching birds)*   The cardinal wears the red hat of the official of the church for whom it was named. It is a member of the finch family, having a stout beak that breaks open seeds with ease. One of the most beautiful of North American birds, the red male cardinal fights for his twig nest, set in low bushes, and tends his drab mate and successive broods of 3 to 4 young. Once considered a southeastern bird, the cardinal has moved as far north as New England and Ontario.

CARIBOU *(even-toed, hoofed mammals)*   The wild reindeer of North America is a stout deer, the bull sometimes weighing over 300 pounds. Antlers appear on both male and female. Its hoofs are wide and rounded for running on snow. The "barren ground" caribou lives in large herds from Labrador to Alaska. The "woodland" caribou lives farther south.

See also *Index*

CARP *(fishes: true-bone)*   The venerable carp, which may weigh more than 60 pounds, actually belongs to the same family as the dainty, silvery minnow and the tawny goldfish. Originally native to Asia, it may now be found all over the temperate world. Many consider it a pest, for it appropriates the food of other, more edible fish.

CAT *(flesh-eating mammals)*   The house cat is related to the lion, tiger, leopard, panther and jaguar. Probably first domesticated in ancient Egypt, it became a pet in Europe before the beginning of the Christian era. Cats breed at 10 months or younger and live about 14 years, but have been known to reach 31. Some house cats have become a wild breed in the forests of North America.

CATBIRD *(perching birds)*   The catbird is one of the mockingbirds. When it cries, it sounds like a cat, but it sings snatches of the songs of neighboring birds. Slate gray except for some underfeathers of bright chestnut, it nests across North America from southern Canada to the northern edge of the Gulf states. It is sassy, friendly and loves yards and crumb-encircled picnic tables.

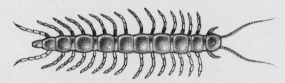

CENTIPEDE *(jaw-footed arthropods)*   Adult centipedes have from 15 to 173 pairs of legs, each one of which ends in a sharp spear. Youngsters start life with as few as 7. The first pair of legs is modified to form poison claws. These paralyze worms and insects and occasionally sicken men. Found under rocks and logs in warm climates the world around, centipedes are soft-bodied and long-legged. Millipedes (double-footed arthropods) are round, hard-shelled, and have short legs.

CHAMELEON *(reptiles: lizards)*   The creature sold in circuses is not a chameleon, but a small iguana. The true chameleon lives chiefly in Madagascar and Africa. A droll lizard, it has quick color changes caused by changes in temperature, light, environment and the chameleon's feelings. A prehensile tail and handlike feet hold it on twigs and upside down on ceilings. Its tongue unfolds in many segments, like a folding drinking cup, to catch an insect.

CHAMOIS *(even-toed, hoofed mammals)*   A European goatlike antelope, the chamois is known for its mountaineering ability and for the soft and subtle quality of its leather, long used for fine polishing and other purposes. Its coat is graded shades of brown; its horns are black. After summering among the peaks, the chamois seeks the protection of mountain forests in the winter.

CHEETAH *(flesh-eating mammals)*   The long and slender cheetah of Africa and Asia is also called the hunting leopard. A creature of the open country, this exquisite animal can reach a speed of 45 miles an hour in 2 seconds. It is trained to hunt black buck in India. Unlike other cats, the cheetah cannot pull his claws all the way in. In temperament he ranges from fierce to gentle.

CHICKEN *(chicken-like birds)*   The first to be domesticated were probably the jungle fowl of Southeast Asia, some 4000 years ago. There are over 100 varieties, of which the Yokohama chicken, bred for its ornamental tail feathers 20 feet long, is the most unusual. The most useful is the white leghorn, which lays an egg almost every day.

CHIMPANZEE *(primates)*   The ape most like man, the chimpanzee of Africa is the most intelligent of all animals. Chimpanzees have memories of visual objects and can use simple tools. Males are about 5 feet tall and weigh 140 pounds. Living in bands of about 40 members, chimpanzees make nests in trees, eat insects and vegetables and have one offspring at a time.

CHIPMUNK *(gnawing mammals)*   This friendly little ground-dwelling squirrel with its striped back is very active by day. From April to October it runs through forests and brushy areas busily gathering food, some of which it stores in cheek pockets and buries underground for the winter. Fallen logs and stone walls are its favorite homes. When startled, the chipmunk utters several rapid "chips" and a long trill.

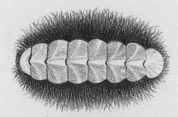

CHITON *(mollusks)*   Allied to snails, the chiton (or sea cradle) is a few inches long and lives in shallow sea water. When a chiton is pulled away from the rock on which it browses, it curls up in a ball like a little armadillo.

CLAM *(mollusks)*   This edible bivalve—it has 2 matching shells —crawls on the bottom of the sea on its single foot. Its nervous system consists of three pairs of ganglia controlling its brain, its foot and its internal organs. It has a heart and blood vessels, outsized gills, where the eggs develop, a digestive tract and kidney. Largest of the many species, the giant clam of Australia weighs up to 500 pounds. A North Atlantic variety is the quahog.

COBRA *(reptiles: snakes)*   The cobra of India, *Naja Naja*, rears when angry and flattens its neck into a hood by expanding its ribs. It is estimated that cobra bites kill some 10,000 Indians a year. Cobras can also squirt their poison into the eyes of an adversary, sometimes causing blindness in humans. They grow to be 6 feet long, are deaf and cannot hear the music of snake charmers: on the alert, they sway back and forth to the motion of the musician, who moves in time to the music. The Egyptian asp is a relative.

COCKATOO *(parrot-like birds)*   A medium-size parrot, the cockatoo has a crested head. The white species is best known. Cockatoos are found in Australia and Indonesia. Elfish in nature and bizarre in appearance, they love to eat orchids, seeds, nuts and fruits. A white cockatoo is a wonderful, though noisy, pet.

See also **Index**

COCKLE (*mollusks*)   The cockle has 2 similar white shells and is found chiefly in European waters. Its shells have bumps that enable the animal to grip the sand, in which it lives buried, moving about on its muscular foot. It eats micro-organisms. Edible cockles are raised commercially.

COD (*fishes: true-bone*)   All but one member of the family, the burbot, live in salt water. The largest—as long as 6 feet—is the Atlantic cod. A well-known smaller member is the haddock. The Atlantic cod may well be the record egg layer in the fish world, one having been credited with 9 million. Among the cod's relatives are the whitings and kingfishes.

CONCH (*mollusks*)   The shell from which cameos are carved is large and spiral, and is the covering of a lively, carnivorous creature that thrives in tropical waters. Like the snail, it can close itself in with a horny door attached to the "foot" on which it moves about.

CONDOR (*daytime hunters*)   This magnificent and powerful inhabitant of southern California is the largest of North American land birds. It is over 4 feet long and may have a wingspread of as much as 11 feet. The condor prefers carrion, though it sometimes kills its own food. Nesting high in cliff caves, it lays but one egg—nearly 5 inches long—at a time. A condor of equal size lives in the Andes Mountains in South America.

See also *Index*

CONY (*hyraxes*)   Not unlike the American cony, or pika, in appearance, the conies of the Near East and Africa, called hyraxes, are actually a mammal order all to themselves. Their heavily padded feet can form a sort of suction cup enabling them to cling to rocks. They are pugnacious and noisy.

COOT (*crane-like birds*)   Member of a family of birds known as the rails, the coot runs with ease through massive clumps of reeds, walks over oozy mud on long toes and dives in and out of the water. It is awkward and somewhat ridiculous; therefore the expression "crazy as a coot." The American coot breeds in marshes over most of temperate North America and south to Colombia and Ecuador. Slate gray and duck-sized, it has a distinct whitish hen-like bill.

CORAL (*sac-like animals*)   A small "jelly" animal, the coral polyp can take the calcium in sea water and turn it into hard calcium carbonate to form a sort of cup around itself. The polyps lay eggs, but also reproduce by budding and thus extend into the magnificent, often branching corals found in warm seas. For food they catch minute animals with their stinging tentacles. Generations of coral colonies build islands, atolls and barrier reefs, which remain when the polyps die.

CORAL SNAKE (*reptiles: snakes*)   In North America the poisonous coral snakes—the eastern and Arizona—are distinguished from similar but harmless snakes by the distinctive, menacing pattern of their colorful bands: red-yellow-black-yellow-red, etc.

CORMORANT *(fully webbed birds: all 4 toes)*   A long-bodied bird with a hook on the end of its beak, it catches fish by chasing them underwater. Some 3 feet long and related to the pelican, the common cormorant breeds on both sides of the Atlantic Ocean. Most species are blackish brown in color. The flightless cormorant of the Galápagos Islands, an expert swimmer, is a rare and strange variety.

COUGAR *(flesh-eating mammals)*   The cougar is also called puma, mountain lion and American panther. Its range extends from British Columbia to the tip of South America. The cougar is either gray or tawny, its head is small, its body long and lithe. A large male is 4 to 5 feet long and weighs about 175 pounds. Cougars give birth to 2 to 5 kittens, which are easily tamed.

CRAB *(crustaceans)*   Most crabs are sea creatures and all have flat bodies and limbs encased in jointed shells. Of the 5 pairs of legs, the front pair end in pincers. The blue crab, a table delicacy, haunts the rocks and backwaters of the Atlantic coast from New England to Brazil. Crabs range from the tiny pea crab to a giant Japanese spider variety whose legs and body span 11 feet.

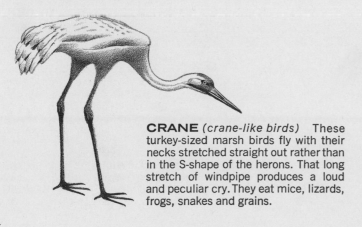

CRANE *(crane-like birds)*   These turkey-sized marsh birds fly with their necks stretched straight out rather than in the S-shape of the herons. That long stretch of windpipe produces a loud and peculiar cry. They eat mice, lizards, frogs, snakes and grains.

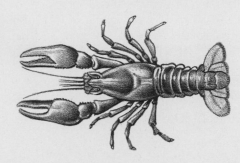

CRAYFISH *(crustaceans)*   The crayfish or crawfish is a small freshwater lobster found under rocks and behind logs in rivers and streams. The swamp dwellers fight for their homes by stacking up small stones, then lunging over the "wall" at other trespassing crayfish. With eyes on stalks they locate snails, fish and tadpoles to eat. The female carries the eggs on her stomach until they hatch. Most remarkably, however, as soon as a leg is lost, a new one starts growing under the shell.

CREEPER *(perching birds)*   The little brown, gray and white bird seen hopping up and down the sides of tree trunks in woodland or backyard is most probably the brown creeper, whose range extends to most cool parts of the world. Its tail is stiff, to brace it against vertical bark. It lives on insects and is often found in pine forests. The nuthatch and chickadee (or titmouse) are relatives.

CROCODILE *(crocodiles and alligators)*   The easiest way to distinguish between an alligator and a crocodile is to note that a large lower tooth on each side is visible when the crocodile's mouth is shut. With the alligator, the upper teeth cover the lower. The American crocodile averages 12 feet in length but has been known to exceed 20. There are other varieties in South America, Africa and Asia.

CUCKOO *(cuckoo-like birds)*   The European cuckoo, a 12-inch bird, lays its eggs in other birds' nests. The foster parents tend the aggressive young until they can fly. Cuckoo clocks imitate the European cuckoo's song. In recognition of their own distinctive calls, American cuckoos have been dubbed rain crow, storm crow, chow-chow or kow-kow. The American cuckoos, yellow-billed and black-billed, are good parents. Shown here is the ani.

See also *Index*

DADDY LONGLEGS *(8-legged spinners)*   It is best not to pick up the harmless daddy longlegs, which may lose a leg if you do, though if still young it can grow a new one. It belongs to the spider family, cannot spin a web, and is officially known as the harvestman because most often seen during harvesting.

DEER *(even-toed, hoofed mammals)*   Bounding and graceful, the deer is the epitome of wilderness beauty. Three kinds live in North America: the mule, the black-tailed and the white-tailed. Found in most parts of the world where there are woodland meadows to browse, the deer breeds in the fall. Fawns are born in the spring and stay with their mothers all summer. Most male deer have antlers that are shed and renewed annually.

DINGO *(flesh-eating mammals)*   This wild dog of Australia wags its tail, howls and looks like an ordinary yellow cur. In the wild, dingos hunt like wolves, in family packs, tracking down wallabies and sheep. They are the only nonpouched carnivores native to the island continent.

DIPPER *(perching birds)*   Mountain birds also known as water ouzels, they are found the world over. Able to stand intense cold, they rarely migrate but remain near swift-running icy streams, swimming underwater after aquatic insects and snails. They build bulbous nests with side openings, like their relatives the wrens.

DODO *(dove-like birds)*   Discovered by the Portuguese on the island of Mauritius early in the 1500's, these fat, flightless 50-pound birds with the curly tail were killed off by 1681. Other species on nearby islands soon followed. They were as stupid and defenseless as they looked. Not even a stuffed one remains.

See also *Index*

DOG *(flesh-eating mammals)*   Fido and man probably became domesticated together in prehistoric times, as they began to hunt the same prey. But the canine or wolf family is at least 10 times older than man! Regardless of man's breeding of dogs into so many shapes for so many purposes, all dogs and members of the wolf family are the same under the skin.

DOVE *(dove-like birds)*   Almost 300 species of dove dwell in trees and on city buildings around the world. There is no real difference between a dove and pigeon, although "dove" usually refers to the smaller species—the mourning doves and turtledoves. All are gentle birds, gregarious and devoted to their nest and young; they are convincing symbols of peace.

DUCK *(goose-like birds)*   On land most species "waddle" because their legs are far back on their bodies, but in the water this arrangement gives thrust to their swimming and diving. The common white barnyard duck is the Pekin, brought from China in 1870. The mallard is both domesticated and wild. Wild ducks fall into 3 groups: river or pond ducks, sea or diving ducks and fish-eating ducks or mergansers. Wood ducks live in tree holes, but most others nest in marshy grasses. Shown here is the pintail duck.

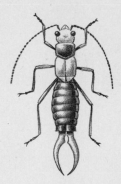

EARWIG *(insects: earwigs)*   Some species of this order are notable because they protect their eggs and young; most insects do not. These garden pests may have got their name from the early belief that they crawled into the ears of sleeping people. The pincers at their hind end are raised when the insect is threatened, but they may be used more in courtship than for fighting.

EGRET *(stork-like birds)*   Egrets are herons, mostly white in color. The snowy egret (shown here) has a magnificent shower of plumes that grow from its head and "shoulders." Demand for these brought the bird close to extinction before it was protected. North America has 3 other species: the great, reddish and cattle. The African cattle egret is a newcomer to America, where he sometimes follows the tractor as well as the cows.

ELK *(even-toed, hoofed mammals)*   The American elk or wapiti weighs up to 1000 pounds, has a mane and a pale rump patch. The male has branching antlers, shed annually. These regal deer graze in herds in lowlands and plains, and migrate seasonally up and down the mountains. In the rutting season, a bull leads his harem into mountain isolation until winter drives them down again. The European elk is what North Americans call a moose.

EMBIID *(insects: embiids)*   Members of this order are low on the ladder of insect life. They spin silk to line the covered runways in which they live in groups. The females lack wings; the males of some species have 2 transparent pairs close to their long, narrow bodies. Unlike higher insects, the embiids change little in appearance throughout their life cycle.

EMU *(casque-headed birds)*   The emu is a large, flightless bird of Australia, the second largest living bird in the world. Five feet high, 3-toed, it has "double" feathers, 2 in one quill. As with its smaller but similar relative the cassowary, the male emu sits on the eggs and tends the young. It eats fruit, herbs and roots and is hated by farmers because of the damage it does to agriculture. Today only one species remains.

FINCH *(perching birds)*   The finches are a family of seed-eating birds that live almost everywhere except Australia. One out of every seven species of bird is a finch: the cardinals, grosbeaks, wild canaries and buntings, as well as the purple finch, house finch and goldfinch. Most have lovely songs.

FLAMINGO *(stork-like birds)*
There are only 6 species in the world, in color pale pink to bright scarlet. Flamingos have swanlike necks and strong bills with "sieves" to wash out the mud from the algae they dine upon. The birds nest in shallow ponds, building strange hillocks of mud. Their young, unable to fly for several months, can run with amazing speed. In the United States, wild flamingos have been hunted out of existence.

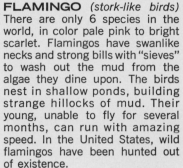

FLEA *(insects: fleas)*   Wingless and disagreeable-looking, the tiny flea can jump farther for its size than any other animal. As an adult, this disease-carrying pest lives on the blood obtained through its notorious itching bites. It mates on the host but vaults back to the ground to lay eggs. The egg hatches into a wormlike creature that lives on refuse.

FLYING FISH *(fishes: true-bone)*   The spreading fins do not flap, but are used only for gliding. These soaring sea creatures take to the air to escape other hungry fish.

FOX *(flesh-eating mammals)*   Sly, quick-footed and yellow-eyed, the fox is a member of the dog family. Several distinct species caper over North America; the most famous is the red fox. Foxes live in earth dens and can almost always outwit a hunting dog. They hunt at night, eating mice and other vermin. Both parents tend and teach their pointed-faced young.

FROGMOUTH *(goatsuckers)*
These unusual, slow-moving night birds of Asia and Australia are plumply fluffy, gray to reddish brown, with huge mouths in relation to their size. The Papuan frogmouth is about 2 feet long. Some scientists believe that their reported habit of sitting motionless on branches with bright yellow-and-pink jaws wide open may lead insects to mistake them for flowers and fly in.

See also *Index*

GAR *(fishes: cartilage-and-bone)* Up to 15 feet in length (the alligator gar), this large freshwater fish is one of the most primitive fishes alive. A long, slender body and a beak armed with sharp teeth identify the gar immediately. Its scales are hard and tough. Gars live in lakes and large rivers from southeast Canada to Costa Rica.

GAZELLE *(even-toed, hoofed mammals)* This delicate group of antelopes is marvelously swift and graceful. They include the gerenuk, the springbok, the impala, Grant's gazelle (shown here) and many other varieties. In recent years their numbers — especially in Africa — have been greatly reduced by hunters, and efforts are being made to protect them.

GIBBON *(primates)* Almost 3 feet tall, with long arms and no tail, the gibbon was once classed as the smallest of the apes, but some scientists now consider it a family by itself. It can whip through the treetops with the speed of a bird. Living in social groups in India, South Asia and the East Indies, gibbons scream at other gibbon clubs if they get too close.

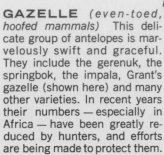

GILA MONSTER *(reptiles: lizards)* This animal and the Mexican beaded lizard are the only two poisonous lizards in the world. The Gila monster lives in the deserts of the American Southwest and northern Mexico and may grow to 20 inches. The poison is carried to a victim through grooves in the teeth. Thumping around by night, the Gila monster eats eggs and baby birds and mammals. The female buries her eggs in shallow ground and leaves them for the sun to hatch.

GNAT *(2-winged insects)* The tiny black bloodsucking member of the fly family—the variety that plagues man and beast from the tropics to the poles—is known as the buffalo gnat. Only the females bite.

GNU *(even-toed, hoofed mammals)* Known as the wildebeest, this African antelope, looking like a "horned horse," has the tail of a horse and the horns of a buffalo—a strange-looking creature. It lives in immense herds. Although they may weigh nearly 500 pounds, gnus like to kick and cavort like playful colts.

GOAT *(even-toed, hoofed mammals)* The male usually wears horns and a beard. Though nourished on grass, these members of the cattle or oxen family will eat almost anything *except* tin cans. Some kinds provide milk for delicious cheeses. The wool of long-haired varieties makes angora and cashmere sweaters. See also Antelope, Chamois, Ibex, Ox.

GOOSE *(goose-like birds)* Closely related to the swan, the goose is in a subfamily by itself. Geese are almost wholly vegetarians. They have great power of flight, migrating from within the Arctic Circle as far as Mexico for the winter. The snow goose, the blue goose, the Canada goose and other species build nests on the ground, lining them with down from their own bodies. They are wary, proud and clannish birds.

GRACKLE *(perching birds)* One of the blackbirds, the grackle is about 12 inches long and mainly black in color, with metallic glints which have led to the names "purple" and "bronzed" for 2 eastern U.S. species. The boat-tailed grackle lives farther south, and west to Mexico. Noisy, strutting birds, grackles like to move about in flocks.

GRASSHOPPER *(straight-winged insects)* Its hind legs are long and slender with heavy thighs designed for jumping, which the grasshopper does all summer. To sing, some species rub their wings together; others rub a hind leg across a fore wing. They hear with an organ under the knees of their front legs or on the sides of their abdomen. Locusts are a species of short-horned grasshopper.

GREBE *(grebes)* These diving birds, an order all to themselves, are highly skilled in the water and clumsy on land. They look very much like ducks, but have lobed rather than webbed toes, henlike bills and no noticeable tail. They have an odd habit of swallowing feathers—no one knows why—even feeding feathers to their young. Grebe nests often float on the water like anchored boats. There are many species on every continent of the world.

See also *Index*

GROUSE *(chicken-like birds)* The ruffed grouse and others are sometimes incorrectly called "partridges." The ptarmigan is the grouse of the mountaintops and far northern tundra, the prairie chicken a grouse of the American West. Male grouse strut, some fan their splendid tails and dance, others "drum" with their wings to attract the female. Most varieties have completely feathered legs.

HORSE *(odd-toed, hoofed mammals)* Horse means work, speed, sport and beauty. By the age of 3, a horse may weigh a ton and stand over 5 feet at the shoulder. The first horse was as small as a fox. A horse's age can be told by his teeth, some of which appear on a definite time schedule. A female horse crossed with a male donkey produces a (nonfertile) mule.

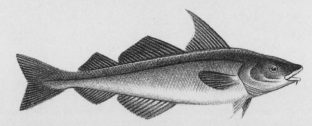

HADDOCK *(fishes: true-bone)* A favorite food fish, this North Atlantic relative of the cod hatches from eggs that drift in plankton, and usually grows up to weigh 3 to 4 pounds. During one phase of its life it hides unharmed in the stinging tentacles of the big blue jellyfish. A handsome fish with a black stripe on its side, the haddock provides New England and the coast of Greenland with a major industry. Smoked, it is served as "finnan haddie."

HYENA *(flesh-eating mammals)* An African or Asian beast, the hyena is of 2 main types—striped or spotted. Strong-jawed and noted for their eerie howl at night (which resembles wild laughter), hyenas are not as brave as they sound. They attack only easy prey, and subsist largely on bones and carrion. They look like dogs with short hind legs and sloping backs, but are not closely related.

HAGFISH *(fishes: jawless)* If netted by a fisherman, this very primitive fish is likely to gut many fish in the catch before it is discovered. It is blind but, with its well-developed sense of smell and sharp teeth, it can prey on helpless sea creatures. Because its skin exudes mucus in remarkable quantities, it is sometimes known as the "slime eel."

IBEX *(even-toed, hoofed mammals)* This is the wild goat of the Himalayas, North Africa, Siberia and the Alps. The Alpine ibex stands 3 feet at the shoulder and weighs about 200 pounds. Both sexes bear heavy ridged horns that curl backward. The male's grow to be 2½ feet long.

HERON *(stork-like birds)* This bird of marshes and waterways is recognizable in flight by the feet stretched out behind and the neck doubled back in an "S." Herons tend to hunt frogs and fish alone, but roost and nest in flocks. A crude mass of sticks in a tree holds 3 to 6 eggs. Our largest herons are the great blue and the great white, standing 4 feet tall. The "fly-up-the-creek," a little green heron, is chicken-sized.

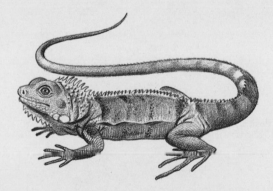

IGUANA *(reptiles: lizards)* This family includes the most spectacular lizards in the New World. A typical iguana is big (some as large as 6 feet) and stupid, with a whiplike tail, a row of comb teeth along its back and a bag of skin hanging ungracefully from its neck. Most species live in trees near rivers and lakes, and feed on leaves, fruit and birds.

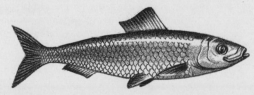

HERRING *(fishes: true-bone)* The world's most important food fishes live primarily in salt water and swim in immense schools. More than 3 billion pounds of herring are taken from the Atlantic Ocean and North Sea every year. Most netted young ones end up in cans; the larger fish are smoked or salted. Anchovies, smelts and sardines are close relatives.

IMPALA *(even-toed, hoofed mammals)* This deer-sized antelope has long, curving horns, a dark red back and a white belly. It lives in southern Africa and can bound 35 feet at a leap.

See also *Index*

JABIRU *(stork-like birds)* This bird is the largest (turkey-sized) of the 3 true storks of the New World. The jabiru eats fish and frogs, and lives from southern Mexico to Argentina. The bare black skin of its head and neck stands out against the alabaster-white feathers of its gangly body. It sports a broad red collar, and looks as if it were laughing.

JAY *(perching birds)* Not quite so large as the crows, to whose family they belong, colorful jays of many species are found in most parts of the world. Intelligent and sly, jays have a civil-defense system that warns of danger. They are persistent nest robbers, and some steal food from camps. In captivity they have a sense of humor, dropping balls to see them bounce, and hiding coins. Shown here is the blue jay. The magpie is a relative.

JACANA *(shorebirds and gulls)* Long legs and large, spread toes hold this ploverlike bird on top of lily pads as it runs lightly after insects. Hidden at the bend of its wings is a nasty spur used like a switchblade against enemies. Jacanas are found in the tropics of the world and are bright chestnut and purple in color.

JELLYFISH *(sac-like invertebrates)* These ocean creatures appear to be lighter than water. Some, like this great Portuguese man-of-war, which stings severely, are actually colonies of specialized animals, achieving buoyancy with floats. One kind, called by-the-wind-sailor, has a "paper" sail. The many varieties include the umbrella-like jellyfishes with stinging tentacles on the underside and the comb jellies or sea walnuts, with 8 bands of "combs" made up of hairlike cilia.

JACKAL *(flesh-eating mammals)* The most common jackal is an African wild dog, curiously marked with a large patch of black on its reddish back. It is fox-sized, scavenges on the remains of a lion's kill and howls at night as it prowls. Easily tamed, the jackal is soon turned from man's door because of its bad odor.

KINGFISHER *(kingfisher-like birds)* This family of many species is almost worldwide. Most have large, crested heads and long, straight bills. Those living near water dive for small fishes from a perch on a branch or from a fluttering halt in flight. Each couple digs a long tunnel into the side of a clay bank and builds a nest at the end, lined with fish bones and scales.

KINKAJOU *(flesh-eating mammals)* A deceptively appealing creature with large, expressive eyes, the kinkajou is often trained as a pet but may become vicious. This tropical member of the raccoon family looks like a small bear with the long, prehensile tail of a monkey. Kinkajous live from Mexico to Brazil and feast at night on honey, insects, fruits and fungi.

JAGUAR *(flesh-eating mammals)* The great cat of the New World, the yellow jaguar has spots like a leopard, but is stockier, sometimes tipping the scales at 250 pounds. It is an excellent tree climber and swimmer, preys on birds and on mammals as large as a horse, and will attack a man. Its terrifying roar may be heard in semitropical forests and grassy plains from southern United States to southern Argentina.

See also *Index*

KIWI *(wingless birds)* A nocturnal, flightless bird of New Zealand, the kiwi differs from all living birds in having nostril openings near the tip of its long bill. The size of a chicken, it has a humped back and stout legs. It screams "kiwi," and usually lays one large egg at a time. Although called wingless, kiwis do possess faint traces of wings.

KOALA *(pouched mammals)* This native of Australia, with its soft fur and lovable nature, reminds many people of a living teddy bear. It carries its babies in a pouch. The koala lives in trees and can eat only a certain kind of eucalyptus leaf. Its relative, the wombat, looks like it.

KUDU *(even-toed, hoofed mammals)* One of the largest African antelopes, the kudu has unusual horns, which stand almost vertical as they sweep up in a magnificent spiral. Its white-ringed body is also an eye-stopper.

LAMPREY *(fishes: jawless)* These are the vampires of the fish world, attaching themselves to a host fish and living on its blood. Although they resemble eels and are sometimes called lamprey eels, lampreys are actually related to the hagfish and were one of the earliest fish to develop.

LARK *(perching birds)* These songsters are primarily Old World birds, although North America has one stunning species, the horned lark, with a display flight somewhat like the European sky lark's. Its nest of grass in a field has a sort of entrance patio of pebbles. The larks are the first songbirds to nest in spring; some have been found incubating their eggs during February snowstorms. Shown here is a skylark.

LEECH *(segmented worms)* The best-known member of this singularly unattractive family fastens itself to animals and fishes to suck their blood. Leeches vary in size and color, and live in the sea, in freshwater ponds and in swamps. Bleeding the sick with leeches was once considered a cure-all. Three small white teeth in the mouth of the medicinal leech pierce the skin of the host; the sucking is done with a white disk-shaped organ.

LEMUR *(primates)* Although it is often hard to guess from their appearance, lemurs are related to apes and monkeys. Some are woolly, many are sharp-nosed and pop-eyed and they vary in length from inches to 4 feet long.

LIZARD *(reptiles: lizards)* Most of the 3000 lizards of all sizes and shapes have dry, scaly skin and hibernate. They love the sun. A number lay eggs; the others give birth to live young. If a lizard's tail is broken off, another grows. The flying lizard glides from tree to tree on sails of skin. The gecko can walk on a ceiling, and the frilled lizard can run on its hind legs. The species shown here is a side-blotched lizard.

LLAMA *(even-toed, hoofed mammals)* A member of the camel family, but without a hump, the llama is the famous beast of burden of South America. As tall as 5 feet at the shoulder, it can travel some 20 miles a day with a heavy pack. The llama is stubborn and temperamental, but highly valued by its Indian masters for its meat, pelt, hide and milk.

LOBSTER *(crustaceans)* This hard-shelled, pincered delicacy of the sea may weigh up to 35 pounds, but those caught in Maine lobster pots are usually only a pound or two. A lobster is vulnerable in early life. One of thousands of eggs carried for 11 months under its mother's abdomen, it hatches into a tiny larva. As it matures on the ocean bottom, it loses its hard shell many times for a slow-growing new one. In 5 years it is old enough to reproduce.

LOON *(loons)* Known for their plaintive cry, echoing over lakes from North America to the Arctic Circle, the common loons have black and white "checkerboard" feathers and short tails. They share with grebes the peculiar gift of being able to settle gently into the water without making one ripple or ring. Loons dive more than 200 feet underwater in search of fish.

See also *Index*

LOUSE *(insects: lice)* These tiny, hairy parasites of animals or plants are ugly and wingless. They have bulbous bodies, hooked feet and beaklike mouth parts for sucking. The female of the body louse (which attacks man) lays her eggs or nits in the seams of under-garments and bedding. The young hatch in about a week and start their sucking careers.

LUNGFISH *(fishes: primitive bone skeleton)* "Living fossils" of Australia, Africa and South America, the lungfishes are an important link between the fishes and the higher land animals. Besides gills, the African and South American species have 2 air bladders that work like lungs. When rivers or lakes run dry, they enclose themselves in mud houses, pressing their mouths against air holes. Living on body tissue, these lungfishes can "estivate" (sleep in a state of torpor) for months until the rains come and set them free.

LYNX *(flesh-eating mammals)* This wild member of the cat family lives in Europe, Asia and North America. Weighing about 30 pounds, it has tufted ears, a stubby tail and handsome sideburns. The lynx hunts in wide circles, for the most part in silence. The Canadian lynx is so dependent on the snowshoe rabbit that when the rabbits die out periodically, many lynxes starve. A near relation is the American bobcat or wildcat.

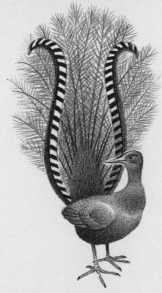

LYREBIRD *(perching birds)* Australia, land of unusual mammals, is also the home of the lyrebird, with its magnificent lyre-shaped tail. It has no close relatives.

See also *Index*

MACKEREL *(fishes: true-bone)* The most popular American species of this valuable food fish of the North Atlantic, a small relative of the tuna, is 10 to 18 inches long. It sports shades of blue and green and has wavy black stripes. In spring mackerel migrate to spawning grounds off Canada and elsewhere, returning to deeper waters in fall. Sharks, porpoises and whales prey on mackerel. Mackerel eat shrimp, anchovies and small herring.

MAMMOTH *(trunk-nosed mammals)* Several specimens of this extinct species of elephant have been found intact, embedded in the ice near a Siberian river. Their tusks were 9 feet long; they must have stood 9 feet high at the shoulder. Unlike today's elephant, the mammoth had a thick, shaggy coat and small ears to prevent loss of heat in the glacial epoch which began more than a billion years ago. It may have survived to relatively recent times.

MANATEE *(siren-like mammals)* Best known of the sea-cow order, this mammal of tropical coastal waters can be seen off the tip of Florida and in nearby river estuaries. About 8 feet long, it has paddle-shaped front flippers and can rest upright on its tail. The nursing female has visible breasts. A strange beast, the manatee has a powerful upper lip for grazing, like a cow, on aquatic vegetation.

MANDRILL *(primates)* This savage baboon of West Africa, with eyes like a pig and a muzzle like a dog, is an ugly creature. Scarlet furrows slash across blue swellings at the sides of his nose, and great patches of red emphasize his rear end. Mandrills walk on all fours; the adults are over 2 feet long and 1½ feet high. Traveling in groups of 50, they prowl the forests, the young screaming as they ride their mothers' backs. They don't like people.

MARMOSET *(primates)* These are the smallest monkeys in the world, about the size of young kittens; one variety, the pygmy, is not much bigger than a mouse. They live in the trees of Central and South America, have long soft fur, hair behind their ears, and long tails. The young reach full size in 6 months, a remarkable rate of growth for slow-maturing primates.

MARMOT (*gnawing mammals*)   Related to the squirrel, these burrowing animals, of which the woodchuck is one, hibernate in the winter. "Hoary" marmots inhabit parts of North America and Siberia. Small, brownish-gray animals with short, bushy tails, they socialize with their fellows and resemble stocky squirrels in appearance.

MARTEN (*flesh-eating mammals*)   Europe's martens include the species that gives us sable. A member of the weasel, badger, otter, skunk and mink family, the marten is about the size of a small fox. Where its cousins haunt the ground or streams, the marten takes to the deep forest. It feeds on mice, fish, rabbits—and even the prickly porcupine.

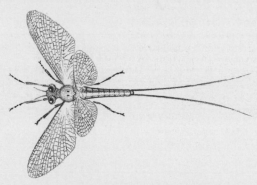

MAYFLY (*insects: mayflies*)   Frilly as a doily, the mayfly adult is a lovely, ephemeral creature that lives from a few hours to a day or so. It does not eat and has no mouth or stomach. It dances, mates, lays its eggs in the waters of streams and ponds—and dies. The eggs hatch into nymphs that live in the water up to 2 years before their maturing transformation. Mayflies differ from true flies in that they have 4 wings instead of 2 and comprise an order by themselves.

MEADOWLARK (*perching birds*)   Not a lark, but an American blackbird, this songster will migrate only as far as it is driven by the snow. Six western states claim this beautiful singer as their state bird.

MOLE (*insect-eating mammals*)   About 6 inches long, the mole looks and acts like a plow, cutting the earth underground with its pointed nose, wedge-shaped head and strong, driving forelegs. It can dig 15 feet an hour seeking earthworms. Moles are almost blind, but they can detect worms eating leaves nearby. The animals nest at the end of deep tunnels in a chamber lined with grass and leaves. Moleskin is used in evening wraps.

MONGOOSE (*flesh-eating mammals*)   Not much bigger than a squirrel, the mongoose is so swift it can kill a poisonous cobra by moving faster than that quick demon. A relative of the civet, the Asian flesh eater, it has been introduced into many parts of the world to control rats. The United States, however, forbids its entry.

MOOSE (*even-toed, hoofed mammals*)   The largest deer in the world, the moose (called elk in Europe) stands some 7 feet high and weighs up to 1800 pounds. Awkward and mighty, the bull wears 2 huge, flattened antlers, each shaped like an open hand, and has a bell of fur-covered skin hanging from its neck. Its big platter feet are designed to run in marshy land and stand in mud and mire. Unpredictable, the moose can be quiet one moment and in a thundering charge the next.

MOUSE (*gnawing mammals*)   The mouse lives everywhere except on a few fortunate islands of the Pacific. The large eyes and ears and long whiskers of house mice are designed for prying into crevices and behind walls. The nicer country dwellers—the field, wood and pine mice—are food for almost every preying animal. Mice are one of the 6400 variations of rodent (the gnawing mammals), like the rats, guinea pigs, beavers, porcupines, squirrels and hamsters, to name a few.

See also *Index*

MOUSEBIRD *(mousebirds)* Also known as the coly, this bird loves fruit and is a pest in central and southern African orchards. Mousebirds are an order all to themselves. Most varieties are grayish or brown with touches of blue; some have red bills. They walk in an ungainly manner, using the lower part of their legs as feet —though they also have feet of the usual kind!

MUSK-OX *(even-toed, hoofed mammals)* Handsome wild relatives of sheep and goats, weighing about 600 pounds, musk-oxen live on the plant-covered tundra in and near the arctic. When a group is attacked, the members stand in a circle facing out, refusing to budge, and can be easily slaughtered by man.

MUSKRAT *(gnawing mammals)* Homely in shape and expression, the humped muskrat, with his small ears and stingy eyes, carries one of the most beautiful and valuable pelts in the world. He lives in marshes and along the borders of rivers and streams, where he builds a house of reeds and roots or finds a hole in a muddy bank. Active day and night, the muskrat eats cattails, iris, grasses—almost anything, in fact.

MUSSEL *(mollusks)* In Europe and wherever gourmets can obtain them from temperate waters, sea mussels are a great delicacy on the half-shell or in a stew. Long hairs attach the sea mussel to its rock. The shell of the freshwater mussel is a source of pearl buttons.

MYNA BIRD *(perching birds)* Charming as he is, the Asiatic myna is a member of the pesky starling family. He is bold and aggressive. His sloppy nest in crevices of buildings does not endear him to man, but his strutting audacity and wry sense of humor do. The talking myna learns to imitate the human voice, and can talk, sing or whistle.

NAUTILUS *(mollusks)* A deep-sea creature with an exquisite spiral shell, the nautilus has tentacles and is related to the octopus. The chambered nautilus of warm southern waters lives in its outer chamber. As it grows new chambers it abandons those behind, filling them with gas to lighten the shell for moving around. Some varieties attain a breadth of 10 inches.

NIGHTHAWK *(goatsuckers)* Not a true hawk, this bird looks like its relative the whippoorwill. About 10 inches long, it is black, white and buff. In subdued light it hunts like a bat, diving and dipping as it catches insects in its wide-open mouth. A loud "peent" identifies it. Cities have been a boon to nighthawk populations. The many flat, gravelly roofs are just what a nighthawk wants for a nest site.

NIGHTINGALE *(perching birds)* One of the thrushes, this fairy-tale bird lives chiefly in central and western Europe. Its voice is plaintive, sad and beautiful, though the bird itself is drab and shy. About 6 inches long, it hides in dark forests and dense hedges. Nightingales migrate to Africa in winter.

OCELOT *(flesh-eating mammals)* To some people this is the most beautiful beast alive. It is one of the New World's small cats, about twice as big as a house cat, and spotted like a miniature jaguar. A denizen of the tropics, the flesh-eating ocelot ranges from southwestern United States to Paraguay.

ORANGUTAN *(primates)* The powerful great ape of the wooded lowlands of Borneo and Sumatra has a large head and arms that reach nearly to the ground. Its face, hands and feet are naked, its hair reddish. Orangutans live in trees, where they build nests and feed on fruits and buds. They are formidable foes when brought to bay, and one of the ugliest mammals alive.

See also *Index*

ORIOLE *(perching birds)* The famous Baltimore oriole, fiery orange and black, took its name from Lord Baltimore of Maryland, who wore such colors. Tropical orioles have been popular as caged birds. The oriole nest is a swinging, sack-shaped cradle which looks as if it would fall—but never does.

OX *(even-toed, hoofed mammals)* This term is applied to castrated bulls used as work animals, but *oxen* is also the zoological name covering a number of bovine animals, including buffaloes, bisons, goats, sheep and domestic cattle. The direct ancestor of modern dairy and beef cattle may have been the extinct aurochs of the Old Testament. Stone Age man painted wild oxen on the walls of his caves.

OYSTER *(mollusks)* The wonderful oyster, popular as food and as a source of pearls, is fastened irrevocably to the stones and rocks of ocean shallows. An Atlantic oyster colony throws out millions of eggs and sperm simultaneously. They meet and rock out to sea, where they hatch. Young oyster larvae twirl freely for a few weeks as their shells grow, before cementing themselves forever to one spot.

PANDA *(flesh-eating mammals)* This relative of the raccoon comes from China and the Himalayas. The giant panda, shown here, is playful and a great attraction at zoos. Its face is bearlike, its tail stumpy and its black-and-white furry coat charming in design. Its diet consists of bamboo shoots and, occasionally, small animals.

PANTHER *(flesh-eating mammals)* In North America this name is applied to a puma, cougar or mountain lion—and in Asia and Africa to a leopard. "Black panthers" are black leopards. The name is loosely used, and even authorities disagree as to whether a panther is just a big cat or a group name for small cats.

PARROT *(parrot-like birds)* Birds of this very handsome, seed-cracking, tropical group have most peculiar toes: the first and fourth—turned backward—enable them to perform feats of climbing. The order of 315 species includes the macaws, true parrots, cockatoos, lories and parakeets. Their tongues are thick, fleshy and somewhat prehensile, enabling them to handle objects with the tongue and upper beak. Some learn to "talk."

PARTRIDGE *(chicken-like birds)* In America the name *partridge* has been applied loosely to varieties of ruffed grouse and bobwhite. The Hungarian partridge of Europe and the chukar of Asia are considered true partridges. Both have been introduced into the United States with considerable success. Shown here is the Hungarian partridge.

PERCH *(fishes: true-bone)* Perches are members of the largest order of fishes, one that contains some 8000 species divided into more than 125 families, some of which are: angelfishes, bluefishes, croakers, porgies, sea basses, snappers and sunfishes. The most familiar perch, the yellow, is found throughout North America.

PETREL *(ocean-dwelling birds)* Storm petrels are the best-known members of this family. Related to the albatross, these little birds also wander over the oceans of the world and come to land only to breed. Sailors believe the storm petrels bring the tempest. Named for St. Peter because they seem to walk on the water, they are also called Mother Carey's chickens by sailors, from Mater Cara ("Dear Mother")—the Virgin Mary.

PHALAROPE *(shorebirds and gulls)* The 3 species of phalarope closely resemble sandpipers. The female is the sirenlike head of the house. She is more vividly colored than the male, picks her mate, makes the love advances, lets him build the nest, then goes off after laying the eggs, leaving *him* to incubate them. The American phalarope nests in the far north and spends the winter at sea off the coast of South America or Africa.

See also *Index*

PHEASANT *(chicken-like birds)* From ancient times man has raised these birds of brilliant colors. The American ring-necked pheasant is a cross between the English (brought to England by the Romans) and the Asian varieties, both of which arrived in the United States in the 19th century. The spectacular gold pheasant of China is rivaled in beauty only by the birds of paradise. The guinea fowls are relatives.

PHOEBE *(perching birds)* Well known for nesting under our eaves, this bossy little bird, with its call, "fee-bee," is related to a whole "tyrant" family of fast-flying catchers of insects. Most of them have whiskery feathers at the bill. They are all audacious. The pee-wee is the sweetest singer among those of the Western Hemisphere.

PIG *(even-toed, hoofed mammals)* Although they love to wallow in mud, domestic pigs are essentially clean animals that do not overeat and have been much maligned. They are, however, apt to be infested by internal parasites like the trichinella, dangerous to man, so eating their meat was early forbidden by certain religions. Today there are over 20 breeds of pig—or hog, as farmers say.

PIKE *(fishes: true-bone)* A mouth that stretches from eye to eye and a vicious set of teeth show how superbly equipped pikes are for dining on smaller fish and even birds and frogs. Pikes and their relatives, the muskellunges and pickerels, are in turn a favorite target of sport fishermen.

PLOVER *(shorebirds and gulls)* Several varieties of golden plover are among the world's greatest migrants, some flying from the arctic to Pacific islands and others from eastern Canada to South America—or as much as 16,000 miles round trip. Plovers nest in open areas, laying 4 eggs colored to match their surroundings. The killdeer is a plover which cries its name.

PYTHON *(reptiles: snakes)* Old World snakes, pythons squeeze their prey to death by suffocation and can swallow even good-sized animals whole (pigs, for example). The reticulate python, more than 30 feet long, is the largest. Pythons shelter their eggs by curling around them.

See also *Index*

QUAIL *(chicken-like birds)* This widespread game bird, represented in the American Northeast and South by the brown-speckled bobwhite, is helpful to man by eating potato bugs. Bobwhites like to huddle together in a circle for warmth and protection. When an enemy appears, they spring into the air and take flight in a confusing bevy.

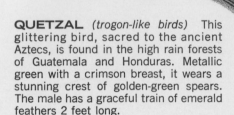

QUETZAL *(trogon-like birds)* This glittering bird, sacred to the ancient Aztecs, is found in the high rain forests of Guatemala and Honduras. Metallic green with a crimson breast, it wears a stunning crest of golden-green spears. The male has a graceful train of emerald feathers 2 feet long.

RABBIT *(leaping mammals)* Long-eared and speedy, these friendly jumpers have two pairs of gnawing teeth in their upper jaw. Rabbits differ from hares in that they have helpless young, born with eyes closed and without fur. Hares give birth to fully furred and wide-eyed youngsters. The North American jack rabbit and the snowshoe rabbit (see page 13) are really hares.

RAVEN *(perching birds)* A large North American cousin of the crow and the European jackdaw, the common raven is about ⅓ bigger and proportionately smarter. It nests on cliffs and in trees and lays from 3 to 8 eggs. Ravens are not so gregarious as most crows, but do spend the winter in flocks. They like the wilderness and make intelligent pets.

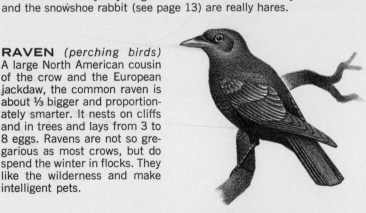

RAY *(fishes: cartilage skeleton)* Terrifying in appearance, flat and powerful, some varieties of ray grow to over 20 feet in breadth. Living at the bottom of the Atlantic and Pacific oceans and in tropical rivers, rays feed largely on worms and shellfish. Some can crush oysters and are a nuisance to the oyster industry; some sting brutally; others give severe electric shocks. Skates are a ray family.

REMORA *(fishes: true-bone)*   This swift swimmer of the tropical seas and open ocean is 2 to 4 feet long. It has a suction cup (an adapted fin) on top of its head which it fastens to whales, turtles, sharks and other large fishes.

RHEA *(rheas)*   Heaviest of New World birds (about 45 pounds), rheas look like small ostriches, but have been put into an order of their own. They live in the open brush country of South America. Like the ostrich, they cannot fly, but run swiftly and well. They can also swim. Each male mates with several females, who lay their eggs in one communal nest on the ground. The male then incubates the eggs and takes care of the young. Rhea-hunting is a sport in South America.

ROBIN *(perching birds)*   Our North American redbreast is a large thrush. (The European and Asiatic robin is quite another bird.) Ranging from Georgia to Alaska, it migrates in winter as far south as Guatemala. Known as spring's harbinger, it is also one of the last migrants to leave in fall. Pairs try to return to the same backyard every year. They make mud nests covered with grass, prefer the fork of a tree and often raise more than one brood a year.

ROC *(ostriches)*   This fabulous bird of Madagascar, reported by Marco Polo and a legend among the Arabs (who gave it its name), is believed by some authorities to have been the extinct elephant bird. A relative of the ostrich, it weighed 1000 pounds. Its bones and well-preserved eggs have been found in Madagascar swamps.

ROLLER *(kingfisher-like birds)*   These stunt fliers tumble and turn in the air on bright blue wings. Testy and pugnacious, they live on insects and very small animals, seeking holes in which to brood, often without bothering to build a nest. Their raucous call is heard in Europe, Asia, Africa and Australia.

SALAMANDER *(tailed amphibians)*   The lizard-shaped salamander lives in many parts of the world and was said in ancient folklore to be immune to fire. Some species have lungs, some have gills and others breathe through their skin. Most fertilize internally, the female gathering up the sperm cells which the male has deposited. The harmless newt and mud puppy are salamanders.

SANDPIPER *(shorebirds and gulls)*   These members of the snipe family have shorter bills than other snipes and prefer shores and beaches. They run in and out with the waves, piping in mellow tones. Some species perform exhaustive 18,000-mile, round-trip migrations, flying from the Northern to the Southern Hemisphere. Of the 82 species in the sandpiper family, 3, the tattlers, use the abandoned nests of other birds; the others nest on the ground.

SCALLOP *(mollusks)*   Scallop shells, 3 to 6 inches across, are most elegant. They have been used for ornament since civilization began. The delicious edible part of the scallop is the large white muscle of the creature living inside the pair of shells. This muscle is cut out—for cooking—like a biscuit. Scallops are found in sea waters around the world.

SCALY ANTEATER *(scaly mammals)*   The seven species of scaly anteater, also known as pangolin, make up an entire mammal order. The tongue of this strange animal is about half the length of the body, not counting the tail; and its covering of hairs, compressed like the rhino's horn, provides an armor of scales.

SEAL *(fin-footed mammals)*   The ancestors of the seal were land animals that returned to water life by developing flippers and blubber. There are two types: the true or hair seals and the eared seals (sea lions and fur seals). Instead of external ears, true seals have only openings in their heads. Most can swim on their backs and all can stay under water 10 to 20 minutes and dive perhaps 200 feet.

SEA URCHIN *(spiny-skinned animals)*   The empty shell picked up at the seashore resembles a hollow decorative doorknob. Alive the sea urchin looks like a pincushion full of pins—the stiff spines with which it protects itself. Large species reach a foot in diameter. Its circular mouth has 5 white horny teeth. Among its relatives are the oval cake urchins (one is the "sea biscuit") and the sand dollars—shaped like fringed pancakes.

See also *Index*

SECRETARY BIRD (*daytime hunters*) Standing out from the head of this African bird are narrow feathers which look like quill pens. Four feet tall, it prefers running to flying, builds a bulky nest in a bush or tree and eats lizards, insects and snakes.

SHEEP (*even-toed, hoofed mammals*) All domestic sheep descend from 2 kinds of wild sheep, the Asian urial and the European mouflon. The largest wild variety is found in the mountains of Siberia. The widest spread of horns is carried by the Marco Polo sheep, first described by that traveler. Wild sheep, high-spirited and daring, move among the tall peaks of this hemisphere in herds.

SHRIMP (*crustaceans*) Shrimps have a thinner shell than their larger relatives, lobsters and crayfish. Trailing long feelers and 5 delicate pairs of legs, they swim backward with the aid of their fan tails, some in salt, some in fresh water. There are many varieties distributed over the world. Most fishermen call the larger shrimps prawns, but the true prawn is distinguished by having pincers on its second pair of legs, unlike others.

SKINK (*reptiles: lizards*) The skink is a bright-eyed lizard of numerous species. The red-headed ranges up to New England and is the most northern lizard found. Another species has a blue tongue and laps milk like a kitten. The "two-headed" skink has scales on its tail that look like a second head.

SNIPE (*shorebirds and gulls*) A game bird, the snipe (like its relative the woodcock) has eyes far back and up on its head, so that it appears to be going the other way. A long, pointed beak droops forward. Crazy, somersaulting sky performances compose its love dance. In North America, snipes breed from Newfoundland to Alaska and even south to Pennsylvania.

See also *Index*

SPARROW (*perching birds*) Some of the most charming birds in the world belong to this family, especially the song sparrow, the white-throated and the field sparrow (shown here). On the other hand, there is the drab and pesky house sparrow, really a species of weaverbird (known as expert nest builders) introduced from Europe. This hoodlum, often called the English sparrow, has become a nuisance in American cities, nesting almost anywhere—in drainpipes, on windowsills, under cornices and on rooftops.

SPONGE (*pore-bearing animals*) The plantlike sponge, often brilliant in color, is among the lowest of the many-celled animals. Fossil remains trace sponges back to the earliest ages. A base or stem holds them to rocks on the sea bottom, most commonly in tropical waters. Small hairs draw water through millions of pores into a central hollow, where cells absorb the microscopic sea life; the water is then ejected. A single sponge may produce both eggs and sperm and can also reproduce by budding.

SPRINGTAIL (*insects: springtails*) Members of one of the most primitive of insect orders, the springtails are also one of the few that can maintain life in the polar regions. Their name comes from their ability to leap into the air by means of a springlike mechanism on the abdomen.

STONE FLY (*insects: stone flies*) The stone flies, delicate creatures with transparent wings and stocky bodies, spend most of their lives as larvae attached to stones on the bottom of streams. They form a separate order of insects.

STURGEON (*fishes: cartilage and bone*) These splendid fishes of north temperate seas and freshwater streams produce the most prized of the eggs known as caviar. Gourmets also value smoked sturgeon. All sturgeons belong to a very ancient group whose sucking mouth and plated body go back several hundred million years. Some varieties have been reported weighing over a ton.

SWIFT *(hummingbirds and swifts)*
The swift, named for its speed, looks like a swallow, but the two are quite unrelated. It flies tirelessly in quick, graceful dips. At dusk it clings by its tiny feet to cliffs and chimneys, the claws acting as hooks. American swifts cement sticks together with saliva to form a nest. And one Asian variety makes its nest entirely of saliva, thus giving us the world-famous "bird's-nest soup."

SWORDFISH *(fishes: true-bone)* The swordfish's sword, actually an extension of its upper jaw, can measure as much as ⅓ of its total length. One of a group known as billfishes, the swordfish has a flattened bill; the bills of the others—sailfishes and marlins, for example—are rounded.

TANAGER *(perching birds)* The most famous, the scarlet tanager, migrates from South America to the United States and Canada, bringing its tropical flaming red. Most tanagers are poor singers.

TAPEWORM *(flatworms)* The miserable tapeworms and flukes invade the intestines and other organs of men and animals. They and other flatworms can lay eggs but also reproduce by splitting in two and budding new heads.

TASMANIAN DEVIL *(pouched mammals)* This ugly beast lives only on the Australian island for which it was named. Although easily tamed, it is ferocious for its size—about that of a badger—and is black with a few white spots. Its too large head is equipped with stout teeth. The "devil" goes abroad at night to kill small animals and, occasionally, victims as large as young sheep.

TERN *(shorebirds and gulls)* Terns hunt along the coasts and inland waters rather than over the open ocean as gulls sometimes do. They pluck shrimp, sand eels and other small fishes out of the water with their long, pointed bills. Like gulls, they nest on the ground in colonies. The arctic tern, a champion migrant, travels an estimated 22,000 miles a year from arctic to antarctic and home again.

THRIP *(thrips)* An order all to themselves, these insects are tiny villains of the greenhouse and garden. Some have wings, some do not. Thrips damage plants in various ways, causing scabs, plant galls (in which the insect lives) and leaf distortion.

THRUSH *(perching birds)* The bluebirds, veeries, wheatears, (American) robins and the wood and hermit thrushes are among the most important American species of this varied worldwide family. They love green woodlands and dark forests, spending much time on the ground, hopping about for worms and insects. The wood thrush is one of North America's most thrilling songsters.

TICK *(8-legged spinners)* This blood-sucking parasite of the spider family inserts its entire head into its victim. It spreads Rocky Mountain spotted fever and other diseases among men and cattle. A smaller relative, one of the mites, is the chigger, whose bite causes severe itching. Ticks and mites are not to be confused with those other parasitic pests the lice and fleas, which are insects.

TINAMOU *(tinamous)* These are an order to themselves, interesting zoologically because they resemble both the chicken-like and the ostrich-like birds. Able to fly only short distances at a time, they make a racket on taking off from the grasslands and jungle floors of their homelands—from Mexico to Argentina.

TOAD *(leaping, tailless amphibians)* They love summer, fresh water, night and insects. The common American toad is warty and has glands behind each eye and in its warts which ooze a poison irritating to its enemies but harmless to man. In spring the toad lays eggs, about 20,000 at a time, in ponds and puddles. Hatching as tadpoles, a few months later these come ashore as adults. The toad's sticky tongue is spectacular, whipping out farther than its body length to snare a bug or worm.

TOUCAN *(woodpeckers)*
An enormous but lightweight bill, sometimes almost as big as its body, distinguishes this tropical bird. The several species are green, black, red and yellow in varying combinations. Found only in the Americas' dense junglelands, toucans are fruit eaters. The long tongue looks like a fuzzy feather. Toucans flock together, calling one another like a pack of baying hounds.

See also *Index*

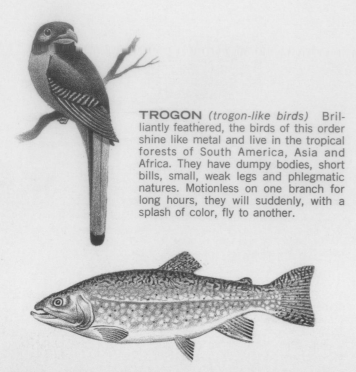

TROGON (*trogon-like birds*) Brilliantly feathered, the birds of this order shine like metal and live in the tropical forests of South America, Asia and Africa. They have dumpy bodies, short bills, small, weak legs and phlegmatic natures. Motionless on one branch for long hours, they will suddenly, with a splash of color, fly to another.

TROUT (*fishes: true-bone*) This famous game fish of many species, a relative of the salmon, is usually found in lakes and streams, though some kinds of trout can live in the sea and occasionally seek it. Originally native to the Northern Hemisphere, they now flourish all over the world. The beautiful and active brook trout, shown here, lives chiefly from Labrador to Georgia and through the Rockies.

TRUE BUG (*insects: true bugs*) This group includes bed bugs, water bugs, water scorpions, assassin bugs, chinch bugs, squash bugs, stink bugs and other plant bugs. All of them bite and suck vegetation, other insects or human beings. Some protect themselves by emitting a disagreeable odor.

TUATARA (*reptiles: tuatara*) Although it looks like a lizard, this creature is actually an order of reptiles all by itself, the last remaining relative of a group of animals that flourished before the Age of Dinosaurs. Today it is found only on a few remote islets off New Zealand. It lives mainly on insects, and its eggs take more than a year to hatch.

TUNA (*fishes: true-bone*) This food fish, also called the tunny, is closely related to the mackerel and the bonito. Tunas are swift swimmers found in both the Atlantic and Pacific oceans. The bluefin of the North Atlantic has been known to weigh 1800 pounds.

UMBRELLA BIRD (*perching birds*) Plumes that canopy its head and feathers hanging from its neck like an umbrella handle give this exotic tropical bird its name. About the size of a crow, it lives in the tops of the highest trees along the Amazon and other rivers of South America and in Central America.

VIPER (*reptiles: snakes*) Snakes with hollow fangs in their upper jaws, both the pit vipers, found chiefly in the New World, and the true vipers of the Old World are poisonous. Pit vipers have heat-sensitive cavities between their nostrils and their eyes which enable them to find warm-blooded prey. The rattlesnake, bushmaster, copperhead and water moccasin are pit vipers. True vipers, lacking the cavities, include the poisonous adders and Russell's viper. Shown here is the moccasin.

VIREO (*perching birds*) The red-eyed vireo is known as the preacher bird because of its persistent and uninterrupted notes. Vireos migrate from South and Central America northward, building deep-cupped nests hanging from the fork of twigs. Other species are the black-capped, white-eyed and yellow-throated vireos.

VULTURE (*daytime hunters*) Several bald-headed birds of prey, ugly in appearance and graceful in flight, are called vultures. The black vulture, California condor, king vulture, Andean condor and turkey vulture are New World varieties. Vultures eat carrion and feed their young by disgorging partially digested food.

WALRUS (*fin-footed mammals*) Long-tusked and bristle-faced, the walrus is the haughty monarch of the Arctic Ocean. It spends most of its time drifting on ice floes, digging shellfish on the ocean floor and occasionally visiting islands and shores. Its heavy tusks protect it from its enemy, the polar bear. The walrus is not harmful if left alone, but a whole herd of walruses will charge, roaring, to defend one molested member.

WARBLER (*perching birds*) These vocal little birds are famous for their busy migrations. In spring some 50 species of New World warblers move in tens of thousands from the tropics to the far north. Inconspicuous when clinging to foliage, woodland warblers are nevertheless some of the most colorful and enchanting birds of North America. Common varieties are the yellow, the black-and-white and the black-throated green warblers.

WASP *(membrane-winged insects)* Wasps either live in societies (yellow jackets and hornets) or are solitary (potter wasps and burrowing species). The female solitary wasp builds a few separate cells, or digs small holes, and lays each egg next to a paralyzed insect—food for the hatched larva. The

hornet queen starts a nest by building a few cells of the comb and laying eggs in each. These hatch into workers that continue to build a "paper" dwelling large enough for many residents. Hornets and yellow jackets sting (but rarely fatally). Wasps eat harmful insects.

WATER BOATMAN *(insects: true bugs)* With hind legs resembling oars, these aquatic insects inhabit freshwater ponds all over the world. A reservoir of air in their bodies allows them to go underwater. Among the most prevalent of the water bugs, they form an order with water skaters and other "true bugs."

WEASEL *(flesh-eating mammals)* This small but vicious cousin of the mink, otter, skunk, badger and European ferret is found in many parts of the world. Several of the numerous varieties assume a white winter coat, the prized ermine, and are known by that name. A foot-long weasel can catch a mouse and disappear under the thinnest cover like a flash of lightning. It will attack animals much larger than itself and is known for its forays on poultry.

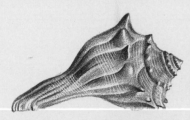

WHELK *(mollusks)* This large sea snail, from 2 to 6 inches in length, lives along the coasts of temperate lands around the world. Its tubular snout makes a hole in the armor of lobsters and crabs, and its sharp teeth scrape bits of the soft tissue of its prey into its mouth.

WHIPPOORWILL *(goatsuckers)* About 10 inches long, this mournful-sounding night flier calls its name, "Whip poor Will!" beginning just at dusk. With a gaping mouth it scoops up insects on the wing. It hides on the ground all day and, since it makes no nest, lays its eggs on the ground, too—among dead leaves.

WOODCOCK *(shorebirds and gulls)* This bird looks very much like its relative the snipe but is much plumper. Its eyes are also far up on the head; its beak is long with a sensitive tip for finding worms. Most American woodcocks winter in the Gulf states, and nest in New Jersey and northward. The males' love flight is spectacular—they utter a "peent" note before take-off, perform a whirling dance high in the sky at dusk or by moonlight, then dive back to earth with a spinning sound.

WREN *(perching birds)* Energetic and with a tail that sticks up like a flag-pole, the little house wren is the original backyard gossip, chattering con-

stantly. It is a delight to gardeners both for its song and for its habit of eating many insects. Each year it raises several broods of 5 to 10 youngsters. Other varieties are the cactus, rock and marsh wrens. All have the same joyous attitude toward life.

YAK *(even-toed, hoofed mammals)* This hairy Asian wild ox carries its head low, weighs up to 1200 pounds and lives only in the high country of Tibet. An agile beast despite its huskiness, the yak can slide down glaciers, swim rivers and leap over rocks. One of the rare beasts of the world, it has been crossed with Mongolian cattle to make a domestic yak useful for carrying burdens.

ZEBRA *(odd-toed, hoofed mammals)* Stunning to behold, vile-tempered and stubborn, the zebra is a member of the horse family. His stripes serve as camouflage in the shade of trees. Most species roam African plains; a few graze the grasses in the rough mountains. All zebras live in bands led by a stallion. They are difficult to tame, but live peaceably with horses.

See also *Index*

CHART OF THE ANIMAL KINGDOM

Scientists have divided the Animal Kingdom into branches, of which the 17 most inclusive are called phyla. The chart below contains the 11 principal phyla. In each phylum there are subdivisions, called classes. The place of each animal listed in the Index is shown on this chart or on the opposite page.

CLASSES

a. Crustaceans (*Crustacea*)
b. Double-footed Animals (*Diplopoda*)
c. Eight-legged Spinners (*Arachnida*)
d. Jaw-footed Animals (*Chilopoda*)
e. Insects (*Insecta*)

BRANCHES
(Phyla)

CLASSES

a. Fishes (*Pisces*)
b. Amphibians (*Amphibia*)
c. Reptiles (*Reptilia*)
d. Birds (*Aves*)
e. Mammals (*Mammalia*)

1
Spinal-cord Animals (*Chordata*)

2
Joint-legged Animals (*Arthropoda*)

3
Mollusks (*Mollusca*) — clams, cuttlefish, mussels, scallops, slugs, snails, squids

4
Segmented Worms (*Annelida*) — earthworm, leeches

5
Spiny-skinned Animals (*Echinodermata*) starfishes, sea urchins

6
Roundworms (*Nematoda*) — nematodes

7
Wheel Animals (*Rotifera*) — rotifers

8
Flatworms (*Platyhelminthes*) — flukes, tapeworms

9
Sac-like Animals (*Coelenterata*) corals, jellyfishes, sea anemones

10
Pore-bearing Animals (*Porifera*) — sponges

11
Single-celled Animals (*Protozoa*) amoeba, foraminifera, paramecium

1 SPINAL-CORD ANIMALS (*Chordata*)

Of this phylum, fishes are the oldest members and so have the most complicated classification, being divided into super-classes, classes, subclasses and superorders. The other groups—amphibians, reptiles, birds and mammals—are classes, and all their orders are listed below with examples.

a. FISHES

Headless Superclass (*Acrania*)
lancelets

Jawless Superclass (*Agnatha*)
hagfishes, lampreys

With-Jaws Superclass
(*Gnathostomata*)

  Cartilage-Skeleton Class
  (*Chondrichthyes*)
  sharks, rays, skates

  Bone-Skeleton Class
  (*Osteichthyes*)

    Primitive Fish Subclass
    (*Choanichthyes*)
    lungfishes, coelacanths

    Ray-finned Fish Subclass
    (*Teleostomi*)

      Cartilage-and-Bone Super-
      orders (*Chondrostei and*
      Holostei)—sturgeon, gars

      True-Bone Superorder
      (*Teleostei*)
      barracudas, mullets,
        silversides
      catfishes
      deepsea anglers
      eels
      electric eels, minnows
      flying fishes
      herrings, anchovies,
        trout, salmon
      mackerels, marlins, tunas
      perch-like fishes
      pikes and their allies
      remoras
      sticklebacks and
        tubenoses

b. AMPHIBIAN CLASS

Leaping, Tailless (*Salientia*)
frogs, toads, etc.

Legless (*Gymnophiona*)—blindworms

Tailed (*Caudata*)
newts, salamanders, etc.

c. REPTILE CLASS

Crocodiles, Alligators, etc.
(*Crocodilia*)

Lizards (*Sauria*)
lizards, chameleons, iguanas, etc.

Snakes (*Serpentes*)
boas, cobras, moccasins, etc.

Tuatara (*Tuatara*)

Turtles (*Chelonia*)
turtles, terrapins, tortoises

d. BIRD CLASS

Casque-headed (*Casuariiformes*)
cassowaries, emus

Chicken-like (*Galliformes*)
grouse, quails, turkeys, etc.

Crane-like (*Gruiformes*)
cranes, coots, bustards, etc.

Cuckoo-like (*Cuculiformes*)
cuckoos, touracos, anis, etc.

Daytime Hunters (*Falconiformes*)
hawks, eagles, vultures, etc.

Dove-like (*Columbiformes*)
pigeons, doves, sandgrouse

Fully Webbed—All Four Toes
(*Pelecaniformes*)
pelicans, anhingas, etc.

Goatsuckers (*Caprimulgiformes*)
nightjars, whippoorwills

Goose-like (*Anseriformes*)
ducks, geese, swans, screamers

Grebes (*Podicipediformes*)

Hummingbirds and Swifts
(*Apodiformes*)

Kingfisher-like (*Coraciiformes*)
kingfishers, bee eaters,
hornbills, etc.

Loons (*Gaviiformes*)

Mousebirds (*Coliiformes*)

Night Hunters (*Strigiformes*)—owls

Ocean-dwelling (*Procellariiformes*)
albatrosses, petrels

Ostriches (*Struthioniformes*)

Parrot-like (*Psittaciformes*)
parrots, parakeets, lovebirds

Perching (*Passeriformes*)—swallows,
thrushes, mockingbirds, etc.

Rheas (*Rheiformes*)

Shorebirds and Gulls
(*Charadriiformes*)
sandpipers, gulls, terns, auks, etc.

Stork-like (*Ciconiiformes*)
storks, herons, flamingos, etc.

Tinamous (*Tinamiformes*)

Trogon-like (*Trogoniformes*)
trogons, quetzals

Wedge-winged Birds
(*Sphenisciformes*)—penguins

Wingless Birds (*Apterygiformes*)
kiwis

Woodpecker (*Piciformes*)—woodpeckers, toucans, honey guides, etc.

e. MAMMAL CLASS

Aardvark (*Tubulidentata*)

Aquatic (*Cetacea*)—whales, porpoises

Claw-winged (*Chiroptera*)—bats

Egg-laying (*Monotremata*)
platypus, echidnas

Even-toed, Hoofed (*Artiodactyla*)
camels, deer, giraffes, etc.

Fin-footed (*Pinnipedia*)
seals, walruses, etc.

Flesh-eating (*Carnivora*)
lions, lynxes, wolves, etc.

Gnawing (*Rodentia*)
mice, rats, porcupines, etc.

Hyraxes (*Hyracoidea*)

Insect-eating (*Insectivora*)
shrews, moles, hedgehogs, etc.

Leaping (*Lagomorpha*)
rabbits, hares

Odd-toed, Hoofed (*Perissodactyla*)
horses, zebras, rhinoceroses, etc.

Pouched (*Marsupialia*)
kangaroos, opossums, koala, etc.

Primates (*Primates*)
marmosets, monkeys, apes, etc.

Scaly (*Pholidota*)—scaly anteaters

Siren-like (*Sirenia*)
manatees, dugong

Toothless (*Edentata*)
anteaters, sloths, armadillos

Trunk-nosed (*Proboscidea*)
elephants

2 JOINT-LEGGED ANIMALS (*Arthropoda*)

For the first four classes in this phylum, only a few easily recognized examples are given. For the largest class, insects, the principal orders are given.

a. **Crustacean Class** (*Crustacea*)
  barnacles, crabs, crayfishes,
  lobsters, prawns, shrimps

b. **Double-footed Animal Class**
  (*Diplopoda*)—millipedes

c. **Eight-legged-Spinner Class**
  (*Arachnida*)—horseshoe crabs,
  mites, scorpions, spiders, ticks

d. **Jaw-footed Animal Class**
  (*Chilopoda*)—centipedes

e. **Insect Class** (*Insecta*)

  Beetles (*Coleoptera*)

  Bristletails (*Thysanura*)

  Caddis Flies (*Trichoptera*)

Earwigs (*Dermaptera*)

Embiids (*Embioptera*)

Fleas (*Siphonaptera*)

Lice (*Anoplura*)

Mayflies (*Ephemeroptera*)

Membrane-winged Insects
(*Hymenoptera*)
ants, bees, wasps

Net-winged Insects (*Neuroptera*)
ant lions, lacewings

Same-winged Insects (*Homoptera*)
aphids, cicadas

Scale-winged Insects
(*Lepidoptera*)
butterflies and moths

Scorpion Flies (*Mecoptera*)

Springtails (*Collembola*)

Stone Flies (*Plecoptera*)

Straight-winged Insects
(*Orthoptera*)
grasshoppers, locusts, roaches

Termites (*Isoptera*)

Thrips (*Thysanoptera*)

Toothed Insects (*Odonata*)
dragonflies, damselflies

True Bugs (*Heteroptera*)
water boatmen, water skaters

Two-winged Insects (*Diptera*)
flies and mosquitoes

INDEX

A figure in italics indicates a page on which an illustration occurs. The terms in parentheses after the name of each animal in the Index appear on the chart on pages 314-315. By looking up these terms on the chart you can locate every creature's place in the Animal Kingdom.

ACKNOWLEDGMENTS

GIANT OF THE DEEP, by Roy Chapman Andrews, from "Just Whales," excerpts from *Whale Hunting with Gun and Camera,* © 1916 and republished 1935 by D. Appleton-Century Co. ONCE THERE WERE BILLIONS, by Maitland Edey, from "Once There Were Billions, Now There Are None," *Life,* Dec. 22, '61, © 1961, Time Inc. THE DINOSAUR AND THE EGG, by Roy Chapman Andrews, from "Consider the Dinosaur," © 1937. GHOSTLY HOOFS ON THE PRAIRIE, by Herbert Ravenel Sass, from "Hoofs on the Prairie," © 1964, The Curtis Pub. Co. THE FISH THAT COULDN'T BE, by James Dugan, from "The Fish Named L. c. Smith," © 1955, The Crowell-Collier Pub. Co. SNAIL FOLK, by William Beebe, © 1960, Natural History. THE CAMEL—DISCONTENTED SHIP OF THE DESERT, by Arthur Weigall, from "Laura, a Camel with a Grievance," in *Everyman's Ark,* edited by Sally Patrick Johnson, © 1962, published by Harper & Brothers, condensed from *Laura Was My Camel,* published by J. B. Lippincott Co. LIFE ABOVE THE TIMBERLINE, by Jean George, from "The Savage Fight for Life Above the Timberline," *Maclean's Magazine,* Sept. 22, '62, © 1962, Maclean-Hunter Pub. Co., Ltd. THE WORM THAT TURNED, by W. Gilhespy, © 1936, John o'London's Weekly. THE QUEEN'S STORY, by Charles D. Stewart, from "The History of the King Bee," © 1931, The Atlantic Monthly Co. AFRICA'S UGLY PRIMA DONNA, by Reed Millard, *Coronet,* Nov. '56, © 1956, Esquire, Inc. NATURE'S SKYSCRAPERS, by George G. Goodwin, *Animal Kingdom Magazine,* June '56. LOOK AT THE OSTRICH —BUT LOOK OUT! by Jan Juta, © 1947, The Atlantic Monthly Co. ALMOST EVERYBODY LIKES HIPPOS, by Colonel Robert Bruce White, *Field & Stream,* Jan. '58, © 1957, Field & Stream Pub. Co. HOW DOTH THE BUSY BEAVER—, by Bill Cunningham, © 1943, The Crowell-Collier Pub. Co. A DAY WITH GORILLAS, by Martin Johnson, © 1960, McCall Corp. THE SNAKE WITHOUT A FRIEND, by Virginia Duncan, condensed from *Southwest Review,* Winter 1945, © 1944, University Press in Dallas. DON'T UNDERRATE BROTHER RAT, by Alfred H. Sinks, published by The Curtis Pub. Co. BURGLAR FROM THE WOODS, by George Heinold, from "Burglar in the Treetops," © 1950, The Curtis Pub. Co. MONKEY TRICKS AND TRAITS, by Martin Johnson, condensed from *Delineator.* MIGRATING MAMMALS, INSECTS AND FISH, by Ivan T. Sanderson, from "The Mystery of Migration," © 1944, The Curtis Pub. Co., permission to reprint granted by Paul R. Reynolds, Inc. CREATURES OF DAY AND NIGHT, by Lorus J. and Margery J. Milne, from "Creatures in the Night," condensed from *The World of Night,* © 1956, Lorus J. and Margery J. Milne, published by Harper & Brothers. ANIMAL POISON, by H. Munro Fox, from "Animal Poisoners," condensed from *The Forum,* July '27.

PHOTOGRAPHIC CREDITS

Alpha Photo Associates: pp. 36-37, 179, 195, 204, Shelley Grossman; p. 36 (inset), Carroll Seghers II. American Museum of Natural History: p. 72 (top). William H. Amos: pp. 79 (purple snail, sea slug, flamingo tongue), 96. Australian News and Information Bureau: p. 82. Bird Photographs, Inc.: p. 257 (bottom), Dr. Arthur A. Allen. Birnback: p. 121, *Australian Women's Weekly;* p. 207, Bob Campbell; p. 130, Simon Trevor. Black Star: p. 48, Lennart Nilsson; pp. 10-11, 127, 157, Emil Schulthess. Dr. Ralph Buchsbaum: p. 79 (periwinkle, garden snail, cowrie). Lynwood M. Chace: pp. 34, 42, 44, 154, 184, 246 (io, white-lined sphinx, leopard and cecropia moths), 248, 274, 276, 285. Cornell University, Department of Plant Pathology: p. 199, H. H. Lyon. Jack Couffer: pp. 218-219 (from the book *Song of Wild Laughter*). Louis Darling: p. 165. Andreas Feininger: pp. 147, 159 (right), 193. Gilloon Photo Agency: p. 68 (left), Charles J. Belden; p. 63, H. E. Lindros. Jerry Greenberg: pp. 186-187. Herman L. Holbrook: p. 70. Dr. Ross E. Hutchins: pp. 49, 105, 107, 246 (luna and underwing moths). *Images et Textes:* p. 159 (3 photographs at left), Jacques Six. Keystone, Germany: p. 287 (penguin). Jürg Klages: pp. 286-287 (rhinoceros, monkey), 288. Cy La Tour: pp. 23, 212, 225, 287 (hippopotamus). Lensgroup: pp. 68 (right), 88, Fred Baldwin. Pierre Marc: pp. 90-91. MGM, Inc. and Cinerama, Inc.: p. 61, buffalo stampede from *How the West Was Won,* © 1963. Monkmeyer: pp. 111, 148, John H. Gerard; p. 281, Carola Gregor; p. 108, Helmut Handrick; p. 227, Louis Quitt; p. 100 (right), Dr. Edward S. Ross; pp. 39, 209, 264 (song sparrow), Leonard Lee Rue III. National Audubon Society: p. 77, Stephen Collins; pp. 21, 242-243, Allan D. Cruickshank; p. 161, Helen Cruickshank; pp. 30, 109, Treat Davidson; p. 242 (left), Walter Dawn; pp. 171, 189, John H. Gerard; p. 55, Karl W. Kenyon; p. 214, Norman R. Lightfoot; p. 57, Bill Reasons; p. 287 (opossum), Leonard Lee Rue III; pp. 75, 201, Grace A. Thompson; p. 224, H. A. Thornhill. Lennart Nilsson: p. 46. Nancy Palmer Agency: p. 174, Juliana Wang. William Partington: p. 184. Klaus Paysan: pp. 95, 177, 197. Peabody Museum, Yale University, New Haven, Conn.: pp. 65-67. Willis Peterson: pp. 93 (inset), 125, 136, 181, 250, 252-253, 257 (top), 259, 270. Photo-Library: p. 15, Morton Beebe; p. 80, Roy Pinney. Photo Researchers: p. 282, N. Chaffer; p. 282, D. Hanley; p. 134, Fritz Henle; p. 264 (nightingale), Eric Hosking; pp. 168, 264 (chaffinch), 267, 278-279, Russ Kinne; pp. 191, 284, John Markham; pp. 234-235, Roger Tory Peterson; p. 264 (catbird), Peter Stibane; p. 18, Ike Vern. Eliot Porter: pp. 139, 153. Rapho-Guillumette: pp. 221, 222, William W. Bacon III; p. 13, Herbert Lanks; p. 216, George Santillo; p. 29, Stan Wayman; pp. 118, 123, 132, 261, 272, Ylla. roebild, Frankfurt: p. 173. Sven Samelius: p. 145. Shostal: p. 26, Mike Hayden; p. 93, Ernest Newell Weber; p. 163, L. Willinger. Arthur Singer: pp. 115, 167. Otha C. Spencer: p. 255. Tierbilder Okapia, Frankfurt: p. 143, Mönch. United Arab Republic Tourist Office: pp. 86-87. U.S. Department of the Interior, Fish and Wildlife Service: pp. 53, 60. William Vandivert: pp. 100 (left), 141, 228. Mort Weldon: p. 102. Wide World Photos: pp. 72 (bottom), 73.